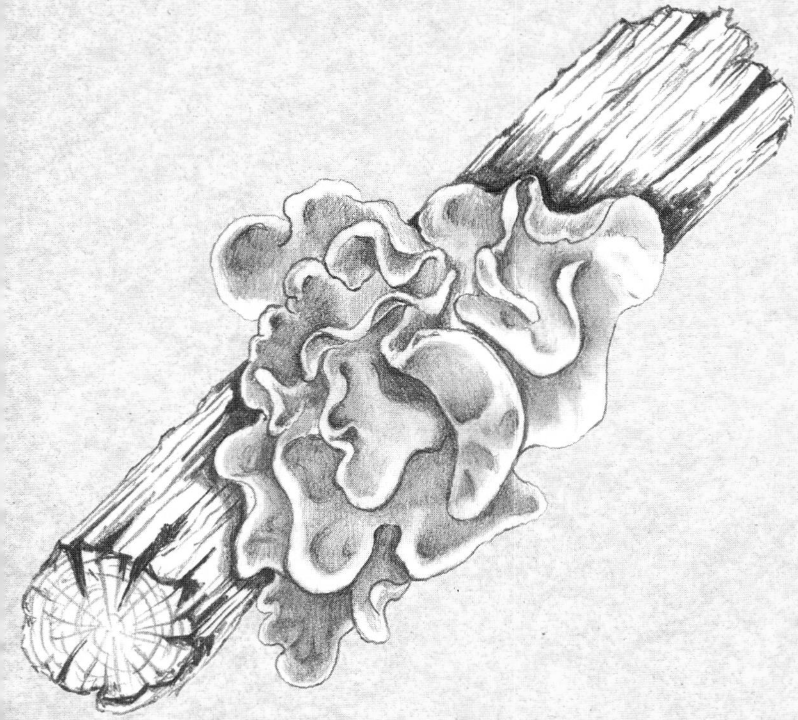

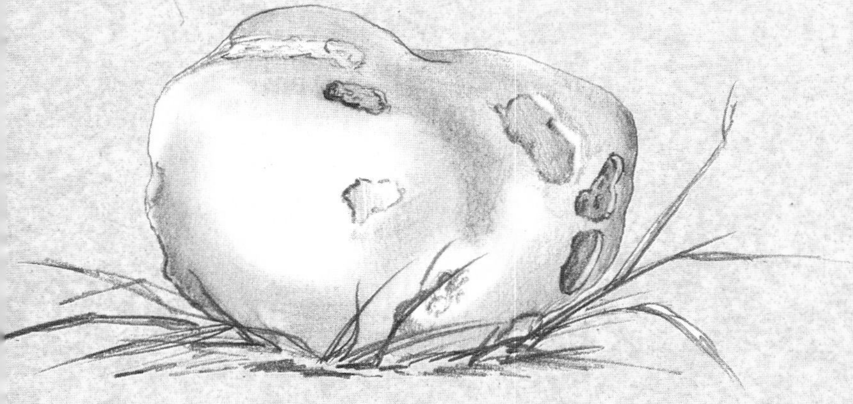

AN ILLUSTRATED GUIDE TO

MUSHROOMS AND OTHER FUNGI OF NORTH AMERICA

GEOFFREY KIBBY

AN ILLUSTRATED GUIDE TO

MUSHROOMS AND OTHER FUNGI OF NORTH AMERICA

GEOFFREY KIBBY

KEY TO SYMBOLS IN TEXT

☠ = Deadly species

(!) = Dangerous and suspect species

DRAGON'S WORLD

Dragon's World Ltd
Limpsfield
Surrey RH8 0DY

First published by Dragon's World 1993

The catalogue record for this book is available from the British Library.

ISBN 1 85028 221 8

Editor: Patricia Burgess
Designer: Mel Raymond
DTP Manager: Keith Bambury
Editorial Director: Pippa Rubinstein

Printed in Italy

CONTENTS

INTRODUCTION

FUNGI: THE UNKNOWN KINGDOM

For most people mushrooms and other fungi are very much an unknown world. Even though they may be familiar with the flowers, birds or animals in their area, the fungi are often hardly noticed. Indeed, many of us can probably remember as children being warned not to touch the "poisonous toadstools", and have carried this image for years afterwards. This is a great pity, since although there are some poisonous and even deadly species, the vast majorityof fungi are harmless, while some are delicious edibles and many are strikingly beautiful. All are fascinating in their manner of growth and dispersal, and some are among the most remarkable organisms in the world in both appearance and life history.

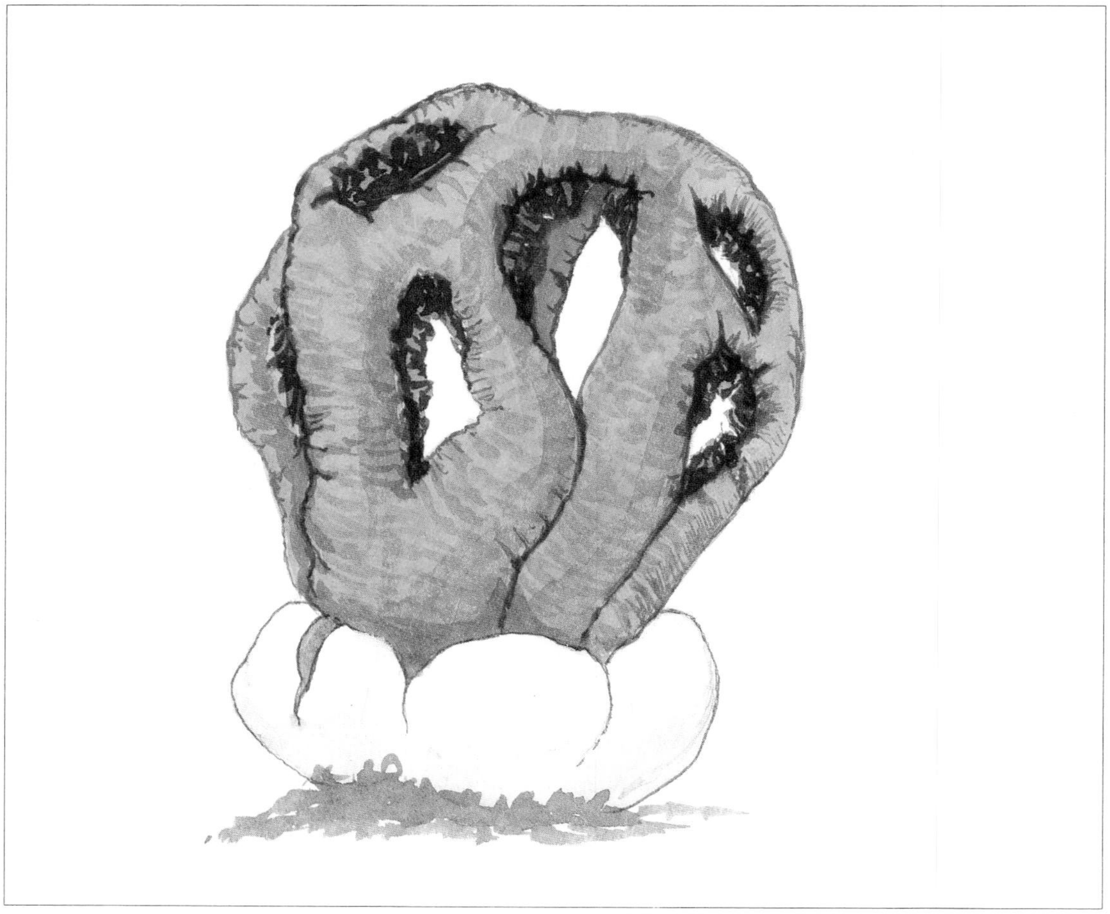

Anyone just beginning to explore this unknown kingdom will soon realize that it is a vast and unending exploration that can easily enthrall you throughout your life. In North America alone there are at least 4000 larger fungi. This comprises only those species that can be easily seen with the naked eye and does not include the thousands of other species best examined with the aid of a lens or microscope. There is almost no part of the world where fungi cannot be found, from humid jungles to arid deserts, from Arctic mountain tops to your own back yard, and it is this enormous variety of habitats that adds to the pleasure of studying fungi.

This book aims to introduce you to some of the variety and beauty of mushrooms to be found in North America and Canada. The 450 covered in this book are the most spectacular, important, or otherwise easily identifiable species you are likely to find. Also included are a number of rare or little-known species, since you are certain to come across at least a few of these and it adds extra enjoyment to anticipate finding a rarity.

CAUTION

All references to edibility are given as a guide only and are based on published reports. As individuals differ in their reactions to different species, only small quantities, even of well-known edibles, should be tried at first. Always try to obtain expert identification if you intend to eat fungi. The author and publishers cannot be responsible for mistakes in picking or adverse reactions. Below are explanations of the terms commonly used to describe edibility in this book.

Edible with caution; can cause upsets = usually edible, but upsets a small percentage of people.

Edible = edible, but not necessarily highly regarded.

Edible and good/excellent = edible and highly regarded.

Edible, but best avoided = edible, but confusion with poisonous species is possible, so best avoided.

Inedible = not poisonous, but distasteful; bitter or too tough to eat.

Doubtful; best avoided = information on edibility is uncertain or contradictory; best avoided for safety.

Unknown; best avoided = no reports on edibility at time of publication.

Poisonous = causes more toxic reactions than simple stomach upsets, e.g. sweating, palpitations, giddiness, hallucinations, but not usually deadly.

Deadly poisonous = often fatal, particularly if untreated; avoid at all cost.

Mushrooms and Toadstools – what is the difference?

When people in Great Britain hear the word mushroom they usually think of the white variety they buy in their local supermarket, or perhaps the white field mushrooms they may have collected in the countryside when they were young. Almost everything else is classed as a toadstool and believed to be inedible. However, Americans and Europeans are much more broad-minded; in parts of Europe dozens of different fungi, each with their own name, are eaten and are commonly on sale in markets. Inedible or poisonous species may also have their own names. The split into two groups so prevalent in Britain is rarely made elsewhere. This reflects the very different historical attitudes to fungi of the different peoples and nations of the world. Britain and one or two other countries are often referred to as mycophobes (fungi-haters), while other countries, such as France, Italy and Sweden are definitely mycophiles (fungi-lovers). Europeans (and, because of their predominantly European ancestry, many Americans too) have always included fungi as a major part of their diet and are much more familiar with the edible and poisonous species.

Thus, the words mushroom and toadstool have no scientific meaning and give no accurate guide to edibility or otherwise. They are simply cultural terms used historically (and very vaguely) by different people in different ways. In this book all species are simply referred to as either mushrooms or fungi, regardless of edibility.

What is a Fungus?

The mushrooms that we see in the woods and fields are just the visible parts of a much larger organism. Usually hidden from sight are masses of almost invisible fungal threads called mycelium, which form the active feeding and growing structures of the fungus. The mushroom that we see is created solely for the production of the spores by which the fungus reproduces itself. This is analogous to the apple on a tree, with the tree representing the mycelium and the apple the mushroom fruiting body. Because of this it is possible to collect the fruiting body without damaging the total fungus. As long as the habitat is not disturbed and reasonable discretion shown in the number of specimens collected, the fungus will carry on growing and fruiting quite happily.

Most biologists now classify fungi as entirely separate from, but related to, the other two major kingdoms with which we are familiar – plants and animals. Although in the long distant past fungi probably shared an ancestry with primitive, amoeba-like or algae-like organisms, they have since diverged in their own unique way. Unlike the green plants, they do not contain the pigment chlorophyll, so cannot produce their own food through the action of sunlight. Instead they must feed directly on other organisms. Many fungi feed on dead and decaying vegetation or wood, or even dead animals, while others have evolved to become active parasites, attacking living plants and animals, including human beings. (Most people have heard of or been "attacked" by Athlete's Foot, a common and very persistent fungal infection.)

Thankfully, the larger fungi usually confine their parasitic attacks to trees and other plants. Many fungi, however, have developed a fascinating and remarkable association with plants which is called mycorrhiza, whereby the mycelium of the fungus surrounds and penetrates the roots of the plant, and plant and fungus begin to swap nutrients back and forth. The association is extremely complex and benefits both fungus and plant; indeed, many forest trees are apparently unable to grow successfully without their fungal partners. Because of this association it is possible to predict in many cases which fungi will be growing with which tree. Some fungi may grow with a number of tree partners, while others grow under only one; for example, *Suillus grevillei* grows only under larch.

All the larger fungi that you will find will produce their spores in one of two basic ways. The majority of the species in this book form their spores externally on a club-like cell called a basidium, and are therefore placed in the class Basidiomycetes. The remainder produce their spores inside a long cell called an ascus, thus forming the class Ascomycetes. These two major groups are further subdivided. In the case of the Basidiomycetes there are different types of basidium. Those with a simple, undivided basidium form the subclass Holobasidiomycetes, while those with basidia divided either longitudinally or laterally form the subclass Heterobasidiomycetes. In both these groups the basidia are spread over gills, tubes, spines, or other structures in a thin layer called the hymenium, and the spores are propelled or flipped off the basidia into the air. A third subclass, the Gasteromycetes, contains those fungi that have simple undivided basidia. However, those basidia are contained within the fruit-body and never project the spores, relying instead on external forces to release and distribute the spores.

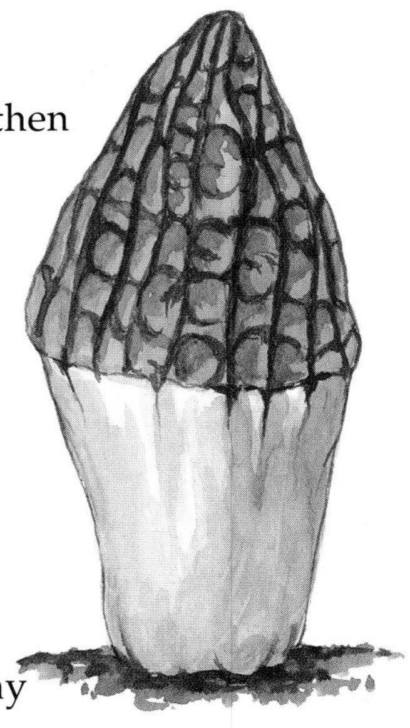

These subclasses are further broken down into orders and then into families based on both visible and microscopic characteristics, chemical reactions, methods of spore dispersal, and many other features. Nine principal orders of Basidiomycetes are dealt with here. These are once again subdivided, this time into genera (singular = genus), then finally into species.

In the class Ascomycetes there are a great many orders, mostly outside the scope of this book, so the Ascomycetes dealt with here are not subdivided into orders, but are grouped together for simplicity. Once again, it is the details of microscopic characteristics that play a great part in determining the divisions.

How to collect and study fungi

With such an enormous number of species available, and those species varying somewhat with age and locality, it may seem a difficult job to identify them with any certainty. For some groups of fungi this is quite true, and they are best dealt with by advanced amateurs, and professionals using specialist literature. Examples of such groups include the genera *Psathyrella*, *Coprinus*, *Inocybe*, and *Cortinarius*. However, many fungi are very distinctive, and with careful collecting, some detailed observation, and practice you will soon find yourself recognizing a number of the commoner species.

To increase your chances of making a correct identification some basic procedures should be followed. First, the material must be collected correctly. You want to minimize any damage to the specimen and make sure that you get the entire mushroom. So, for example, with a typical gilled mushroom with a cap and stem you should carefully lift the specimen out of the soil using a knife or trowel, making sure you do not leave any part of the stem behind. In many mushrooms, such as species of *Amanita*, this is vital since there may be a volval sac at the stem base. Try to avoid handling the specimen as many species have delicate features that bruise easily and rub off, or even change color when touched. Wrap the specimen carefully in a piece of waxed paper with the ends twisted like a candy wrapper. This helps prevent the specimens being crushed in a bag or basket, and also keeps moisture in the specimen. *Never use plastic bags:* the fungi will soon sweat and collapse, sticking to the sides and forming a mush that is impossible to identify. When you get the specimens home, make careful notes on color, texture, any rings or bags on the stem, smell the gills,

and even taste a tiny portion. The last-mentioned may seem alarming to the beginner, but if only a tiny portion is rolled on the tongue and then spit out, it is quite safe, even with poisonous species. However, most mycologists make a point of learning to recognize well-known poisonous species to avoid having to taste them. Taste is very important in many groups of fungi, varying from mild to peppery, burning, bitter, or otherwise distinctive.

The next important step is to make a spore print or deposit since it is vital to record the color of the spores (this is not usually done in the case of Gasteromycetes). This is very easy and great fun to do since the colors vary from pure white to rust-brown, pink, purple, or even black. Simply place a mushroom cap with the gills, tubes, or other spore-bearing surface down on a sheet of white paper and cover with a container for a few hours. After this period carefully lift the mushroom cap, and underneath you should have a good deposit of spores (it is often possible to peek under much sooner and determine the color that is forming). Let the deposit dry for a few minutes, then carefully scrape the spores together to determine the color as accurately as possible.

The size of the spores is very important, as is their shape, and whether or not they have any warts or spines. For this examination a microscope is required. Although it is possible to study mushrooms in some depth without one, a microscope is nevertheless a great asset, often vital for the identification of many species, as well as adding to the enjoyment and fascination of the hobby. In this book the spores of all species are described, and the microscopic details of length and breadth are given. For example, spores 7–8 x 4–5µm means that the spores vary from 7 to 8 micrometers in length and 4 to 5 micrometers in width. A micrometer (often called a micron) is one thousandth of a millimeter.

Some basic chemical reactions are given, and some of the chemicals involved are easily obtainable; these include ammonia (window cleaner with ammonia will do) or caustic soda, KOH. Others are more specialized and their formulae are given in the glossary.

Few mushrooms have a common name – only the well-known edible or poisonous species – so most are called by their scientific name. This should not cause problems; after all, we speak of chrysanthemums and pelargoniums, both of which are scientific names. The mushroom's scientific name consists of two Latinized words followed by the names of the authors who described it. For example, if we look at *Russula lutea* (Hudson ex Fries) S.F. Gray, the first name is the genus (*Russula*) always with an initial capital and in italics, while the second name is the specific epithet (*lutea*), always in lower case italics. This mushroom was described by Fries based on the earlier description of Hudson, but moved to the genus *Russula* by S.F. Gray. As many mushrooms have been placed in different genera by different authors, and as the names may vary from book to book, the best-known synonyms are given wherever possible. Remember, the mushrooms do not change, just our ideas about them.

Pictorial Key to Major Groups

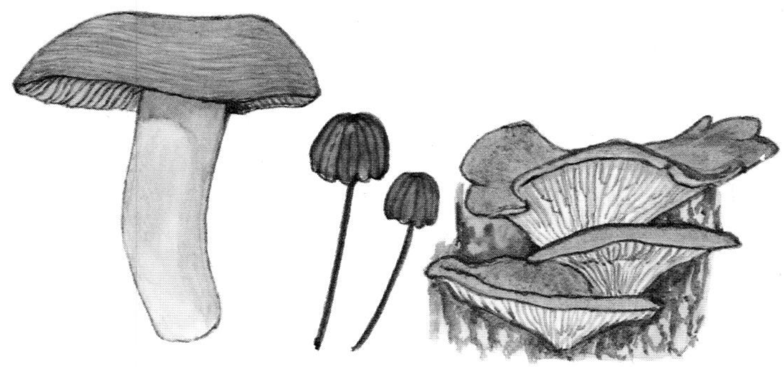

Mushrooms with gills
These form the largest portion of the book. They include species with and without stems, and are found both on the ground and on trees. They vary from the most delicate, fragile forms to large, robust fruiting bodies. All have radial flaps of tissue called gills, or lamellae. The thickness, attachment to the stem, and the spacing of these gills can be important characteristics for separating different genera and species – see pages 37–134.

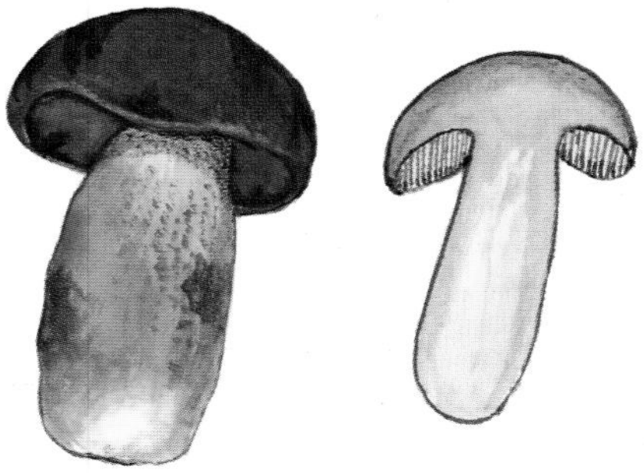

Boletes
Fleshy fungi with a cap and stem similar to some gilled mushrooms, but rather than gills on the underside of the cap they have a layer of vertical, spongy tubes with the openings forming a layer of pores. The size and arrangement of these pores varies from genus to genus – see pages 18–36.

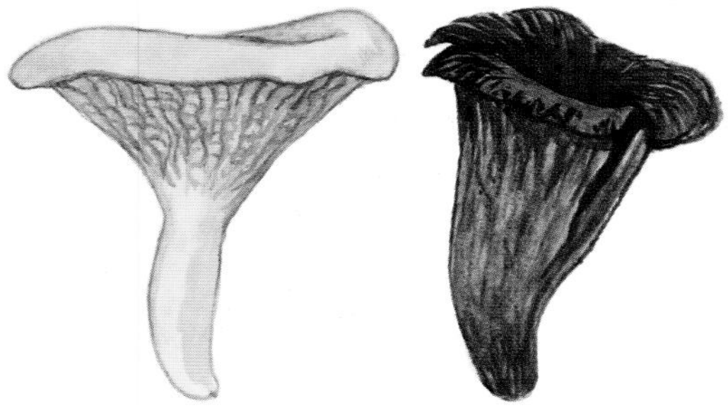

Chanterelles
Sometimes confused with the gilled mushrooms and vice versa, but they never have true, narrow gills. Instead they have blunt-edged wrinkles, often multiply forked and interveined with cross-ridges. Some forms are almost completely smooth on the outer surface of their trumpet-like forms – see pages 135–8.

Puffballs, Earthstars, and Bird's Nests
Never with gills or pores, they all have some form of ball-like structure containing the spores, often elevated on a stalk or, as in the Earthstars, with an outer skin that splits into star-like arms. In the Bird's Nests these spore-masses are very tiny and contained in a cup- or nest-like structure – see pages 159–67.

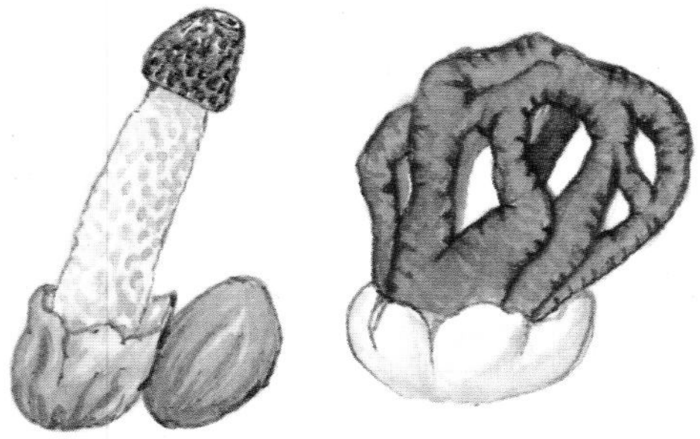

Stinkhorns
Bizarre fungi that "hatch" from an egg, and whose spores are spread over specialized structures. The spores liquefy to produce a foul odor, hence the common name, and are usually eaten, and thus dispersed, by insects – see pages 154–8.

Toothed Fungi
Fungi with a cap and stem, and hence growing on the ground; or completely stemless and shelf-like; or even like undersea corals growing on a tree. All share the common feature of downward-pointing spines or teeth on which the spores are formed. The spines vary from extremely tiny and densely packed to over an inch in length and more widely spaced – see pages 144–6.

Polypores, Bracket Fungi, and Crust Fungi
Often very hard, or at least very tough and fleshy, fungi, usually with one or more layers of downward-pointing tubes on the undersurface. The majority grow on trees, although some are found on soil. The crust-like fungi may or may not have a tube layer. Some polypores and brackets can grow from year to year, others are annuals and produce a new body each year – see pages 143–53.

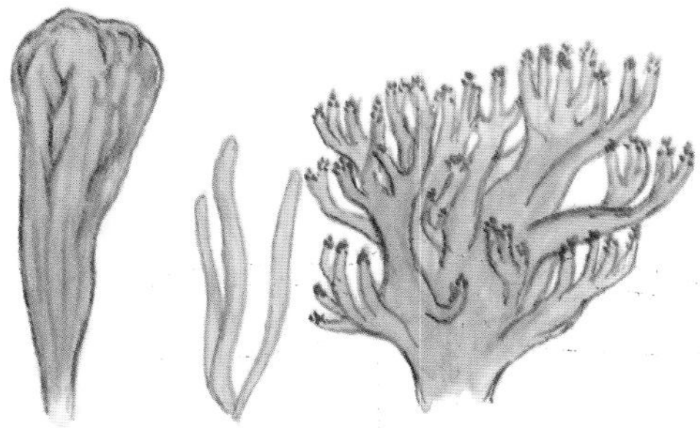

Club-shaped and Coral Fungi
These fungi range from the simplest of club-shaped fruiting bodies to extremely complex and quite large coral-like structures where the clubs are multiply branched, and forked at the tips. The majority grow on the ground, although there are exceptions. The spores are produced over most of the outer surface of the clubs – see pages 139–42.

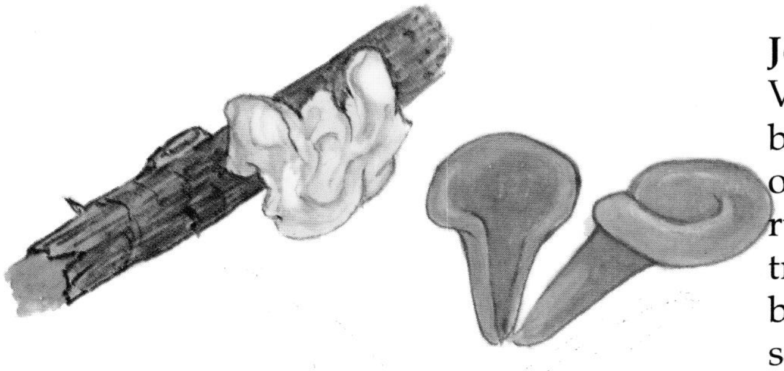

Jelly Fungi
Very variable in form and size, from almost microscopic blobs of shapeless jelly, to more complex shapes like ears or tongues, but all with a soft, jelly-like or sometimes rubbery texture. They grow both on the ground and on trees. Their spore-forming basidia are divided internally by cross-walls, either longitudinally or transversely – see pages 168–70.

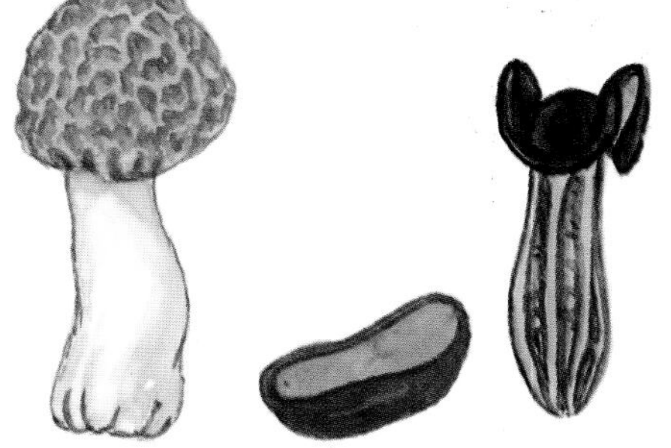

Morels, False Morels, and Cup Fungi
From the simplest of cups, often microscopic in size, to complex, brain-like or sponge-like structures raised on a stem. They are usually brittle in texture. All form their spores in an ascus, which is usually spread over the cup surface, or in the pits of the sponge-like forms. The spores may often be seen ejecting in a dust-like puff when the fungus is disturbed – see pages 171–9.

Development of a Mushroom with Volva and Ring

The universal veil (1) enclosing the mushroom ruptures to leave a volva (4) at the base, and fragments on the cap. The partial veil (3) covers the gills (2), then is pulled away to form a ring on the stem. This is the most advanced form of veil development; other mushrooms may have just the partial veil (3), the universal veil (1), or, of course, no veils at all.

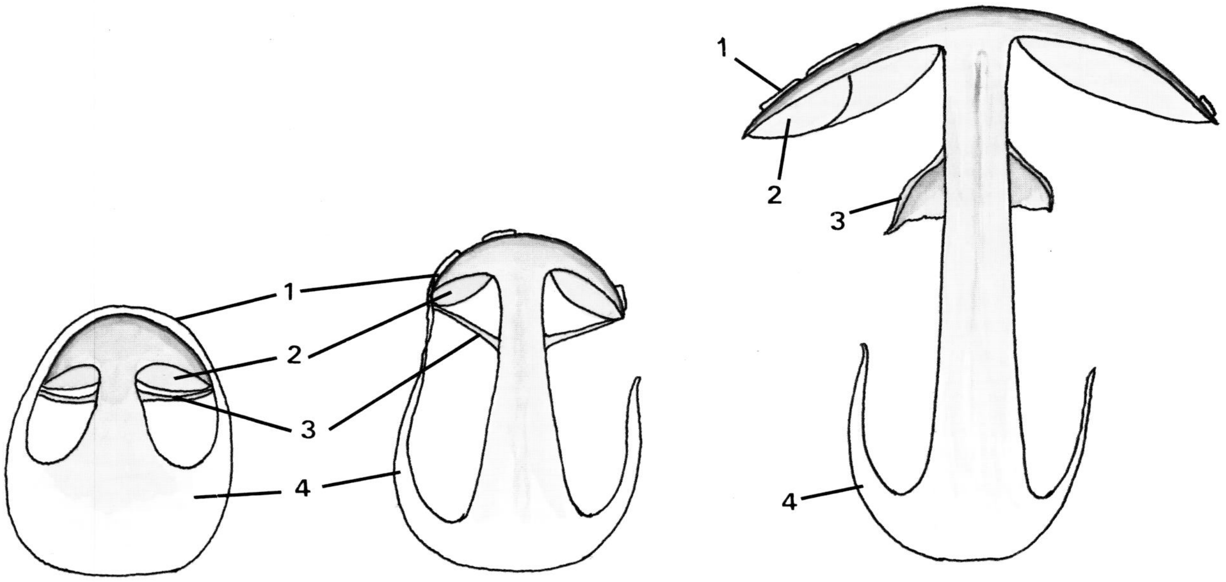

Types of Gills Attachment to the Stem and Cap shapes

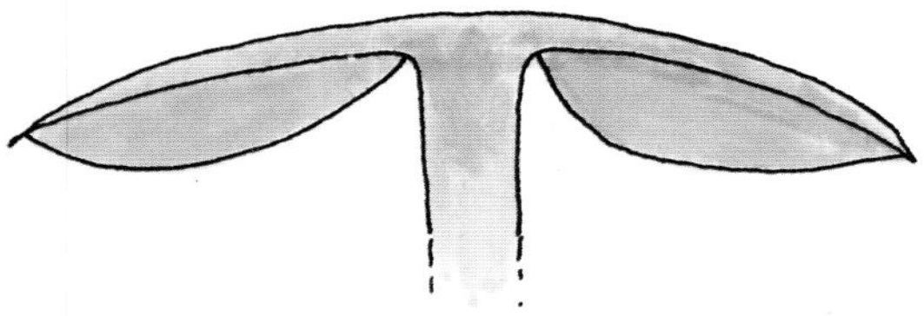

Free gills are completely clear of the stem, they are shown here on a rounded or convex cap.

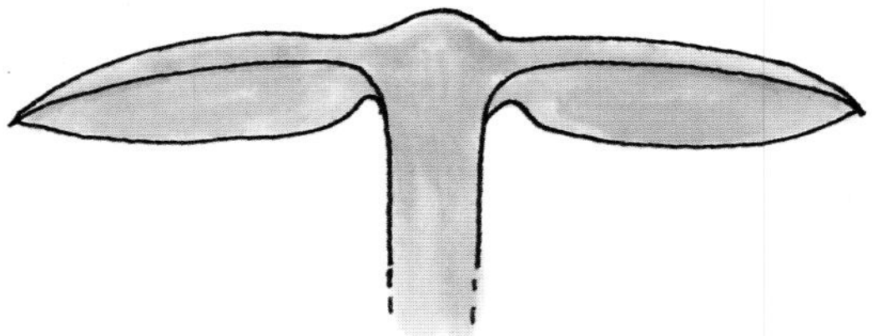

Sinuate or notched gills have a sudden curve just before they join the stem, often with a slight downward bend where they touch. The cap has a central bump or dome and is called umbonate.

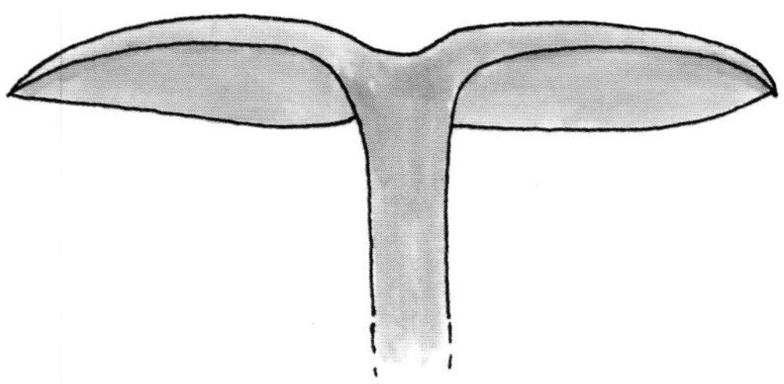

Adnate gills join the stem over their entire width (if they do not join on part of their width, they are often described as adnexed). This cap has a central hollow and is described as depressed; if the depression is extreme, like a navel, it is called umbilicate.

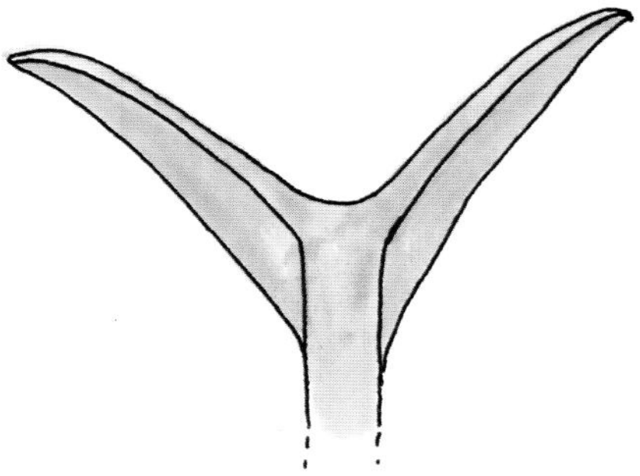

Decurrent gills join the stem and run down it for a greater or lesser amount; in some mushrooms it can be quite extreme. This cap is funnel-shaped or infundibuliform.

Common Mushroom Structures

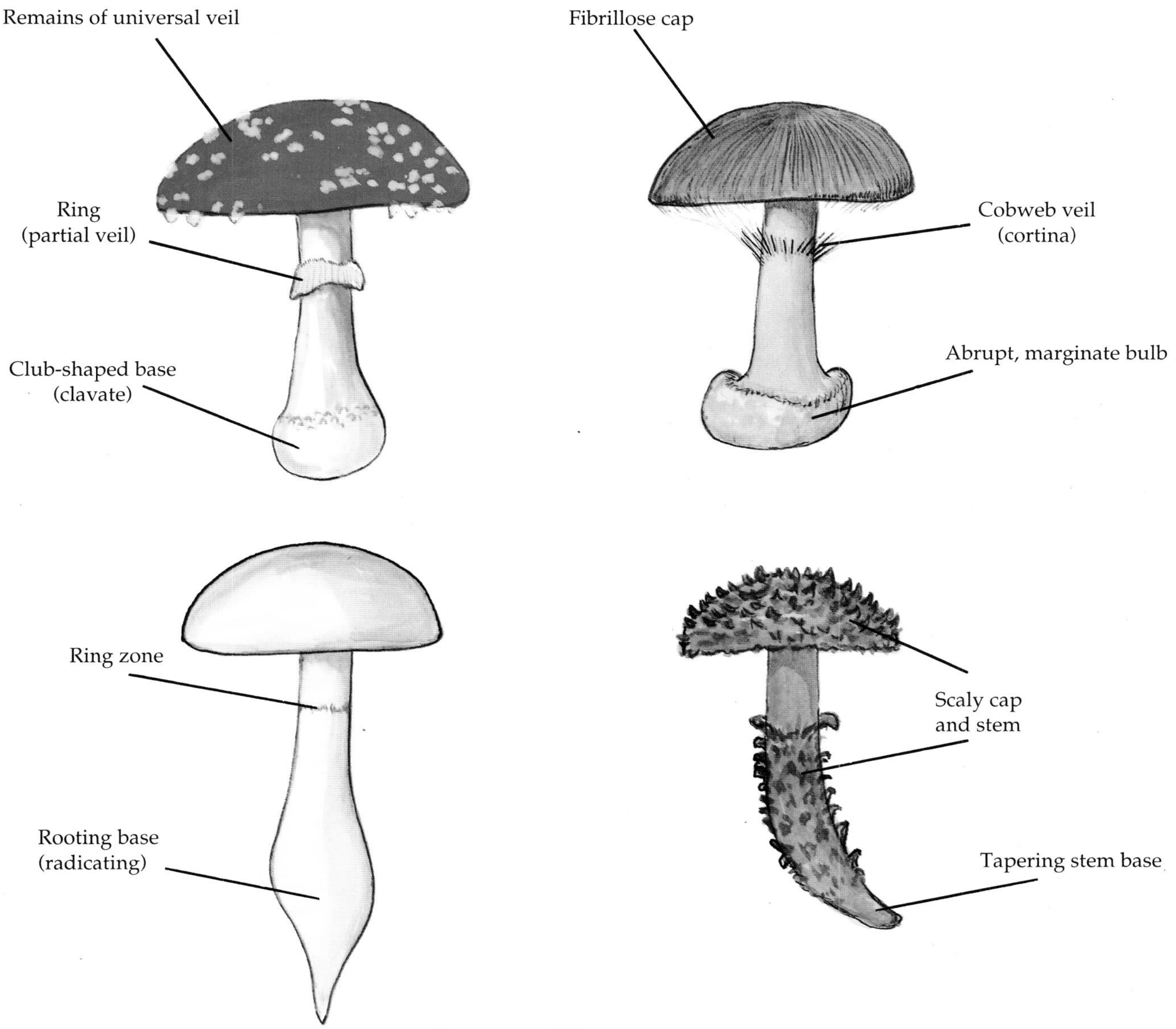

Spore Types

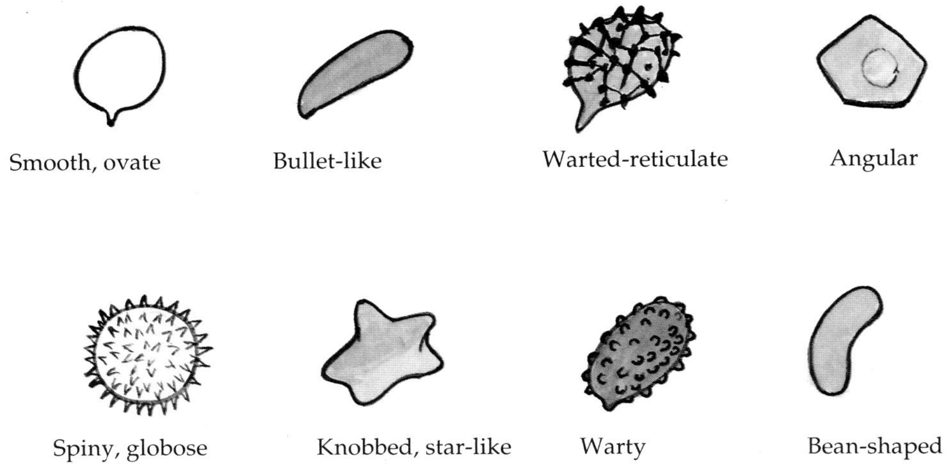

Examples of different Basidia

Holobasidiomycetes
(Typical Mushroom)

The basidia here are simple, undivided cells, usually forming 1–4 spores on short sterigmata and arranged in a layer called the hymenium, spread over gills, tubes, or other structures.

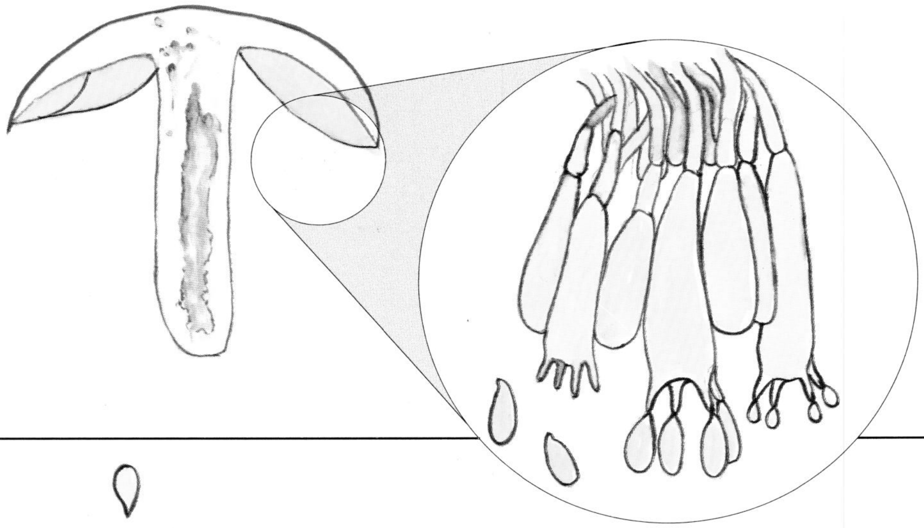

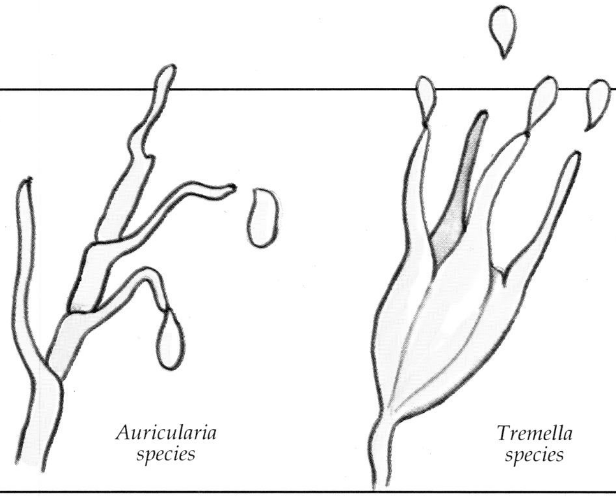

Heterobasidiomycetes
(Jelly Fungi)

Often rather strange, complex cells, with dividing cross-walls (septate) runnng either laterally or longitudinally. Usually 2–4 spores on extremely long sterigmata. Basidia are spread over the external surface of the fungus.

Ascomycetes
(Cup Fungi)

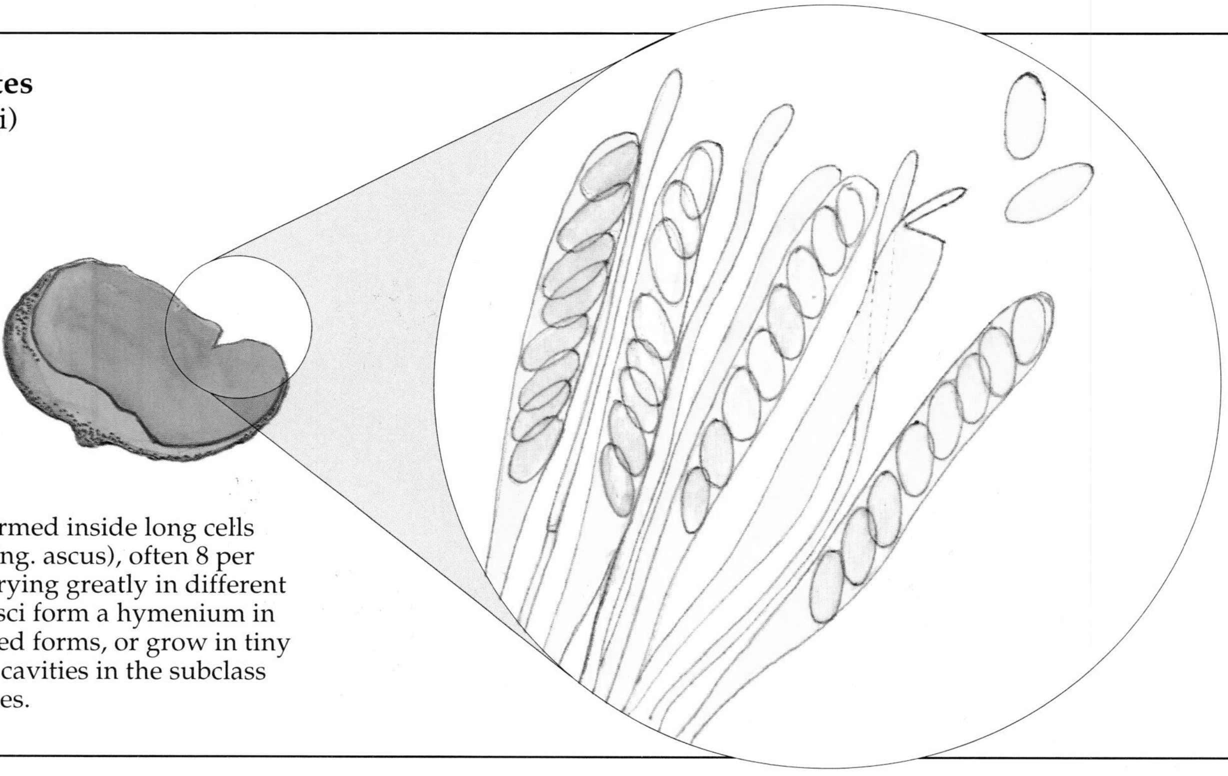

Spores are formed inside long cells called asci (sing. ascus), often 8 per ascus, but varying greatly in different genera.The asci form a hymenium in the cup-shaped forms, or grow in tiny flask-shaped cavities in the subclass Pyrenomycetes.

CLASS BASIDIOMYCETES

This class of fungi includes the majority of those illustrated in this book. They all share the common feature of producing their spores externally on a club-shaped or complex cell called a basidium, usually forming either two or four spores, although other numbers can be found. These basidia may form in an external layer called the hymenium, or may form in a mass called the gleba, within the fruiting body. The Basidiomycetes are further divided into three subclasses based on the structure of the basidium: the Holobasidiomycetes, Heterobasidiomycetes, and Gasteromycetes.

ORDER: BOLETALES

All boletes share common features: a soft, fleshy body; the basidia produced in a vertically arranged layer of minute tubes (the pores) on the underside of the cap; the forming of an association with specific trees. Their spores vary from round to – more commonly – long and bullet-shaped. The spores may be smooth or ornamented and range in color from yellowish to olive-brown, pinkish, or even black.

Many species display a remarkable change in color when their flesh is cut or bruised. This is caused by the reaction of certain chemicals in the flesh with oxygen, and may be almost instantaneous. Some boletes have distinctive tastes or odors, and in others identification is often aided by the use of chemical tests.

In size they range from under 1in (2cm) to over 2ft (60cm) across the cap in some tropical species; even in the USA they can reach 12in (30cm). The Boletales also include some gilled mushrooms, namely *Paxillus, Phylloporus,* and *Gomphidius,* but they are treated with the other gilled mushrooms for convenience since most beginners would expect to find them there.

BOLETACEAE
Bolete Family

These fungi include some of the most sought-after edible species. Mushrooms such as *Boletus edulis* are eaten all over the world either fresh, or dried in mushroom soups. The USA is rich in bolete species and they form one of the most attractive and readily visible groups of fungi throughout its woodlands.

Boletus edulis Bulliard ex Fries – "Cep", "Steinpilz"

Cap: 3–10in (8–25cm)
Spores: olive-brown, 13–19 x 4–6.5μm
Edibility: edible and excellent

PoRCiNi

The most sought-after edible bolete in the world, it occurs over the whole northern temperate region of the USA, Europe and Asia. It grows in both mixed conifer and deciduous woodlands, and a number of varieties and subspecies have been described from under different trees. Distinguishing features are the young pores, which are white, maturing to yellow-olive; the unchanging flesh when cut; and the fine white network which covers the stem. The cap color varies from a light yellow-brown to a deep reddish-brown, often with a lighter, whitish margin. The flesh has a mild, nutty flavor and dries well, making it invaluable in commercial mushroom soups. It is collected in enormous numbers in Europe for sale and processing, as well as for personal use.

Boletus aereus Bulliard ex Fries

Cap: 3–8in (8–20cm)
Spores: olive-brown, 12–14 x 4–5μm
Edibility: edible and excellent

A wonderful species with its dark chocolate-brown to blackish cap, often huge size, and excellent flavor. The cap is dry and finely granular in texture, frequently cracking into a fine mosaic. When covered in leaves it becomes blotched with paler, discolored patches. The tubes and pores begin white but soon age yellowish. The stem is distinctive with a brownish ground overlaid with a darker, fine network overall, unlike the better known *B. edulis,* which has a pale, whitish stem. The flesh is white with a sweet, nutty flavor, making it a popular edible. Found under tan oaks, madrone or live oak in California, it is a rather uncommon species.

Boletus barrowsii Smith

Cap: 3–10in (8–25cm)
Spores: olive-brown, 13–15 x 4–5μm
Edibility: edible and excellent

This wonderful species is considered a rival to the well-known Cep or King Bolete, *B. edulis,* for flavor and texture. The often huge white cap, pallid pores, and swollen stem with a fine reticulum are very distinctive. The cap surface is dry and almost velvety when young. It can be quite common in parts of western North America and Mexico, and grows under oaks and pines. It is named after the late Chuck Barrows, a very well-known collector of mushrooms, and the discoverer of several new species – a good example of the contribution an amateur can make.

Boletus seperans Peck

Cap: 2–6in (5–15cm)
Spores: olive-brown, 11–15 x 3–5μm
Edibility: edible and good

This is a good example of how a simple chemical test can instantly identify some species where variations in color and shape can otherwise make them a little tricky. Although the cap color varies from deep liver-brown to dull reddish, and the stem from the palest pinkish-buff to deep purplish-wine, the reaction with a drop of household ammonia is constant – a deep, vivid sea-green. This easily separates it from the similar *B. edulis*. It is not common but is widespread throughout the northeast under mixed deciduous trees. There is some discussion as to the correct name for this species, and some authors have described it as a new species, *B. pseudoseperans*, although the differences, if any, between the two seem slight.

Boletus regius Krombholtz

Cap: 3–8in (7–20cm)
Spores: olive-brown, 12–16.5 x 3.5–5μm
Edibility: edible

Certainly one of the most beautiful species of bolete anywhere, the deep rose-red to dark red cap contrasts with the bright yellow pores and stem. The latter has a fine network overall, and the flesh stains a pale blue. It is more frequent in the western states than in the east, and seems to prefer oak as its host tree. It is quite widely regarded as a good edible, but is often spoiled by insect larvae, a common problem with many boletes and, indeed, many of the best edible fungi of all sorts. More commonly found in the northeast is *B. pseudopeckii*, which has a pale rose cap rapidly turning dull brick-red, and a very fine network only visible at the apex of the stem. It prefers conifers to oaks.

Boletus appendiculatus Schaeffer ex Fries

Cap: 4–8in (10–20cm)
Spores: olive-brown, 12–15 x 3.5–5μm
Edibility: edible

Originally described from Europe, where it grows under beech and oak, it can also be found in California and some other western states growing likewise under oak. It is quite a handsome species, with a dry cinnamon-brown cap and bright yellow pores and stem, with the latter possessing a fine yellow network and often stained reddish-brown at the base. Both pores and flesh bruise pale blue. The flesh may have a rather pungent, almost unpleasant odor, but it is usually regarded as a good edible.

Boletus calopus Fries

Cap: 3–8in (7.5–20cm)
Spores: olive-brown, 10–14 x 4–6μm
Edibility: inedible, extremely bitter to taste

Many species of boletes are distinguished by having a bitter taste, although they are in fact edible, just distasteful. In North America there is a complex of closely related species all sharing this characteristic, many of them quite beautiful in appearance. This species occurs in the western states under conifers, and is distinguished by its red stem with a white network, whitish-olive cap, and yellow pores. Similar species include *B. rubripes*, also in the west and with a red stem, but without a network; *B. coniferarum* has a network, but usually lacks red tints and is common in the Pacific Northwest, while *B. inedulis* occurs in the east and has a slender, reddish stem with only a partial to minute network.

Boletus subvelutipes Peck

Cap: 3–6in (7.5–15cm)
Spores: olive-brown, 12–18 x 4–6μm
Edibility: doubtful; best avoided

When young and fresh this can be a quite spectacular species, with bright orange-red to deep blood-red colors in its cap, stem, and pores. Add to that the instant change to deep indigo blue when bruised and it is a truly memorable species. Growing under beech or pine, the stem is minutely speckled with tiny dots, and no network is present. At the base are fine reddish hairs. This is now known to be a complex of several very similar species which mainly differ microscopically, including *B. rufocinnamomeus*, which only differs macroscopically by the yellow wooly coating on the stem base, and is probably equally common. See also *B. subluridellus* below.

Boletus subluridellus Smith & Thiers

Cap 2–6in (5–15cm)
Spores: olive-brown, 11–15 x 4.5–5μm
Edibility: doubtful; best avoided

Often confused with the previous species, this is in fact even more beautiful when young, with a deep, blood-red coloration in all parts of its fruiting body, bruising deep blue-black when handled. As it ages, the cap fades to orange-red, and the stem becomes orange-yellow with fine red dots. The base of the stem has a pale yellow wooly coating. It is quite common in warm, wet summers and the fall in the northeast, and prefers oaks as its host.

Boletus frostii Russell

Cap: 2–6in (5–15cm)
Spores: olive-brown, 11–15 x 4–5μm
Edibility: doubtful; best avoided

This would, I think, get my vote as the most spectacular bolete, and indeed one of the most spectacular of all fungi, in North America. A fresh specimen in its prime is a bright apple-red to blood-red all over, with a shiny, slightly viscid cap surface. The stem has a strongly raised network all the way down, and the deep, almost blackish-red pores often weep droplets of amber liquid. The flesh turns a deep blue when cut. It is not very common, but is found most years growing under oaks in the eastern and southern states, and is quite unmistakable.

Boletus satanus Lenz - "Satan's Bolete"

Cap: 3–12in (7–30cm)
Spores: olive-brown, 11–15 x 4–6μm
Edibility: poisonous, causes acute gastric distress

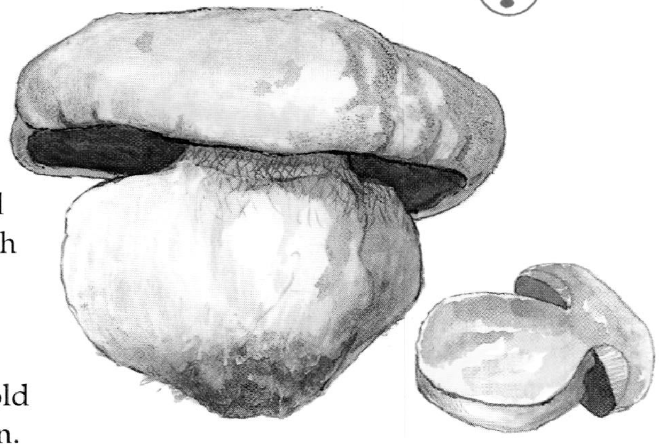

The mycologist who described this species stated that its emanations were so malign that he felt ill even at a distance! Certainly it looks rather lurid, although no one has reported such drastic effects since then. The huge grayish-olive cap soon discolors pinkish, while the swollen stem has a very fine reddish network. The pores are red and bruise blue to the touch, as does the pale yellow flesh. It is quite frequent in some years in parts of California, growing under oaks, and is one of the few boletes reliably known to cause poisonings. It is worth noting that *B. satanus* as described and found in Europe is different in many respects: the cap is whiter, does not flush pink, and the flesh develops a repulsive odor of rotten garlic with age. The American fungus should probably have its own name; *B. eastwoodiae* is another old name for the same fungus and could be used if the difference is proven.

Boletus pulcherrimus Thiers & Halling

(= *B eastwoodiae*)

Cap: 4–6in (10–15cm)
Spores: olive-brown, 11–13 x 4.5–6μm
Edibility: probably poisonous

This species was known for many years under the name *B. eastwoodiae*, but when the original specimen of that species was examined it turned out to be the same as *B. satanus*, described above. Thus, a new name had to be given to this species, and it was called *B. pulcherrimus*, which means beautiful. Certainly it is very striking, although not as bulky and fat as the previous species, and the cap is a darker olive to reddish-brown. It also occurs on the west coast and is considered mildly poisonous.

Boletus pseudosensibilis Smith & Thiers

Cap: 3–6in (7.5–15cm)
Spores: olive-brown, 9–12 x 3–4μm
Edibility: edible, but best avoided

Sometimes, when there is a group of closely related, and very similar, species, it can be very useful if there is one outstanding characteristic that separates at least one of the species from the others. In this case it is the vivid green reaction caused when a drop of ammonia is placed on the cap. Only this species has this reaction, compared with the other species in the group, such as *B. bicolor* (see below), *B. sensibilis*, or *B. miniatoolivaceus*, all of which have rather similar external colors. *B. bicolor* can be distinguished by the very weak blue staining reaction in its flesh and its redder colors. *B. sensibilis* has a spicy, nutty odor, stains deep blue, and has a tiny network at the apex of the stem (use a lens). *B. miniatoolivaceus* lacks the odor, but stains deep blue and has a smooth stem all the way up.

Boletus bicolor Peck

Cap: 2–6in (5–15cm)
Spores: olive-brown, 8–12 x 3.5–5μm
Edibility: edible, but best avoided

The lovely rose-red to carmine cap soon fades to a dull pinkish-brown and may often crack in dry weather. The bright yellow pores are usually slightly decurrent and bruise deep blue; this contrasts with the flesh which only very slowly bruises palest blue, if at all. The stem is reminiscent of rhubarb, with its deep purplish-red colors at the base. It can be a very common species in warm, wet years and grows under oaks throughout eastern North America down into Florida. Compare carefully with *B. pseudosensibilis,* shown above; it stains deep blue and reacts green with ammonia on the cap surface.

Boletus longicurvipes Snell & Smith

Cap: 1–2in (2.5–5cm)
Spores: olive-brown, 13–17 x 4–5μm
Edibility:edible

A strange species, which has also been placed in the genus *Leccinum* with which it shares some characteristics, but is probably best placed here. The specific name means "long curving stem", which fits admirably, since it nearly always has a long, slender, and curved stem. The cap is tacky to viscid to the touch and a rather bright orange-brown, while the stem is flushed pinkish-brown to reddish-orange and speckled with minute floccules. The flesh is white and unchanging when cut. Although uncommon overall, it can be locally common in mixed conifer woods in the northeast south through North Carolina.

Boletus subglabripes Peck

[= *Leccinum subglabripes*]

Cap: 2–4in (5–10cm)

Spores: olive-brown, 11–14 x 3–5μm

Edibility: edible

Another species which cannot quite decide which group it belongs in, as the synonym shows. It demonstrates that many of these divisions into genera are man-made, and that fungi will not always conform to our rules. The slightly wooly-floccose stem is reminiscent of a species of *Leccinum* shown later, but the small wooly scales do not darken as they do in that genus. The cap is slightly tacky and often lumpy or irregular, and a rich cinnamon-brown to orange-brown. The pores are yellow and do not change color when bruised. The flesh is pale yellow. It can be very common in mixed woods throughout the eastern states.

Boletus ornatipes Peck

Cap: 2–6in (5–15cm)

Spores: olive-brown, 9–13 x 3–4μm

Edibility: edible

With many boletes the surface of the stem, whether it is smooth or has a network, is very characteristic and important for identification. In this species and a few others the network is greatly developed, although it is even more extreme in other species. The lines of the network are raised into distinct ridges and flaps, hence the Latin name *ornatipes*, which means "ornate stem". The cap is unusual in that it begins life a deep gray-brown but soon flushes yellow, then bright yellow-gold. The stem, pores, and flesh are all yellow. It is a fairly common species along roadsides, banks, and woodland edges throughout the northeast.

Boletus griseus Frost in Peck

Cap: 2–6in (5–15cm)

Spores: olive-brown, 9–12 x 3.5–4μm

Edibility: edible

A close relative of the previous species, this also has a well-developed network on the stem, and in some forms can be confused. In this species, however, the colors are much duller, more whitish-gray, particularly the pores and tubes, which are pallid gray, and the flesh, which is whitish. The base of the stem has a yellow flush and may become yellow overall. This is a common species in open oak woods throughout the northeastern states.

Boletus parasiticus Fries

Cap: 1–3in (2.5–7.5cm)
Spores: olive-brown, 12–18 x 3.5–5μm
Edibility: edible

Unique and unmistakable among American boletes, this species has developed a most remarkable method of growth. It occurs only on fruit-bodies of the common Earthball, *Scleroderma citrinum*, often with several boletes pushing up from the base of the Earthball. It does not seem to cause undue damage to its host, since the Earthball continues to produce its own spores, even though its tissues are invaded by the mycelium of the bolete. A locally common species, it may appear in large numbers in wet seasons.

Boletus pulverulentus Opatowski

Cap: 2–4in (5–10cm)
Spores: olive-brown, 11–14 x 4.5–6μm
Edibility: edible

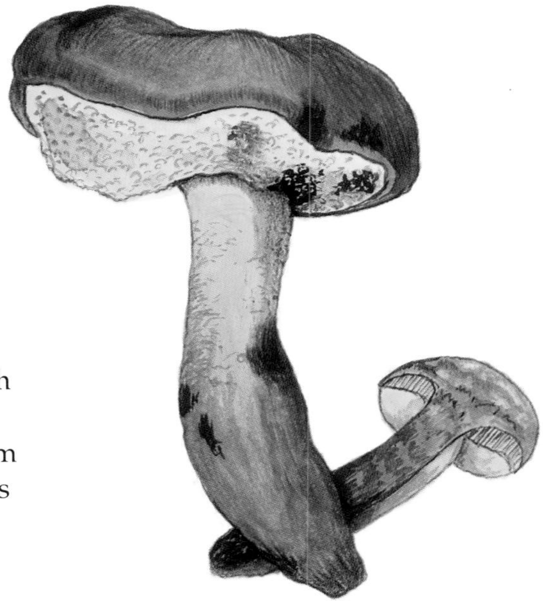

Although many fungi, and particularly boletes, change color when cut or bruised, there are few mushrooms as remarkable as this species in the intensity of the change. When any part of the mushroom is handled, and particularly when cut open, there is an almost instantaneous change to the deepest cobalt blue or blue-black. When fresh the bolete has a reddish-brown cap with yellow pores, and a yellow stem flushed with red. By the time you get it home it may be almost unrecognizable from the staining and bruising. This is a locally common species found mostly under oaks in the northeastern states.

Boletus badius Fries

Cap: 2–4in (5–10cm)
Spores: olive-brown, 10–14 x 4–5μm
Edibility: edible and good

Found throughout the northern and eastern states, and, indeed, across most of the temperate northern hemisphere, this chestnut-brown species has a slightly velvety cap when young, with yellowish-cream pores which bruise dull blue-gray. The cylindrical stem is smooth and colored like the cap. It occurs in both conifer and deciduous woods, especially under beech. Specimens from the latter habitat tend to be brighter in color and much more velvety, and are sometimes referred to as a separate species, *B. vaccinus*, by some mycologists.

Boletus rubellus Krombholtz

Cap: 1–2in (2–5cm)
Spores: olive-brown, 7–17 x 4–7μm
Edibility: edible

There are few boletes, or indeed any other fungi, as attractive as this small species. To see the clusters of bright scarlet or blood-red caps nestled deep in the grass along paths or on lawns under oaks, where it likes to grow, is one of the delights of mushrooming. Both cap and stem are red and bruise blue when handled, while the pores are pale yellow. It is always found close to oak trees, usually out near the root tips in damp grass soon after the first of the late summer rains, and is common throughout much of eastern North America.
Other similar small red species, including *B. campestris* and *B. fraternus,* are distinguished microscopically but are otherwise identical. Although edible, the insects also find it attractive, so it is usually rather buggy inside.

Boletus mirabilis Murril

Cap: 2–6in (5–15cm)
Spores: olive-brown, 19–24 x 7–9μm
Edibility: edible and excellent

This large bolete is one of the few species to fruit regularly on old, rotten logs, and this, combined with its striking liver-brown to chocolate colors, makes it easy to recognize. The stem is roughened and almost reticulate in texture, while the flesh is pallid and unchanging when cut. Under a microscope the spores are exceptionally large. This is a western species and is considered by many to be an excellent edible fungus.

Boletus affinis Peck

Cap 2–4in (5–10cm)
Spores: yellow-brown, 12–16 x 3–3.5μm
Edibility: edible

This species occurs in two common forms, one with a uniformly colored cap, the other with the surface spotted to a greater or lesser degree with pale-colored spots. There are no other differences between the two, and it seems this is just a natural variation in the pigment of the cap, although it is not known why it occurs. The spotted form is shown here. The cap is usually dry and rather dull in texture. The pores are white to pale buff, and the stem is pale reddish-brown and quite smooth to touch. Because of the yellowish spores without any olive tints normally found in bolete spores, this species is sometimes placed in the genus *Xanthoconium*.It is very common throughout the northeastern states down into Florida, although the spotted form seems not to occur very commonly in the south.

Boletus piperatus Fries

Cap: 1–4in (2.5–10cm)
Spores: cinnamon, 9–12 x 4–5μm
Edibility: inedible, very peppery to taste

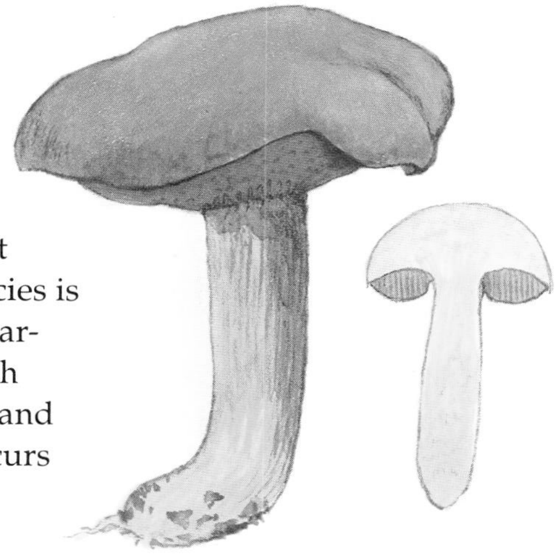

Unusual flavors are very rare in the majority of boletes, the most common being a bitter taste. The hot, peppery flavor of this species is almost unique. A small, pretty bolete, it has cinnamon to cinnabar-red pores, and the stem is bright yellow at the base, as is the flesh inside. The last feature is perhaps the best distinguishing mark, and you can identify even old, faded specimens by this means. It occurs most commonly under birch, occasionally under pine, and is widespread throughout the northern and northeastern states.

Boletus caespitosus Peck

[= *B. auriporus* Peck?]

Cap 2–3in (5–7.5cm)
Spores: olive-brown, 9–11 x 4–4.5μm
Edibility: unknown; best avoided

Very few boletes have the habit of growing in clumps (caespitose is the technical term for this, hence the Latin name), although all may do so on rare occasions. This species almost always does so. The other distinguishing features are the slightly sticky cap, the brilliant golden-yellow, unchanging pores, and the smooth, spindle-shaped stems. Most importantly, when cut open the flesh has a strong, pungent, rubber-like odor exactly like that of the common Earthball *Scleroderma citrinum*. It is rather rare and grows in warm, wet summers in the eastern states under oak and beech. There is a suggestion that it is the same as *B. auriporus*, also described by Peck, and that name would have preference if this is proven. Until then I prefer to use this very descriptive name.

Boletus spadiceus (Fries) Quélet

Cap: 2–4in (5–10cm)
Spores: olive-brown, 9–14 x 4–5μm
Edibility: edible

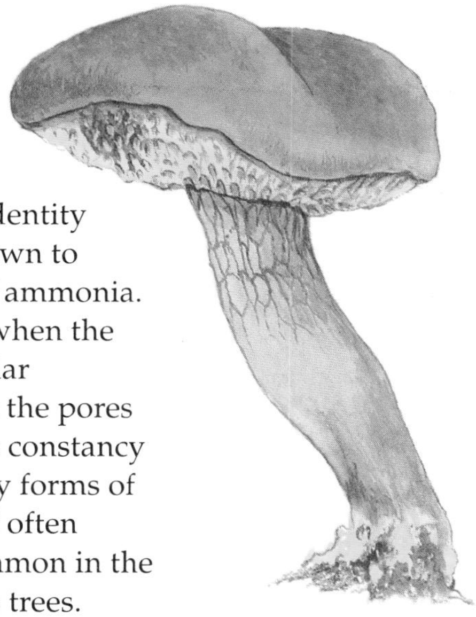

A bolete where a chemical reaction gives a good clue as to identity when combined with other visible features. The reddish-brown to yellow-tan cap is velvety, turning deep green with a drop of ammonia. The other important feature is the lack of any color change when the yellow pores are bruised. This is in contrast to the very similar *B. illudens*, where there is also a green ammonia reaction but the pores bruise slowly blue. There is some doubt, however, about the constancy of these characteristics, and it is possible that they are merely forms of one variable species. The stem of both species has a series of often prominent ridges and lines at the apex. Both species are common in the northern and eastern states under oaks and other deciduous trees.

Boletus chrysenteron Fries

Cap: 2–3in (5–8cm)
Spores: olive-brown, 9–13 x 3.5–5µm
Edibility: edible

Perhaps the best known of the smaller boletes in both Europe and North America, this species is to be found in almost any woodland throughout America. The brownish cap soon develops fine cracks which expose the reddish flesh beneath. The pores are yellowish and bruise blue. The slender stem is yellowish-white above, shading to purplish-red below, and has pale flesh which also stains blue when cut. Although variable in cap color (more olive or reddish forms are common), the cracking is a consistent feature of older specimens. Similar species are *B. zelleri* on the west coast, which has a very dark, blackish cap, often extremely wrinkled and lumpy, and *Boletellus intermedius* in the northeast, which is almost identical but stains deep blue everywhere, and has spores which are truncate and have faint spiralling grooves.

Boletus ravenelii (Berkeley & Curtis) Murrill

Cap: 2–4in (5–10cm)
Spores: olive-brown, 8–10 x 4–5µm
Edibility: edible

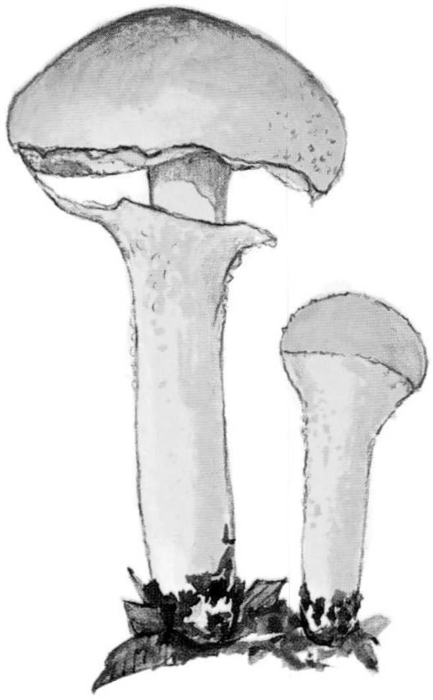

This bolete has such distinctive and almost unique characteristics that it is quite unmistakable and is often placed in a separate genus called *Pulveroboletus*.The entire fungus is bright yellow to slightly orange in the center, and is dry and powdery to touch. When picked up, the yellow powder, which is the remains of an enveloping outer veil, may often come off on your fingers. There is also a prominent ring at the top of the stem. The yellow pores bruise slightly blue when touched. It is a locally common species with a very scattered distribution, but is found from the southeastern states up to Maine and into Canada, and grows under pines.

Tylopilus alboater (Schweinitz) Murrill

Cap: 3–6in (7.5–15cm)
Spores: reddish-brown, 7–11 x 3.5–5µm
Edibility: edible

Although the majority of species of *Tylopilus* are bitter to taste, this one is an exception, having a mild, nutty flavor. It is, besides, so distinctive with its deep blackish-gray coloration that it can hardly be confused with any other bolete. When young the cap is almost velvety but becomes smooth and often cracks with age. The flesh turns reddish-gray then black when cut, but, as with all mushrooms, such color changes are no indication of edibility or toxicity; in this instance it is a good edible. It can be quite common in some parts of the east and northeast, and grows under oaks.

Tylopilus felleus (Fries) Karsten

Cap: 2–8in (5–20cm)
Spores: reddish-brown, 11–15 x 3–5µm
Edibility: inedible, extremely bitter to taste

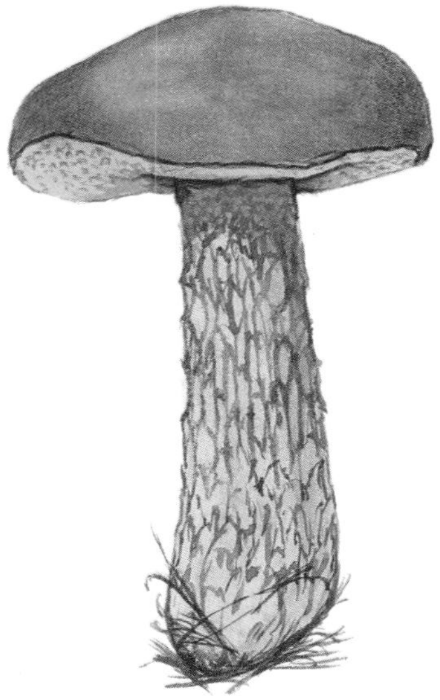

Many a meal of mushrooms has been spoiled by this species, particularly when the collectors thought that they were picking the delicious Cep bolete, *Boletus edulis,* which this resembles. However, one taste of this species will soon show you the error you have made. It tastes almost as bitter as quinine, and the flavor is not improved by cooking. Like *Boletus edulis,* this species has a network on its stem, but unlike that species the overall coloration is yellow-brown and the mature pores take on a distinct pink flush. The spores differ also in their pinkish-brown to purplish color. A common species under mixed trees throughout the east from Florida up to Maine and into Canada.

Tylopilus eximius (Peck) Singer

Cap: 2–6in (5–15cm)
Spores: reddish-brown, 11–15 x 3–5µm
Edibility: possibly poisonous

Not easily recognized as a *Tylopilus,* and it has in fact been placed in other genera by different authors. It seems to combine the features of different boletes, having the pinkish or wine-brown spores like a *Tylopilus,* but the speckled, wooly stem of a *Leccinum.* The pores are unlike almost any other bolete, with their very dark purple-brown color, a very strange bolete indeed. The flesh is whitish to light purplish-brown, and is mild to taste. This has traditionally been considered a good edible, but some recent poisonings from a "large, dark brown bolete" in areas where this species is common seem to refer to it and might mean that this opinion must be reconsidered. It is recorded from Florida to Maine, but has a very scattered distribution and seems commonest in the north.

Tylopilus plumbeoviolaceus

(Snell & Dick) Singer

Cap: 2–6in (5–15cm)
Spores: reddish-brown, 10–13 x 3–4µm
Edibility: inedible; very bitter

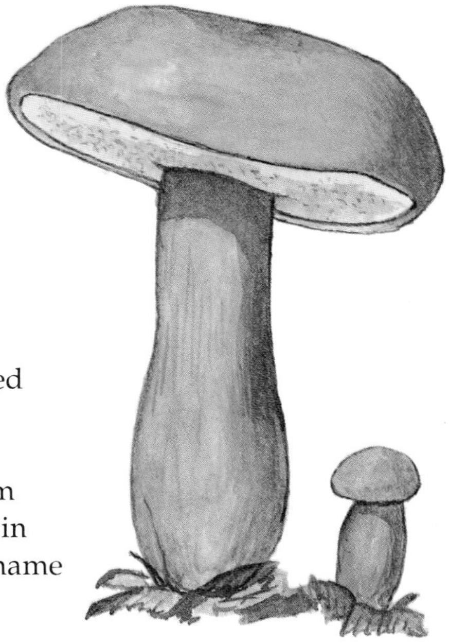

When young and fresh this is one of the most remarkable and easily identified boletes in the USA. It is the only species with deep violet-lavender colors, especially in the stem, and this contrasts with the whitish pores. As it ages, however, the cap colors rapidly fade to a dull pinkish-gray, although the stem usually retains its violet flush longer. It can be extremely common and grow in very large numbers in mixed woods throughout the eastern states. What a shame such a beautiful and edible-looking bolete should be so bitter and inedible!

Tylopilus chromapes (Frost) Smith & Thiers

Cap: 2–6in (5–15cm)

Spores: reddish-brown, 11–17 x 4–5.5μm

Edibility: edible

If one were to design a bolete with the most unlikely color combinations and features, this species might well be the result. This remarkable species is beautiful, with its pale strawberry-pink to reddish cap, pink stem with darker red wooly scales and a brilliant yellow base, and its white pores turning pale pink. Because of the speckled stem it has sometimes been placed in the genus *Leccinum*, but the resemblance is only superficial. It is fortunately a common species in deciduous woods throughout the eastern states.

Tylopilus ballouii (Peck) Singer

Cap: 2–4in (5–10cm)

Spores: reddish-brown, 5–11 x 3–5μm

Edibility: edible

An example of the enormous color range to be found in the genus *Tylopilus*, this species is a bright burnt-orange fading to orange-tan with age. It is rather unusual in that where the cap is chewed by slugs or rodents the orange cuticle often regrows over the eaten-out areas. The pores are creamy to pale pinkish, while the short, stocky stem is whitish and smooth. This species has a distinctly southern distribution and grows from Florida up into southern New Jersey and coastal areas of New York, Rhode Island and neighboring areas.

Boletellus russellii (Frost) Gilbert

Cap: 2–6in (5–15cm)

Spores: olive-brown, 15–20 x 7–11μm, with longitudinal grooves

Edibility: edible

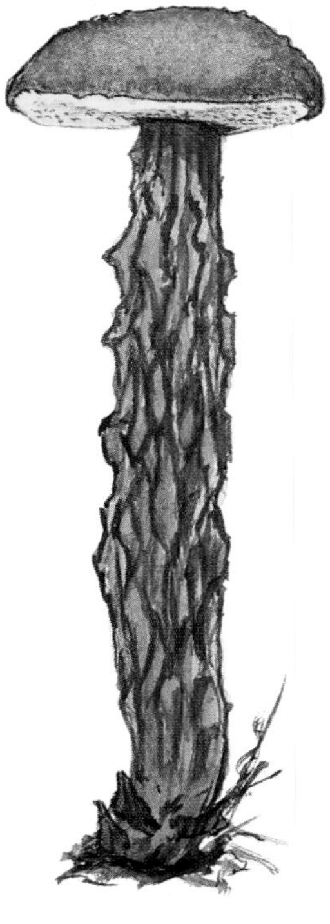

A rather weird-looking bolete, with its tall stem covered in a shaggy network of ridges, and grooves extending out into flaps, this is rather typical of many members of the genus *Boletellus*, but not all. The genus is characterized by its grooved and pitted spores, but is a rather mixed assemblage of boletes, and is probably not worth separating off from the genus *Boletus* on this one feature. We now know that many boletes have finely grooved spores when viewed under very high-powered electron scan microscopes. This rare species grows under oaks and pines throughout the eastern states.

Leccinum atrostipitatum

Smith, Thiers & Watling

Cap: 3–8in (7.5–20cm)

Spores: olive-brown, 13–17 x 4–5μm

Edibility: doubtful; best avoided

When young this has the most beautiful pale pink cap which is felty to touch; as it ages, it turns a pinkish-buff to pale apricot, and may form flattened wooly scales at the center. The young pores are cream, while the stout, often massive stem is covered with dense black squamules even when young. The entire genus *Leccinum* is characterized by the presence of these wooly squamules, which usually darken with age and are formed of a mixture of sterile cells and fertile basidia. The white flesh turns slowly wine-red to violaceus-gray to blackish when cut. It is frequently found under birches in eastern and northern states up into Canada.

Leccinum insigne Smith, Thiers & Watling

Cap: 2–6in (5–15cm)

Spores: olive-brown, 13–16 x 4–5μm

Edibility: edible

This was formerly confused with the well-known *L. aurantiacum*, but there are several differences. Both species have bright tawny orange to reddish-orange caps, although *L. insigne* seems to be consistently darker, and both have white stem squamules which rapidly turn deep rust-brown to blackish-brown. The flesh in *L. insigne* turns grayish-purple then purplish-black, while *L. aurantiacum* passes through a burgundy-red stage before becoming purplish-black. Both species grow under aspen, but *L. insigne* can also be found under birch. The two species are common over much of North America and Canada.

Leccinum rugosiceps (Peck) Singer

Cap: 2–4in (5–10cm)

Spores: olive-brown, 16–21 x 5–5.5μm

Edibility: edible

This all-yellow to tawny orange species is distinctive because of its wrinkled, lumpy cap surface which often cracks with age. The stem is yellow with tiny, concolorous wooly squamules, which darken with age or handling. The flesh when cut is yellow turning reddish. It is frequent in mixed woods, especially under oaks in the eastern states. Compare it carefully with the similar *Boletus subglabripes*, shown earlier, which looks superficially similar but has a less lumpy, irregular cap, extremely tiny stem squamules that do not darken, and often a reddish flush in the stem surface, and finally has flesh which does not turn dull reddish when cut.

Leccinum albellum (Peck) Singer

Cap: 2–3in (5–7cm)
Spores: olive-brown, 15–20 x 4–6μm
Edibility: edible

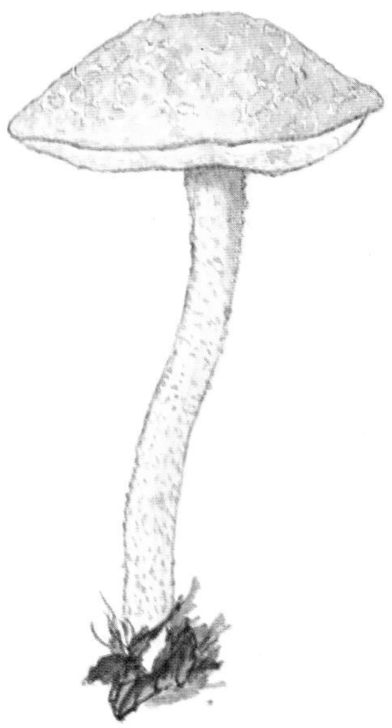

All-white boletes are quite uncommon, and this one is easily distinguished both by its very slender, rather soft fruit-body and the way in which the cap cuticle cracks like a mosaic as it matures. The fungus can also take on a grayish-buff hue with age. The flesh when cut is pallid and unchanging. It is rather common and grows under oaks throughout the eastern states. The similar *L. holopus* is also white, but rarely cracks, and has flesh often flushing pink when cut. The white body also turns greenish with age.

Leccinum scabrum (Fries) S.F. Gray

Cap: 2–6in (5–15cm)
Spores: olive-brown, 15–19 x 5–7μm
Edibility: edible

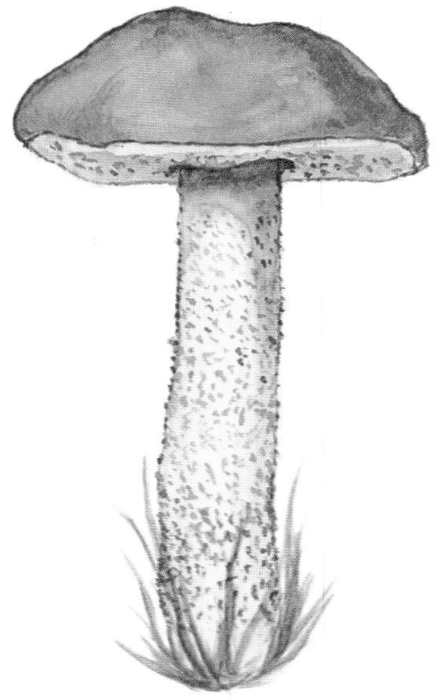

Although commonly reported and often included in guide books, this is in fact a much rarer species in North America than it is in Europe, and is frequently misidentified. The true *L. scabrum* has a soft, yellow-brown to buff-brown cap which is easily dented by the pressure of a finger, pale cream-buff pores that hardly stain when bruised, and stem squamules which start white and age blackish-brown. The flesh is pallid and, when cut, hardly changes, turning only very slightly pinkish-buff in the stem apex. There may be bluish-green stains in the stem base. Other similar species stain a much brighter pink in the cap and stem, and have firmer flesh. It grows exclusively under birch, and is spread throughout the northern and eastern states up into Canada.

Gyroporus purpurinus (Snell) Singer

Cap: ½–2in (1–5cm)
Spores: yellowish, 8–11 x 5–6.5μm
Edibility: edible

The genus *Gyroporus* is distinguished by the following characteristics: brittle flesh, stem usually hollowed out into chambers, and spores distinctly yellowish rather than olive-brown. This is the one of the rarest species and has a beautiful bright reddish-purple hue overall, unlike almost any other bolete. The pores are white to cream and unchanging when bruised. It is also unusually small for the genus. It grows under oaks and other deciduous trees in the southern and eastern states.

Click to LOOK INSIDE!

Share your own customer images
Search inside this book

Start reading Mushrooming Without Fear on your Kindle **in under a minute**.

Don't have a Kindle? Get your Kindle here, or download a **FREE** Kindle Reading App.

Mushrooming without Fear: The Beginner's Guide to Collecting Safe and Delicious Mushrooms [Paperback]

Alexander Schwab (Author)

(23 customer reviews) | (144)

List Price: ~~$14.95~~
Price: $9.11 & eligible for **FREE Super Saver Shipping** on orders over $25. Details
You Save: $5.84 (39%)

Only 8 left in stock (more on the way).
Ships from and sold by **Amazon.com**. Gift-wrap available.

Want it delivered Monday, September 17? Order it in the next 43 hours and 14 minutes, and choose **One-Day Shipping** at checkout. Details

25 new from $9.11 **20 used** from $5.97

Formats	Amazon Price	New from	Used from
Kindle Edition	$8.65	--	--
Hardcover	--	$16.25	$15.24
Paperback	$9.11	$9.11	$5.97

Quantity: 1

Yes, I want **FREE Two-Day Shipping** with Amazon Prime

or

Sign in to turn on 1-Click ordering.

Sell Us Your Item
For a **$1.35** Gift Card
Trade in
Learn more

More Buying Choices
45 used & new from $5.97
Have one to sell?

Share

Book Description

Publication Date: **October 17, 2007**

Novices eager to collect tasty wild mushrooms will find this unique guide invaluable. Unlike others, it focuses only on those types that are both safe to eat and delicious. Most important, it presents the eight rules of mushroom gathering in a straightforward fashion—including "Never, never take a mushroom with gills" and "If a mushroom smells rotten, it is rotten." Among the many mushrooms covered are the cep; the red-cracked, larch, bay, and birch boletes; hen of the woods, chanterelle, trumpet chanterelle, hedgehog fungus, common puffball, horn of plenty, and cauliflower mushroom. Each is identified with several color photographs and identification checklist, and there's also information on mushroom season, handling, storage, and cooking, complete with recipes.

Frequently Bought Together

 +  + 

Price For All Three: $48.77

Show availability and shipping details

- ☑ **This item:** Mushrooming without Fear: The Beginner's Guide to Collecting Safe and Delicious Mushrooms by Alexander Schwab Paperback $9.11
- ☑ National Audubon Society Field Guide to North American Mushrooms (National Audubon Society Field Guides) by Gary H. Lincoff Paperback $13.27
- ☑ Mushrooms Demystified by David Arora Paperback $26.39

Customers Who Bought This Item Also Bought

Page 1 of 25

National Audubon Society Field Guide to North ... Gary H. Lincoff

Mushrooms Demystified › David Arora (85)

All That the Rain Promises and More: A Hip Pocket ... › David Arora

The Complete Mushroom Hunter: An Illustrated ... › Gary Lincoff

Gyroporus castaneus (Fries) Quélet

Cap: 1–4in (2.5–10cm)
Spores: yellowish, 8–12.5 x 5–6μm
Edibility: edible and delicious

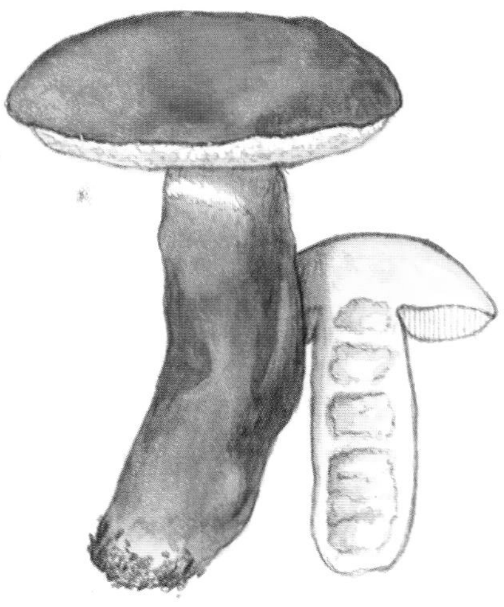

The commonest species of the genus, this is found all across the northern temperate regions of the world and also extends down into the subtropical regions. The rich chestnut to yellow-brown cap and stem are often rather irregular and lumpy, and, like other species in the genus, are usually hollowed out and brittle. It is extremely common in North America, where it grows under a variety of trees, but especially oaks, and is a valued edible species with a nutty flavor.

Gyroporus cyanescens (Fries) Quélet

Cap: 2–5in (5–12.5cm)
Spores: yellowish, 8–10 x 5–6μm
Edibility: edible

This species cannot be mistaken for any other bolete, with its overall whitish-straw colors combined with the quite remarkable depth of the color change when cut. All parts turn an intense cobalt-blue within a few moments of bruising or cutting. The stem is hollowed, as in other *Gyroporus* species, while the cap surface is fibrous and roughened. It is rather uncommon, but is found under pines and birches on sandy soils from Florida up to Maine and into Canada. A variety may be found where the color change is to deep violet rather than blue, var. *violaceotinctus;* this is much more uncommon.

Suillus granulatus (Fries) Kuntze

Cap 2–4in (5–10cm)
Spores: olive-brown, 7–10 x 2.5–3.5μm
Edibility: edible with caution; can cause stomach upsets

The genus *Suillus* is typified by the arrangement of special cells (cystidia) in the tubes, by the small, glandular dots on the upper part of the stem in many species, the often sticky cap (although a few species are dry and scaly), and the strict relationship with certain conifers. This species has all these features. The cap is cinnamon-brown to orange-brown, and the pores are pale yellow and often weep milky droplets when young. This is a common species under pine, often found in large numbers. Like many *Suillus* species, it is edible to some, but causes upsets in others.

Suillus luteus (Fries) S.F. Gray – "Slippery Jack"

Cap: 2–4in (5–10cm)
Spores: olive-brown, 7–9 x 2.5–3μm
Edibility: edible with caution; can cause upsets

The common name refers to the viscid, glutinous cap in wet weather. The rich reddish-brown cap is often streaky or fibrous under the gluten. The stem is very distinctive, with glandular dots at the apex and a thick, membranous white ring. The ring is usually flushed lilac on the underside. Although widely collected as a good edible, the viscid cap cuticle seems to cause stomach upsets in many people, so is best removed. It grows under pines and is quite common.

Suillus grevillei (Klotzch) Singer [=*S. elegans*]

Cap: 2–6in (5–15cm)
Spores: olive-brown, 8–10 x 3–4μm
Edibility: edible with caution; can cause upsets

This is one of the commonest species of *Suillus* throughout the north temperate regions of the world and is very attractive with its bright yellow-orange cap and stem. The pores are yellow and bruise reddish-brown. The stem has a white, cottony ring at the top. In some areas a deep reddish-chestnut form is found, but it agrees in all other essential details. This species is specific to larch and is found wherever this tree grows, often in a circle around the tree. As with other *Suillus* species, if you intend to eat it, it is best to remove the slimy cuticle which seems to be the cause of the upsets that some people experience after a meal of these fungi.

Suillus tomentosus (Kauffman) Singer, Snell & Dick

Cap: 2–6in (5–15cm)
Spores: olive-brown, 7–10 x 3–5μm,
Edibility: edible with caution; can cause upsets

This is something of an exception to the usual *Suillus* species in that it has a dry, wooly-velvety cap, but is sticky below the wooly layer. The color varies from pale yellow to orange-yellow, the same as the cap. The pores are dark brownish-cinnamon. When cut, the yellowish flesh turns pale blue and has an acidic, fruity odor. It grows under two-needle pines and is quite common in the western states. It seems likely that this is the same as *S. variegatus* found in Europe.

Suillus americanus (Peck)
Snell ex Slipp & Snell

Cap: 1–4in (2.5–10cm)
Spores: brown, 8–11 x 3–4µm,
Edibility: edible

This extremely common species varies greatly in its cap color; although the basic color is a bright golden yellow, this may be blotched and streaked with bright red spots, and when old may fade to a dull yellow-brown. The cap is often conical and is very viscid when wet. The margin often has a soft, cottony veil hanging down. The stem is yellow with large, brown glandular spots, and the yellow pores are large and honeycomb-like. It often grows in large circles around white pine, and is found throughout the northern and eastern states.

Suillus pictus (Peck) Smith & Thiers

Cap: 2–6in (5–15cm)
Spores: brown, 8–11 x 3.5–5µm
Edibility: edible

A magnificent species when young and fresh, with very bright colors, starting a bright carmine-red to purplish-red, then fading to reddish-brown when old. Unusually for a *Suillus,* it has a dry, felty-scaly cap and stem. There is a prominent whitish ring at the stem apex. The large pores are bright yellow and rather decurrent down the stem. It is a common species, growing under white pine throughout the north and east.

Suillus cavipes (Opatowski) Smith & Thiers

Cap: 2–4in (5–10cm)
Spores: brown, 7–10 x 3.5–4µm
Edibility: edible

One of the dry, scaly species, this has an attractive reddish-brown to tawny cap. The specific name of *cavipes* refers to the usually hollow stem, which also has a white ring zone at the apex, although the latter often vanishes quite quickly. The pores are yellow, large, and angular. Found only under larch, *S. cavipes* grows from Nova Scotia to Washington. Thanks to its distinctive characteristics, this and other similar dry species are sometimes placed in a separate genus – *Boletinus.*

Boletinellus meruloides (Schweinitz) Murrill

Cap: 2–4in (5–10cm)
Spores: brown, 7–10 x 6–7.5µm
Edibility: inedible

If you have ash trees anywhere in your vicinity, there is a good chance that you will find this species as it is specific to that tree. It has what must be one of the most remarkable ecologies of any fungus. It was first thought that it was mycorrhizal with the ash, but the ash does not form external mycorrhiza with mushrooms. Then it was discovered that under the soil were small balls of hard fungal tissue (sclerotia) and that these were hollow. Inside some of these sclerotia are found a species of soil-dwelling aphid (a relative of the common greenfly found on roses). Apparently, what is happening is that the aphid is excreting waste chemicals that the fungus finds useful, and in return the fungus encloses and presumably protects the aphid.
This dull brown bolete has an excentric, short stem and shallow, almost gill-like pores.

Strobilomyces confusus Singer

Cap: 2–6in (5–15cm)
Spores: black, 10–12.5 x 9.5–10µm
Edibility: edible

There are two very common members of this genus which can be found widely distributed – this species and the better known *S. floccopus* (some others grow only in the southern states). Although the latter species is more often mentioned in field guides, *S. confusus* can in fact be the commoner species in many areas. *Strobilomyces* is distinguished by its black, often rounded and ornamented spores, and these are the best way to distinguish these two very similar species. In this species they have a broken or partial network, while in *S. floccopus* there is a complete network. *S. confusus* also has smaller, sharper, and much tougher warts on the cap; in *S. floccopus* they are soft, broad, and rather flattened. Both species are found in mixed woods from late summer through the fall.

ORDER: RUSSULALES

Gilled mushrooms with flesh composed of groups of spherical cells (sphaerocysts) enclosed by long, cylindrical cells, and with spores ornamented with amyloid warts or ridges. Consists of only one family.

RUSSULACEAE
Russula Family

In any walk through the woods the members of this family of mushrooms will form one of the most prominent and brightly colored groups you will see. Although their identification can be very difficult and a matter for the specialist, there are, nevertheless, a number of species which have good distinguishing characteristics and can be tackled by the amateur. A number are also good edibles.

The two genera *Russula* and *Lactarius* are usually placed in their own order – the Russulales – because they differ so markedly from other gilled mushrooms. They have a characteristic brittle, crumbly texture in the hand, reflecting the unique cellular structure of their tissues, and their spores are ornamented with a variety of warts and ridges which stain blue-black when treated with a special iodine solution (Melzer's solution). Other important features are the taste of the cap flesh and gills, the odor, and the color of the spore deposit. The latter is placed on a scale of pure white to ocher, designated by eight letters (A–H) shown below, and is vital to accurate identification, especially in *Russula*.

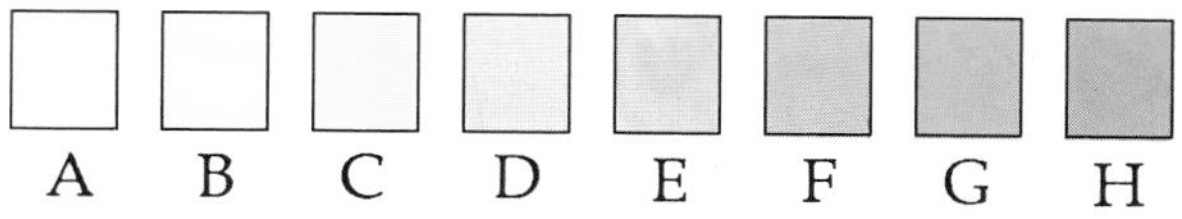

Lactarius differs from *Russula* in its usually duller colors and in its flesh, which oozes a sticky latex when cut. This latex may be clear, white, or colored. The spore color is less variable in *Lactarius*.

Russula dissimulans Shaffer

Cap: 2–6in (5–15cm)
Spores: white (A), 7.5–11 x 6.5–9µm, with a fine network
Edibility: inedible; often regarded as poisonous

A very common species under conifers in much of North America, this fungus was formerly referred to as *R. nigricans*, actually a very uncommon species in the USA. *R. dissimulans* has a white cap which rapidly ages blackish-brown and looks as if it has been in a fire. The gills are moderately widely spaced and thick (in *R. nigricans* they are very widely spaced). All parts of the mushroom bruise strongly reddish before turning black, and the taste varies from mild to burningly hot. A related species, *R. subnigricans*, is apparently poisonous, so all these white, blackening species should be avoided.

Russula albonigra Fries

Cap: 2–4in (5–10cm)
Spores: white (A–B), 7–10 x 6–7µm, with low warts and a partial network
Edibility: inedible; often regarded as poisonous

This and the previous species both blacken with age, but in this instance there is no intermediate red stage, and there is often a striking contrast between the white mushroom and its black stains. The gills are also more crowded than in *R. dissimulans*, and the taste of the flesh is odd – mild with a menthol-like aftertaste. It is not as common, but is widespread in the USA under beech and pine.

Russula brevipes Peck

Cap: 3–6in (7.5–15cm)
Spores: white to pale cream (A–C), 8–10.5 x 5–8.5µm with warts up to 1.7µm and a good network
Edibility: inedible; best avoided

Often to be found bursting up through the leaf litter where it develops underground until it starts to expand, this all-white species soon becomes funnel-shaped. The gills are crowded and sometimes have a faint bluish tint. The taste is mild to quite peppery in some forms. There is sometimes a thin blue line at the top of the stem, and this form is often referred to as a variety, var. *acrior*, which also has a very acrid taste. It is widespread throughout North America.

Russula variata Banning & Peck

Cap: 2–6in (5–15cm)
Spores: white (A), 7–10 x 5.5–8μm, with small, isolated warts
Edibility: edible and good

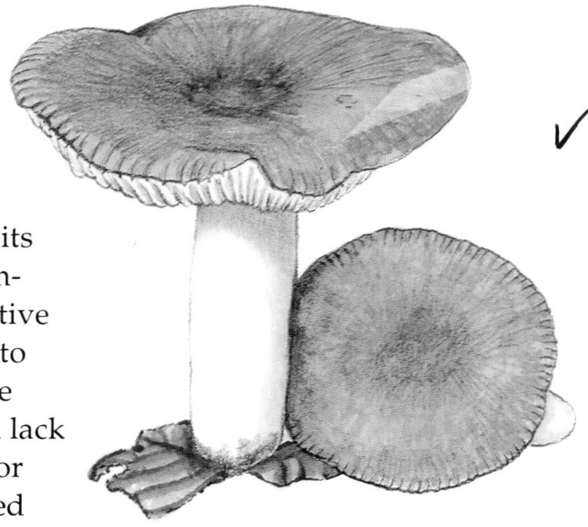

One of the commonest species, this is something of a chameleon in its color variations. It can be a mixture of lavender, green, and purplish-brown, or any one of these colors can predominate. Its most distinctive feature is the rather crowded white gills which fork repeatedly out to the cap margin and are greasy and quite flexible to the touch, unlike almost all other species. Another unusual feature is the almost total lack of chemical reaction to iron sulfate ($FeSO_4$); most species turn pink or green. The taste is peppery. The firm stem is white. It grows in mixed deciduous woods, especially beech and oak, sometimes under conifers.

Russula virescens (Schaeffer) Fries

Cap: 2–4in (5–10cm)
Spores: white (A), 6–9 x 5.5–7μm, with isolated warts, or sometimes with a few connecting lines
Edibility: edible and good

A beautiful species, with the cap in delicate shades of gray-green, blue-green, or yellowish-green, and easily distinguished by the cap surface, which soon breaks up into fine, flattened wooly patches. This can be an unusually firm and fleshy species as *Russula* species go, has a mild taste, and is a popular edible. Unfortunately, it is equally attractive to the many fly larvae which like to infest mushrooms, so it can be hard to find one that is untouched. An uncommon species, it occurs under mixed woods in eastern North America west to Texas. The much commoner *R. crustosa* looks almost identical but differs in its cream spores (C–D).

Russula aeruginea Lindblad

Cap: 2–4in (5–10cm)
Spores: deep cream (D–E), 6–10 x 5–7μm, with low warts and a few connecting lines
Edibility: edible

The genus *Russula* has a number of green species, most of which are easily distinguished either by spore color or other features of the cap. This species can be a bright grass-green, or vary to a yellow-green, frequently with slight rust-brown spotting. The spores are a deep cream (D–E) compared to other green species such as *R. virescens* and *R. variata,* which have white spores. Like them, it has a mild taste. This is a common species in mixed deciduous woods throughout the USA.

Russula rugulosa Peck

Cap: 2–4in (5–10cm)
Spores: deep cream (C–D), 7–9 x 5.5–7μm, with warts sometimes joined together in short ridges
Edibility: edible; mild with an odd metallic aftertaste

This bright red species has an oddly wrinkled and pimpled cuticle, rather shiny and sticky when wet, and peels about halfway to the cap center. The gills are pale cream and the stem white. Often mistaken for the well-known *R. emetica,* the latter differs in its pure white spores, smooth red cap, and very acrid taste. *R. rugulosa* has proved to be very common in mixed woods throughout the eastern and northern states.

Russula betularum Hora

Cap: 1–2in (2.5–5cm)
Spores: white (A), 8–10.5 x 6.5–8μm, with warts connected by a partial network
Edibility: inedible; very acrid to taste

A pretty little species of the most delicate pastel pink fading to almost white; the cuticle peels almost completely. The gills and slender stem are snow white,and the flesh has a fiercely hot taste. There is a delicate odor of coconut. This is widespread throughout the USA in damp birch woodlands, but should be carefully compared with *R. fragilis,* which grows in similar habitats and can also be pink in some of its color forms.

Russula silvicola Shaffer

Cap: 1-3in (2.5–7.5cm)
Spores: white (A), 6–10 x 5–9μm, with a well-developed network
Edibility: inedible; painfully hot to taste

This common species has a pale pinkish-red cap which can wash out to a yellowish-pink at the center. The gills and stem are white. It is unusual in that it often grows attached to very old, rotten logs, as well as in leaf litter. It is widespread throughout North America. This is another fungus which was formerly confused with *R. emetica*, a species with a bright red cap confined to northern, boggy pine woods.

Russula puellaris Fries

Cap: 1–2in (2.5–5cm)
Spores: pale ocher (D–E), 6.5–9 x 5.5–7μm, with rather tall, isolated warts
Edibility: edible

Many *Russula* species change color when bruised or with age, and this species is easily distinguished by the deep ocher-yellow stains that appear over the entire mushroom in a few hours. The small, reddish-brown to purplish-brown cap is rarely seen without some yellow discoloration at the margin and on the gills. The soft, fragile stem usually looks waterlogged and dull yellow. The taste is mild. A common species, it is found in rather wet areas of mixed woods throughout much of the USA.

Russula polyphylla Peck

Cap: 3–6in (7.5–15cm)
Spores: white (A), 7–10 x 5.5–7μm, with warts connected by a partial network
Edibility: unknown; best avoided

A rare and little-known species, it is nevertheless very distinctive. The large, funnel-shaped cap is whitish to pale ocher with fine, pinkish-brown scales at the center. The decurrent gills are very crowded and pale cream. All parts of the mushroom stain a dull reddish-brown when scratched, and the flesh has a strong, unpleasant, and alkaline odor, and a similar taste. It grows under beech trees in eastern North America.

Russula claroflava Grove

Cap: 2–4in (5–10cm)
Spores: pale ocher (E–F), 7.5–10 x 6–7.5μm, with more or less isolated warts
Edibility: edible and excellent

This species presents one of the brightest caps of any mushroom in the woods, the clear, vivid yellow color being easily visible in the wet, boggy areas under birch where it grows. All parts, however, will slowly blacken over the course of a few hours, or sometimes in minutes if scratched. The broad gills are cream to pale ocher. It usually grows in sphagnum moss and is found across the whole of the north temperate regions of the world. Despite its color and blackening flesh, it is an excellent edible mushroom. An extremely similar species, tentatively identified as *R. seperina*, differs in the flesh turning briefly red then black, and microscopically has cap cystidia which *R. claroflava* lacks. This second species has proved very common in some eastern states and has undoubtedly been confused with the species illustrated here.

Russula fucosa Burlingham

Cap: 1–2in (2.5–5cm)
Spores: pale ocher (E–F), 8–10 x 6–8µm, with tall, isolated warts
Edibility: edible

A small but very attractive species which deserves to be better known, particularly as it is quite common in some areas. The blood-red cap has a white bloom like a grape, and the white stem soon stains brown on handling. The taste is mild, but the smell becomes fish- or crab-like with age. If iron sulfate ($FeSO_4$) is rubbed on the stem, a deep olive-green reaction occurs, typical of a number of species placed in the so-called *R. xerampelina* group. *R. xerampelina* is larger, has a deep red stem as well as a purple-red cap, and grows under pines. *R. fucosa* grows under mixed trees in the northeast.

Russula ballouii Peck

Cap: 1–3in (2.5–7.5cm)
Spores: white (A–B), 7–9 x 5.5–7.5µm, with warts joined by a partial network
Edibility: edible

A strange species with the ocher-yellow cap cracked into fine scales like a mosaic. Similar fine scales are seen at the base of the stem. The gills are white and the taste is quite peppery. An uncommon but easily recognized species, it grows in deciduous woodlands. The similar *R. burlinghamiae,* also with a cracked yellowish cap, differs in its mild taste and cream spores (C–D).

Russula olivacea (Schaeffer) Fries

Cap: 4–6in (10–15cm)
Spores: deep ocher (G–H), 8–11 x 7–9µm, with very tall, isolated warts
Edibility: edible and excellent

This magnificent species rarely follows its specific name since it is most often deep purple in color, although olive-colored specimens can sometimes be found. The cap surface is dry and finely shagreened, and there are often slight concentric bands apparent in the cap color. The broad gills are deep ocher with the edges often marked in red. The robust stem is white flushed pink over the upper half, and the flesh has a mild taste. It is found in northern and eastern states under beech trees, and is sadly rather uncommon. The similar *R. davisii* differs in its yellow cap, but is otherwise identical and is perhaps best considered a variety.

Russula fragilis Fries

Cap: ½–2in (1–5cm)

Spores: white (A–B), 6–9 x 5–8µm, with a well-developed network

Edibility: inedible; extremely acrid to taste

Very variable in color, the cap may be shades of purple, pink to deep green, or even black at the center. The gills and stem are white and the taste is very hot. This small species is not common, but is widespread in the north and east in wet, mixed woodlands. The similar *R. aquosa* is larger, a clearer purple-red, with a wet, greasy-looking cap and waterlogged stem. The taste is less acrid.

Russula compacta Frost

Cap: 2–6in (5–15cm)

Spores: white (A–B), 7–10 x 6–8µm, with low warts and a fine network

Edibility: edible

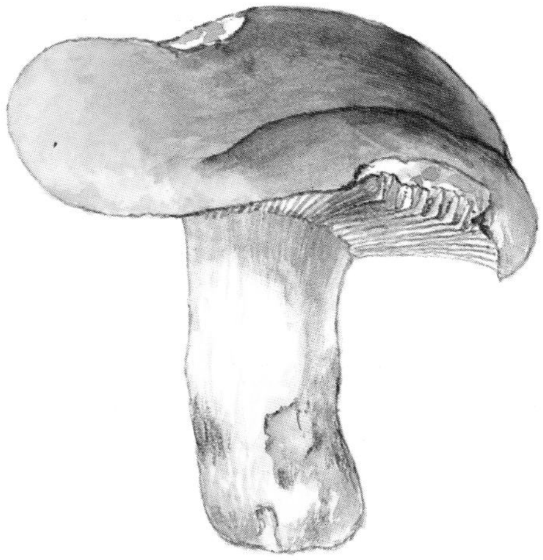

All parts of this robust, thick-fleshed white mushroom age and stain deep reddish-brown, and develop a strong odor of crabs or fish when old. The cap is dry and smooth to slightly roughened. Iron sulfate ($FeSO_4$) turns the flesh a deep blackish-green. Often abundant, this species grows in mixed woods and is widespread in both eastern and northern states.

Russula vinacea Burlingham
[= *R. krombholtzii*] Shaffer

Cap: 2–4in (5–10cm)

Spores: white (A), 7–9.5 x 6–8µm, with a fine partial network

Edibility: edible

The rich purple-red cap may be almost black at the center, and is sometimes irregularly blotched with paler areas. The cream gills are often spotted rust-red. The stem is white, sometimes flushed gray with age. The taste varies from mild to quite hot. Very common in mixed woods, especially under oaks, throughout the USA. Although often called *R. krombholtzii*, Burlingham's species was published much earlier, is identical, and therefore takes precedence.

Russula earlei Peck

Cap: 2–4in (5–10cm)
Spores: white (A–B), 5.5–7 x 3.5–5.5μm, with a fine partial network
Edibility: unknown; best avoided

This strange species gives us a glimpse at what all species of *Russula* probably looked like in the dim, distant past, since this is considered to be a very primitive species in terms of its appearance and characteristics. The smooth, almost waxy cap is dull ocher and often pitted, and has a wavy, irregular outline. The gills are widely spaced, very thick, and soft and waxy. The stem is whitish-ocher. The flesh has a mild to slightly peppery or bitter taste. The spores have among the lowest ornamentation of almost any *Russula.* This little-known species has proved to be common in many eastern states, and grows under beech.

Russula brunneola Burlingham

Cap: 2–5in (5–12.5cm)
Spores: white (A–B), 6–9.5 x 4–7μm, with small warts, mostly isolated
Edibility: edible

Some cap colors can be very difficult to describe or characterize, and this is certainly the case here. It varies from a pinkish-brown, or even slightly purplish, to very deep purple-brown, often unevenly colored. Once you have seen a few specimens, however, it is actually quite distinctive. A good clue is the intense salmon-brown reaction of the flesh to iron sulfate ($FeSO_4$). The flesh is more or less odorless and has a mild taste. It is very common in parts of the north and east in mixed woods.

Russula lutea (Hudson) Fries

Cap: 2–3in (5–7.5cm)
Spores: deep ocher (G–H), 7–9 x 6–8μm, with rather tall, isolated warts
Edibility: edible

The sense of smell is a very elusive and variable thing when tested across a range of people, and mushroom smells can be some of the most difficult to describe. This species has a very delicate and rather faint odor, but most people relate it to fruit – peaches or apricots – or to honey as it gets older. It is the gills which give off most of the scent, and indeed this is true for most mushrooms. Apart from the odor, it can be distinguished by its small, delicate caps, lovely rosy-peach to yellow color, and very deep ocher spores. The taste is mild. It is uncommon, found under deciduous trees, especially beech, throughout the northern and eastern states.

Russula mariae Peck

Cap: 2–3in (5–7.5cm)
Spores: pale ocher (D–E), 7.5–9.5 x 6.5–8μm, with a prominent network
Edibility: edible

A beautiful species, it exhibits a feature which is frequent in certain groups of *Russula*, and in other genera too. The cap surface is minutely velvety or matt in texture, and this is produced by thousands of microscopic, finger-like cells standing up from the surface like a turf. The colors are rich reddish-purple to violet, and both the stem and gill edges may be flushed with pinkish-purple. It varies greatly, however, and some caps can be found which are yellowish with brownish-purple, or even greenish, flushes. The taste is mild to very slightly peppery. A very common species, it grows in mixed woods and gardens from Canada down to Florida.

Russula flavida Frost

Cap: 2–4in (5–10cm)
Spores: deep cream (D–E), 5.5–8.5 x 5–7μm, with warts in a partial network
Edibility: edible

This species almost glows, it is such a bright golden yellow on its cap and stem. The gills are pale yellow, and the white flesh is firm to hard. The taste is mild. Sadly rather uncommon, it grows in deciduous woods and is quite widespread. The similar *R. ochroleucoides* differs in its duller yellow-ocher colors, very matt, pruinose cap, white spores, and very firm, hard flesh.

Russula fragrantissima Romagnesi

Cap: 2–4in (5–10cm)
Spores: cream (C–D), 6.3–9 x 5.5–7.7μm, with a partial network with large warts and ridges
Edibility: inedible

Nowhere is the strangeness of some mushroom odors better demonstrated than in this species. It has the most wonderful smell of bitter almonds or marzipan blended with a sour undertone which increases as it ages. Its taste can be quite hot and also unpleasant. The often very viscid cap is coarsely ridged and pimpled at the margin, and both the cap and stem are a pale honey brown. A much rarer species, *R. laurocerasi*, is very similar, but differs in its clearer, cleaner cap colors and appearance, rather taller stem, and incredibly fragrant odor of marzipan or almonds, just like confectionery, without the sour undertone of *R. fragrantissima*. Its spores are also remarkable for the huge ridges and flanges with which they are ornamented.

Russula foetentula Peck

Cap: 2–4in (5–10cm)
Spores: pale yellow (D–E), 7–9 x 5.5–7μm, with tall, isolated warts
Edibility: inedible

This common species has a strong odor, which is a blend of marzipan or almonds with a sour, unpleasant component. The cap is orange-brown, coarsely ridged, and pimpled at the margin. The stem is pale cream ocher, but soon stains deep rust-red to orange at the base. The taste is both acrid and unpleasantly oily. It grows in mixed woods and is often called *R. subfoetens*, but that appears to be strictly European.

Russula amoenolens Romagnesi

Cap: 2–4in (5–10cm)
Spores: cream (B–D), 6–9 x 5–7μm, with mostly isolated warts
Edibility: inedible

Perhaps the dullest species in appearance, the cap is in shades of drab brown and sepia, with strong marginal grooves and ridges. Combined with the fetid, cheesy odor and unpleasant, acrid taste, it has little to commend it. It can be a very common species in woods, parks, and gardens under a variety of deciduous trees, often forming a circle around their base. It is widespread throughout the USA.

Russula ventricosipes Peck

Cap: 3–6in (7.5–15cm)
Spores: deep cream (D–E), 7–10 x 4.5–6μm, unusually long and slender, with minute, isolated warts
Edibility: doubtful; best avoided

To find this species you must search in southern or coastal areas in sandy soils where it likes to grow, often completely buried below the surface, only pushing through as the cap expands. The broad cap is dull yellow-ocher with a strongly grooved margin. The short, stout stem is spotted and stained red below. The taste is strongly acrid. The spores are remarkable for a *Russula* species, and provide instant confirmation of its identity.

Russula simillima Peck

Cap: 2–3in (5–7.5cm)
Spores: white (A–B), 6.5–9 x 5.5–7µm, with tall warts in a partial reticulum
Edibility: inedible

This species is specific to stands of beech trees, and blends in perfectly with the yellow-brown fallen leaves. The entire mushroom is a dull honey yellow and is usually odorless, but may occasionally have a faint odor of household geraniums (Pelargonium). The taste is very acrid. It is closely related to the European *R. fellea,* which always has a strong geranium odor and looks identical. It may best be considered as a variety of that species.

Lactarius deliciosus (Fries) S.F. Gray – "Saffron Milk Cap"

Cap: 2–4in (5–10cm)
Spores: cream (B–D), 7–10 x 6–7µm, with a fine network
Edibility: edible and good

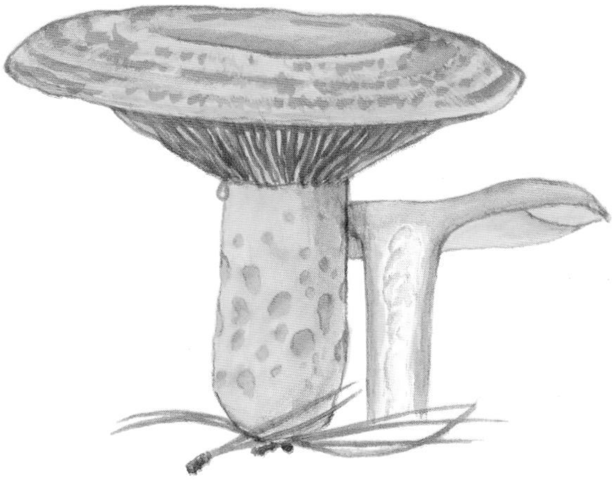

One of the brighter *Lactarius* species in the USA, the bright orange, zonate caps stain or discolor green with age. The stem is orange and often has small round pits or spots on the surface. When broken, the gills and flesh ooze an orange milk which hardly changes color (see below). The taste of this latex and of the flesh is mild to slightly soapy, and is considered a good edible. It grows often in large numbers under pine throughout North America. The superficially similar *L. chelidonium* can look similar when old, but when young has a distinct silvery-blue color. When cut, the flesh in the cap is pale blue and oozes blue latex.

Lactarius thyinos Smith

Cap: 2–4in (5–10cm)
Spores: cream (C–D), 9–12 x 7.5–9µm, with a partial network
Edibility: edible

A beautiful species, the entire mushroom is a bright, clear orange without any green staining. The cap may be faintly zoned and the stem slightly pitted with darker spots. The latex is orange, becoming slowly darker, and has a soapy, bitter flavor. It is associated with northern white cedar and seems to be most common in the colder boggy woodlands of the northern states.

Lactarius subpurpureus Peck

Cap: 2–4in (5–10cm)
Spores: cream (C–D), 8–11 x 6.5–8μm, ridged and warted with a partial network
Edibility: edible

A strikingly colored species and difficult to confuse with any other when fresh, as the entire mushroom is a bright wine-red to purplish-pink, and the cap zoned and soon stained with green. The stem is smooth and slimy when wet, spotted and pitted with darker red. The latex is scarce, wine-red, and tastes slightly peppery. A rather uncommon species, it grows under pines from Maine down through the eastern states, and becomes commoner in the southeast.

Lactarius indigo (Schweinitz) Fries

Cap: 2–6in (5–15cm)
Spores: cream (C–D), 7–9 x 5.5–7.5μm, with an almost complete network
Edibility: edible

Perhaps the most remarkable species in the genus – indeed, one of the most remarkably colored fungi in the world. When fresh and young the deep indigo blue cap, gills, and stem are unmistakable and beautiful. The cap is zoned with slightly silvery bands, and the stem is pitted and spotted with darker spots. When old the mushroom fades to a pale silvery blue. The flesh and latex are a deep indigo blue, turning slowly greenish. It is widespread and locally common in the northeast under oak and pine, although curiously absent in some areas, such as New Jersey.

Lactarius torminosus (Fries) S.F. Gray

Cap: 2–4in (5–10cm)
Spores: cream (C–D) 7.5–10 x 6–7.5μm, with a network
Edibility: inedible; often regarded as poisonous

When fresh and in good condition this can be one of the most spectacular species. The deep pink, zonate cap is remarkably shaggy-hairy all around the margin, which starts off quite inrolled. The gills are pinkish-white and the smooth stem is also pink. The white latex is copious when the flesh is broken, and tastes painfully acrid and burning. It is frequent under birch throughout the more northerly states and into Canada. A closely related species, *L. pubescens,* is much paler, almost white, usually without any zones, and is less shaggy. It is uncommon, but found in similar situations.

Lactarius aquifluus Peck

Cap: 2–6in (5–15cm)
Spores: buff (D–E), 6–9 x 5.5–7.5μm,with mostly isolated warts
Edibility: inedible; often regarded as poisonous

This is a large species with a strong odor, making it easy to identify in the field. The odor is variously described as chicory, burnt sugar, or curry powder among others, but all agree it is spicy and quite pleasant. The cap is a pale cinnamon brown, dry, and slightly roughened. The latex is thin, watery, and mild to taste. This is a fairly common species in mixed woods throughout the northern states and in Canada. There is little doubt that what is called *L. helvus* in Britain is the same species, but the Peck name is the correct one for this fungus.

Lactarius rufus (Fries) Fries

Cap: 2–4in (5–10cm)
Spores: cream (C–D), 7.5–10.5 x 5–7.5μm
Edibility: inedible

This is a deceptive species as far as its taste is concerned, and often catches out the unwary. Its white latex starts mild and only very slowly turns acrid, by which time it is too late to get rid of the taste. The cap is a deep fox-red to brick or bay, and usually has a sharp, central knob or umbo. The stem is similarly colored, but has a whitish base. A very common species, it occurs in both pine or birch-woods, but usually prefers boggy areas.

Lactarius hygrophoroides Berkeley & Curtis

Cap: 2–4in (5–10cm)
Spores: white (A–B), 7.5–10μm, almost globose, with a fine network
Edibility: edible and good

The rich, orange-brown cap and stem are dry and almost suede-like, and usually have a characteristic puckered, wrinkled surface. The gills are cream and very widely spaced (see half cap illustrated far right). When any part of this species is cut a copious white, sticky latex oozes out, making it difficult to handle. It is thought that the latex in this and other species may be a deterrent against insects that like to feed on mushrooms, by glueing up their mouth parts. The taste is quite mild, and there is an odd odor of shrimp or fish when mature. It is a very common species in deciduous woods throughout the southern, eastern, and northern states. The similar *L. volemus* differs in the crowded gills (see illustration of half cap, lower right) and the brown stains which develop on the broken gills.

Lactarius corrugis Peck

Cap: 2–6in (5–15cm)
Spores: 9–12 x 8.5–12µm, with a network
Edibility: edible

Although somber in color, this is nevertheless a beautiful species, with a dark, almost matt cap which is curiously wrinkled and corrugated at the margin. The gills are a deep ocher-brown, and the smooth stem a deep brown also. The latex is white, very copious and mild tasting. A fish-like odor can develop with age. It is frequent to common under deciduous trees in eastern and northern states. Often found growing with *L. volemus*, the two species may sometimes look alike, but *L. volemus* is rarely as dark or wrinkled. Both are edible.

Lactarius lignyotus Fries

Cap: 1–4in (2.5–10cm)
Spores: bright ocher (E–G), 9–10.5 x 9–10µm with a network
Edibility: edible

When fresh and young the surface of this mushroom looks like black velvet, and it is one of the loveliest of the *Lactarius* species. It is also distinctive for the sharp umbo or point at the center of the cap, and for the contrasting white gills. To add to the exotic appearance, the white, copious latex soon stains bright rose, and the taste is peppery. Found under conifers, especially spruce, it is widespread in the eastern and northern states.

Lactarius camphoratus (Fries) Fries

Cap: 1–2in (2.5–5cm)
Spores: yellowish (D–E), 7–8.5 x 6–7.5µm, with a few connecting lines
Edibility: edible

Although rather nondescript in appearance, this is usually fairly easy to identify by the strong odor of curry powder, burnt sugar, or chicory, which develops with age. With experience one can, however, learn to recognize it even without the odor, as the cap and stem have a characteristic reddish-brown to liver color, and the cap has a small umbo at the center. The latex is scanty, watery-white, and mild to taste. A very common species, this is found in mixed woods throughout the USA.

Lactarius deceptivus Peck

Cap: 3–10in (7.5–25cm)
Spores: buff (D–E), 9–13 x 7.5–9μm, with very fine ridges
Edibility: inedible

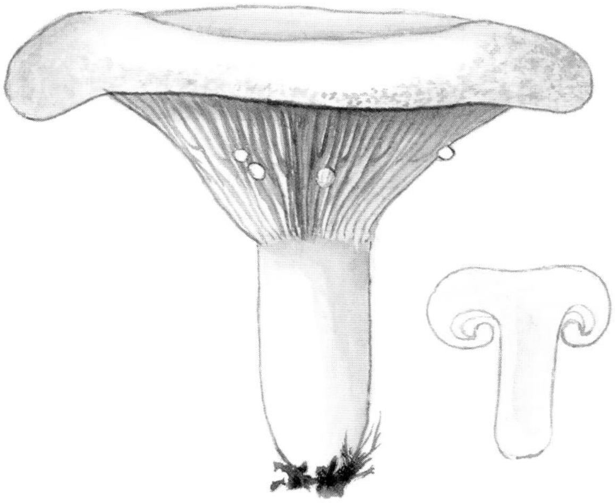

Often forming huge fruit-bodies, this all-white to ivory species soon becomes deeply funnel-shaped, but the margin begins tightly rolled up with a soft, cottony margin (best seen by sectioning), and slowly unrolls. The stem is very short and hard, and like the cap is slightly velvety to the touch. The gills are fairly closely spaced and yellowish-cream. The latex is white, abundant and very acrid to taste. This is a common species and often bursts up through the leaf litter of the forest floor in eastern woods west to Michigan and Ohio. Similar species include *L. subvellereus*, which differs in its less cottony-wooly margin, more crowded gills, and smaller spores with lower warts (0.2–0.5μm). It is also widely distributed in eastern states as far south as Alabama.

Lactarius piperatus (Fries) S.F. Gray

Cap: 2–6in (5–15cm)
Spores: white (A–B), 6–8 x 5–5.5μm, with a faint network
Edibility: inedible; very acrid

The gills of this species are so narrow and so closely packed that they often seem to present an almost smooth surface on the underside of the cap. The entire mushroom is white and slightly velvety, and soon becomes funnel-shaped. The latex is white and copious, extremely acrid to taste, and in some forms will dry to an olive green. A quite common species, it is frequent under deciduous trees in eastern North America west to Michigan. There are few species it could be confused with if the extremely crowded gills are looked for. Most other white species have strongly inrolled cap margins and wider spaced gills, as well as larger spores. The stem of *L. piperatus* is usually rather taller in proportion to its cap diameter than other species. The green-staining variety is var. *glaucescens*.

Lactarius thejogalus (Fries) S.F. Gray

Cap: 1–3in (2.5–7.5cm)
Spores: cream (C–D), 7–9 x 6–7.5μm, with tall ridges forming a partial network
Edibility: edible

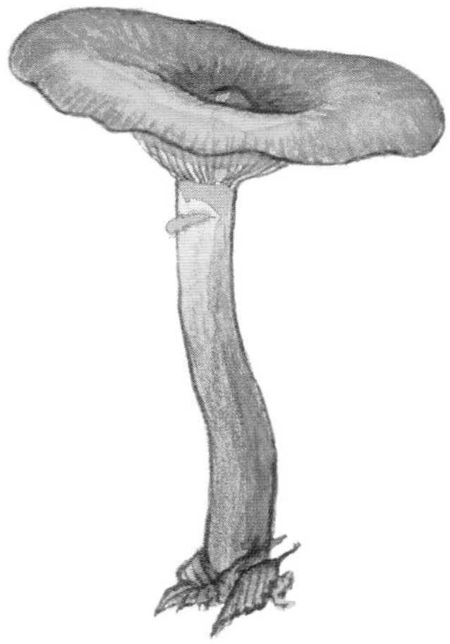

This small, cinnamon orange to brick-colored mushroom has a small, sharp umbo at the cap center, but it otherwise appears rather ordinary. Its most characteristic feature is the latex, which is white but slowly turns yellow if smeared on a handkerchief. The latex is scanty and rather acrid to taste. A very common species throughout the USA in mixed deciduous woods in wet, boggy habitats.

Lactarius chrysorheus Fries

Cap: 1–3in (2.5–7.5cm)
Spores: pale yellow (D–E), 6–8 x 5.5–6.5μm,with isolated warts and a slight network
Edibility: edible

A rather attractive species with a pale pinkish-cream to yellowish cap with noticeable concentric zones and/or watery spots. Like the previous species, this has latex which changes to yellow, but here the white latex is abundant and will stain bright yellow, even on the gills and cut flesh. The taste is quite mild. Another clue is that this species is found growing only under oak trees, where it forms a characteristic part of the oak flora in the fall. One should also look out for the very similar *L. vinaceorufescens*, which differs in developing dull purplish-brown stains over most of the mushroom.

Lactarius glyciosmus (Fries) Fries

Cap: 1–3in (2.5–7.5cm)
Spores: cream (C–D), 6–8 x 5–6μm, with bands and ridges forming a broken network
Edibility: edible

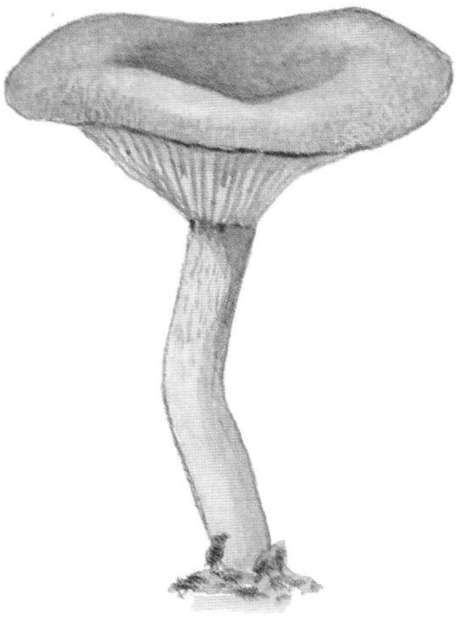

Mushroom odors can be quite amazing, and some, as in this case, are very specific indeed. This species has a strong odor of desiccated coconut (the dried, processed coconut one can buy in packets), not, it should be noted, of fresh coconut. The smell, combined with the overall pale grayish-lavender colors, makes it easy to recognize. The latex is white, unchanging in color, and slightly acrid to taste. A common species in mixed woods. Despite the wonderful aroma, it is rather poor in flavor.

Lactarius atroviridis Peck

Cap: 2–4in (5–10cm)
Spores: pale cream (C–D), 7–9 x 5.5–6.5μm, with a partial network
Edibility: inedible

The deep, blackish-green color of this mushroom is difficult to mistake for any other species. The cap is dry and roughened to touch, while the stem is often pitted with darker spots. The latex is white, plentiful, and very acrid to taste. It may stain the gills slowly olive with time. This is a rather rare species and difficult to spot in the leaf litter of the shady woods where it grows in eastern North America. It is one of a complex of similar species, including *L. sordidus*, but that species is yellow-brown to olive, never dark green.

Lactarius quietus (Fries) Fries

Cap: 2–4in (5–10cm)
Spores: cream (C–D), 7–9 x 5.5–7μm, with mostly isolated warts and ridges
Edibility: edible

The reddish-brown to liver-brown cap is faintly zoned, while the stem is usually darker below. The crowded gills are pale buff-brown, and when cut ooze a white to slightly yellowish latex which is at first mild, but soon slightly acrid. The odor is difficult to describe, but distinctive; most people compare it with sweet, oily substances. It occurs quite frequently in northeastern states. Although not often reported in the literature, this species is not uncommon in some of the eastern states, where it is confined almost entirely to oaks. The habitat, combined with the faint odor and zoning, are good clues to its identity, but when old and faded it can be much more difficult to identify.

ORDER: AGARICALES

An enormous group of fungi which share the common feature of having the spore-bearing basidia spread over thin gills (there are a very few exceptions which have developed without gills, just a smooth surface). They may have a central or oblique stem, or have no stem at all, and emerge directly from the substrate on which they grow. The tissues are almost entirely filamentous, except in the outer layers, where globose cells may appear. The order is divided into a large number of families, often with very different spore colors.

HYGROPHORACEAE
Hygrophorus Family

All these mushrooms share the common features of thick, waxy gills and smooth, white spores formed on very long basidia. *Hygrophorus* species are usually thicker, fleshier, and duller colored than the fragile, often brilliantly colored *Hygrocybe.*

Hygrocybe pratensis Persoon

Cap: 2–4in (5–10cm)

Spores: white, 6–7 x 4–5μm, smooth

Edibility: edible and quite good

As the late summer and fall days move in, and the fields and woods are soaked with rain, the species of *Hygrocybe* appear, and this is one of the commoner and least brightly colored of them. The flattened, top-shaped caps are a pale orange-buff, and the gills run down the stem. It may also appear in grassy woodland clearings and garden lawns, and, like most *Hygrocybe* species, prefers a light, calcareous soil. This is among the few species of *Hygrocybe* that are considered good edibles. There are few other species it might be confused with, although it can look a little like some species of *Clitocybe*. Many of the latter are poisonous, so care should be taken to observe the features of *Hygrocybe*: thick, waxy gills and often brittle flesh compared with the thin, moist gills and more flexible tissues of *Clitocybe*.

Hygrocybe virginea (Wulfen ex Fries) Orton & Watling [=*H. niveus*]

Cap: 1–2in (2.5–5cm)
Spores: white, 7–10 x 5–6μm, smooth
Edibility: edible

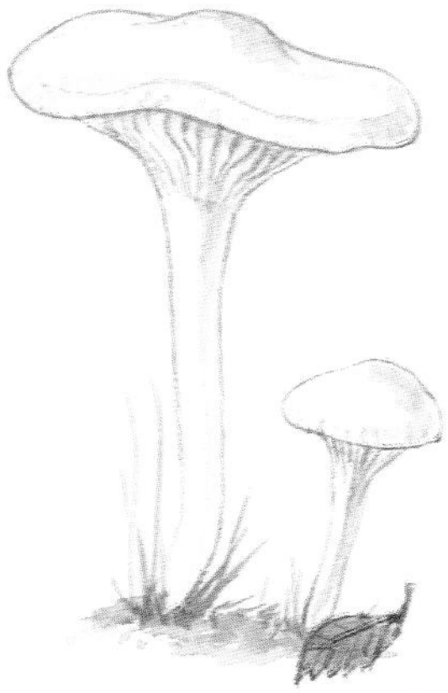

A number of white species have been described and are quite difficult to separate without a microscope, and even then not all experts agree on the names. Many mycologists consider *H. niveus* (regarded here as a synonym) to be a good species in its own right. *H. virginea* is characterized by its smooth, slightly greasy, and hygrophanous cap with a translucent, striate margin. The gills are distant and run down the stem. This is a common species of fields and woods in the western states. In the east it is replaced by the almost identical *H. borealis,* which has a dry cap.

Hygrocybe conica (Scopoli) Kummer

Cap: 1–2in (2.5–5cm)
Spores: white, 8–12 x 5–7μm, smooth
Edibility: doubtful; best avoided

A distinctive species, it is also very attractive. The sharply conical cap is bright red, while the tall, slender stem is yellowish flushed red. The gills are pallid to yellowish. All parts rapidly bruise or age black, and within a matter of hours the entire mushroom will look completely blackened. This is a common species in fields and grassy woodlands everywhere. Another species, *H. pseudoconica*(=*H. nigrescens*), is often separated out by its more obtuse, blunt cap, larger and more robust fruit-bodies and 4-spored basidia compared to *H. conica's* usually 2-spored basidia. Many authors consider them as merely forms of one variable species,

Hygrocybe punicea (Fries) Kummer

Cap: 2–4in (5–10cm)
Spores: white, 8–11 x 5–6μm, smooth
Edibility: edible

A magnificent species with a bright scarlet to blood-red cap and stem, with a silky or greasy surface. The gills are yellowish to orange and only narrowly adnate, often with a slight decurrent tooth. Both the flesh and the base of the stem, however, are whitish, and this forms a key characteristic of the species. It is widespread in woods and grassy areas in the western states late in the year through January. The closely related *H. coccinea* differs in being smaller and having reddish flesh and broadly adnate gills, but is otherwise similar in color.

Hygrocybe miniata (Fries) Kummer

Cap: 1–2in (2.5–5cm)
Spores: white, 7–9.5 x 4–5.5μm, smooth
Edibility: edible

There are a number of small, bright red species, often quite difficult to separate, although by careful examination of some characteristics (a hand lens is often required) several can be identified with reasonable accuracy. This species has a rough, scaly-squamulose cap surface with the scales often paler and yellower against the bright red background. The gills are broadly adnate with a small decurrent tooth, and the flesh is odorless. The very similar *H. quietus* differs in its truly decurrent gills and the unpleasant oily smell it leaves on the fingers when the fungus is crushed and rubbed.

Hygrocybe psittacina (Schaeffer ex Fries) Wünsche – "Parrot Mushroom"

Cap: ½–1in (1–2.5cm)
Spores: white, 8–10 x 4–5μm, smooth
Edibility: edible

This species well deserves its common name of Parrot: it is one of the few truly green fungi to be found, and like a parrot can be a mixture of different shades mixed with yellow and orange, fading as it ages. The cap is smooth and viscid when wet, and the gills are adnate, often with a notch where they join the stem (compare with *H. laeta*, below). A common species, especially later in the season, it occurs in grassy woodlands, fields, and pastures everywhere.

Hygrocybe laeta (Persoon ex Fries) Kummer

Cap: ½–1in (1–2.5cm)
Spores: white, 5–7.5 x 4–5μm, smooth
Edibility: edible

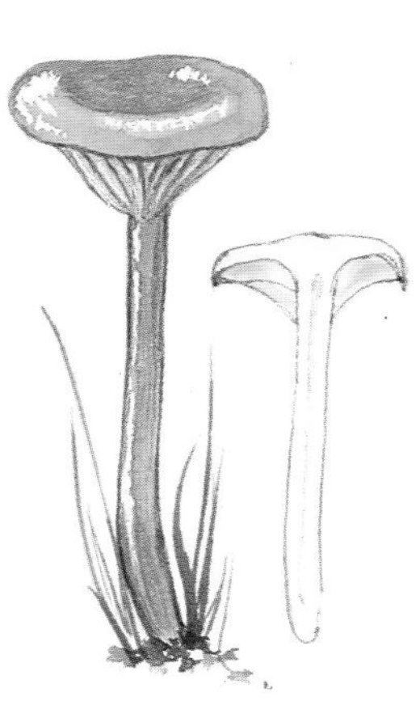

This is often confused with the previous species, but there are some clear differences. The green tints in this species are confined to the gills and stem apex, while the cap is in shades of orange to olive-brown or orange-brown. The gills vary from whitish to olive to grayish-pink, and are very broadly adnate to decurrent. The tall, slender stem is yellowish-green to grayish-orange. Both cap and stem are very slippery, glutinous when wet. A common species, it grows in pastures, fields, and woods across the United States.

Hygrocybe unguinosa (Fries) Karsten

Cap: 1–2in (2.5–5cm)
Spores: white, 6–8 x 4–6μm, smooth
Edibility: edible

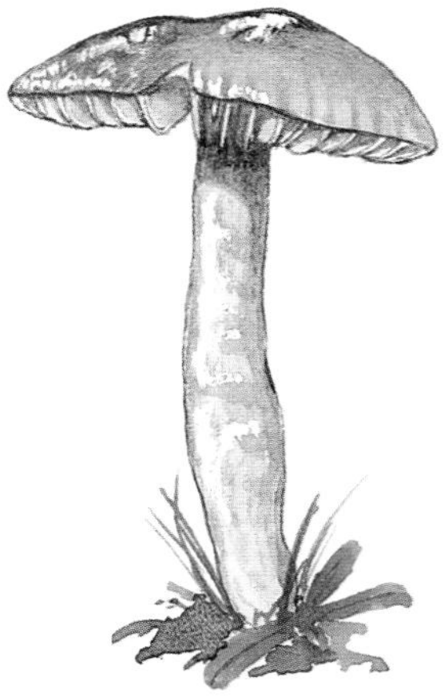

An unusual color for a *Hygrocybe*, the gray to gray-brown cap and stem are both very glutinous and slippery, and contrast with the white gills. The cap margin is often translucent-striate, and the gills show through from below. A rather uncommon species in many areas, it grows, as do so many other *Hygrocybe* species, in fields and grassy woodlands.

Hygrocybe ovina (Bulliard ex Fries) Kühner

Cap: 1–3in (2.5–7.5cm)
Spores: white, 7–9 x 4.5–6μm, smooth
Edibility: doubtful; best avoided

A very somber-colored member of this genus, the entire mushroom is a dark blackish-gray when moist, fading to gray-brown or buff when dry. All parts bruise red and then black when scratched or handled roughly, and there is often, but not always, an odor of ammonia or bleach. A very uncommon species, it grows in deciduous woodlands in the eastern states. The similar *H. nitiosus* is found under redwoods in California.

Hygrophorus chrysodon (Batsch ex Fries) Fries

Cap: 1–3in (2.5–7.5cm)
Spores: white, 8–11 x 3.5–5μm, smooth
Edibility: edible

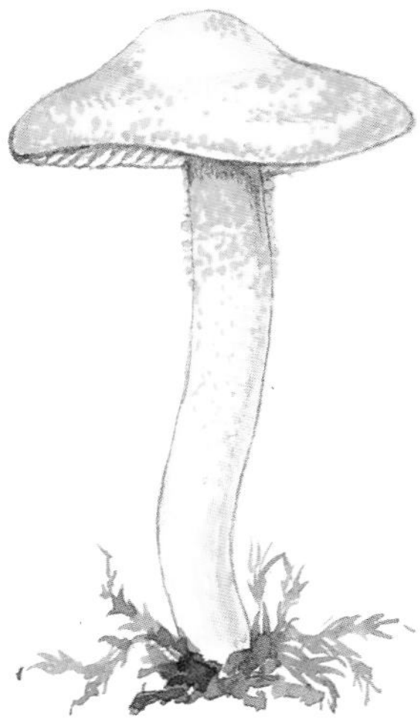

This is one of a number of white species of *Hygrophorus* to be found in woodlands, and is the easiest to distinguish by means of the bright golden yellow flecks which dot the cap margin and stem apex. The cap is slimy-viscid when wet, as is the stem over its lower half. There is a distinct odor, said to resemble artichokes or bitter almonds. Although an uncommon species, it is widespread in woods of oak and pine throughout the western states. While there are other white species with distinct odors, and some are also viscid, as in the species illustrated here, none has the distinct yellow flecks on cap and stem which make this species so distinctive. Although edible, it must be rated rather poor in comparison with other edible fungi.

Hygrophorus penarius Fries

Cap: 2–4in (5–10cm)
Spores: white, 6–8.5 x 3–5μm, smooth
Edibility: edible

One of the larger and more robust of the white, woodland *Hygrophorus* species, the caps soon flatten out, have rather wavy, undulating edges, and are slightly downy to touch. The gills are thick, widely spaced, decurrent, and pale cream in color. The stem is stout and short. The cap and stem surface are quite dry to touch and have no particular odor. Found under beech trees, it is not uncommon in eastern and northern states. Although usually called *H. sordidus,* there seems little doubt that it is the same as *H. penarius* of Fries, which was described much earlier.

Hygrophorus russula (Schaeffer ex Fries) Quélet

Cap: 3–6in (7.5–15cm)
Spores: white, 6–8.5 x 4–6μm, smooth
Edibility: edible, but sometimes bitter

A beautiful species with its large, whitish-pink caps mottled and spotted with dark wine-red blotches, becoming totally reddish-purple with age, including the stem and the crowded gills. It is a robust, fleshy mushroom, often growing in large numbers or even in fairy rings in beech woods late in the year, but sadly is an uncommon species found in the northeast across to the northwest. It prefers calcareous soils.

Hygrophorus hypothejus (Fries) Fries

Cap: 2–4in (5–10cm)
Spores: white, 8–9 x 4–5μm, smooth
Edibility: edible

There are a number of species which appear very late in the year, just before the winter sets in, and which have a distinct veil on the stem. This species is very common and is distinguished by its glutinous, yellow-brown to olive-brown cap, whitish-yellow, decurrent gills, and slender stem with a sticky coating below a faint ring zone. It grows under conifers and is widespread in the USA. The similar *H. persoonii* differs in its more umber, reddish-brown cap and similarly colored bands of veil on the stem. It is common in California.

PLEURОТАСЕАЕ
Pleurotus Family

The genera which make up this family usually grow on wood, and in the majority of species have the stem reduced or completely absent. The spores vary from white to pale lavender, or even faintly pinkish. Some mycologists consider these to be closer to the tubed polypores rather than the other gilled mushrooms, and place them in the Polyporaceae family with the bracket fungi.

Pleurotus ostreatus (Jacquin ex Fries) Kummer – "Oyster Cap"

Cap: 2–6in (5–15cm)
Spores: pale lilac, 8–9 x 4–5µm, smooth
Edibility: edible and considered a great delicacy

This well-known species is now such a popular edible that it is cultivated commercially and is available from many supermarkets and specialty food stores. The caps usually have no stem but grow directly from dead or dying timber, and are a deep bluish-gray to gray-brown. The narrow, crowded gills are white to grayish and there is a pleasant odor. It grows, often in enormous numbers, late in the year from fallen or standing timber throughout the USA. The similar *P. pulmonarius* is usually almost white or cream and appears much earlier in the year. It is equally common and edible.

Pleurotus cornucopiae Paul ex Fries
[= *P. sapidus*]

Cap: 2–6in (5–15cm)
Spores: pale lilac, 8–11 x 3.5–5µm, smooth
Edibility: edible and good

A rather unusual species, it produces large clusters of fruit-bodies, often fused together, and each cap has a more or less central and quite well-developed stem. The gills are deeply decurrent down the stem. There is usually a delicate odor, rather like aniseed. Although a common species on fallen elms, it is regarded as a good edible, but is perhaps not quite as well known as the Oyster Cap, *P. ostreatus*.

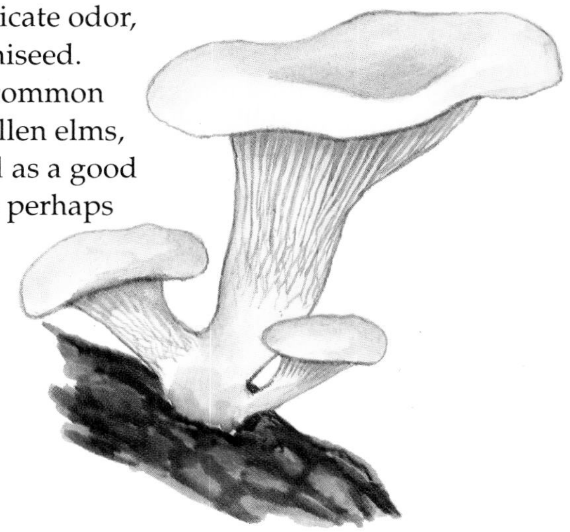

Phyllotopsis nidulans (Persoon ex Fries) Singer

Cap: 1–3in (2.5–7.5cm)
Spores: pale yellowish-pink, 4–5 x 2–3µm, smooth
Edibility: inedible

A striking species in color, which is deep yellow-orange, and odor, which is rank and unpleasant, rather like rotted cabbage. The wooly-surfaced, kidney-shaped cap has no stem, and the bright yellow-orange gills are narrow and crowded. It grows on fallen conifers, and is widespread in the USA, usually being seen late in the year through to early spring.

Panus tigrinus (Bulliard ex Fries) Singer

Cap: 1–3in (2.5–7.5cm)
Spores: white, 7–8 x 3–3.5μm
Edibility: inedible

The key characteristics of this species are the decurrent white gills with finely serrated edges, the slightly funnel-shaped cap which is cream with fine brownish scales, and the almost central stem which is tough and fleshy. The spores are also distinctive, being very narrow, almost cylindrical. It is an uncommon species, preferring fallen timber of poplar and willow, and seems to be commonest in the northern states.

Panellus serotinus (Hoffmann) Kühner

Cap: 2–4in (5–10cm)
Spores: yellowish, 4–6 x 1–2μm, smooth
Edibility: edible

This striking species is not often collected, but this is mostly because it grows very late in the year when most mushroom hunters have stopped collecting until the coming spring. The semicircular caps are a deep olive-green to ocher-green, sometimes with a flush of violet, and the surface is decidedly velvety. The gills are crowded and pale yellow-orange. There may be a very short stem present. It is widespread in the USA on fallen timber.

Panellus stipticus (Bulliard) Karsten

Cap: ½ –1in (1–2.5cm)
Spores: white, 3–5 x 1.5–3μm, smooth
Edibility: inedible

This small, rather inconspicuous mushroom is unusual in that it occurs in two forms, depending on whether you collect it in Europe or in North America. The American form is brightly luminescent, the gills glowing yellow-green. Sadly, the European form is non-luminescent. The two forms will interbreed in culture, so are considered as being one species, although why such a striking difference should occur is uncertain. The shell-shaped cap is dull ocher-buff with a rough surface, and a distinct but short stem is present at the trailing edge. The ocher-brown gills are crowded. The flesh is astringent and very distasteful. It is a common species on fallen timber everywhere, especially late in the year.

TRICHOLOMATACEAE
Tricholoma Family

This is an enormous family of mushrooms, varying greatly in size and appearance, and very difficult to define. Some have stems, some do not, some have even lost their gills and have a smooth undersurface. They all share white or at least very pale spores, some being yellowish or pinkish. The gills range from sinuate through adnate to decurrent, but are never free. Many genera have some sort of veil present.

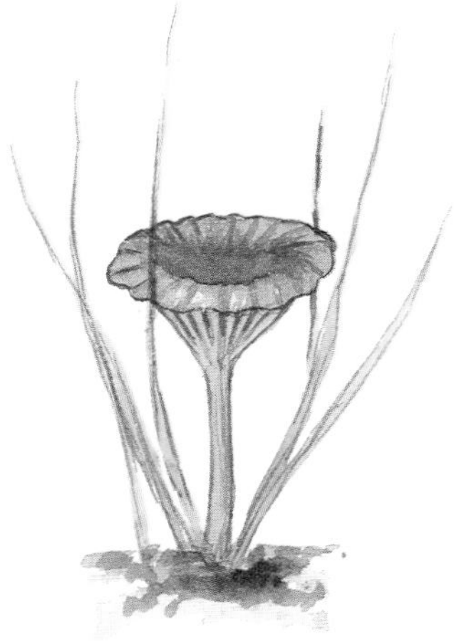

Omphalina pyxidata (Bulliard) Quélet

Cap: ¼–1in (0.6–2.5cm)
Spores: white, 7–10 x 4.5–6μm, smooth
Edibility: doubtful; best avoided

This tiny, delicate species is common in grassy woodlands and lawns everywhere. The funnel-shaped cap is rusty brown with a fluted margin. The decurrent gills are slightly paler, as is the rather short stem. This is one of a number of small species varying in cap color and other details, which really require specialized literature to identify them. It may be considered typical of its type.

Rickenella fibula (Bulliard ex Fries) Raith

Cap: ¼–½ in (0.6–1cm)
Spores: white, 4–5 x 2–2.5μm, smooth
Edibility: doubtful; best avoided

This species shows a definite preference for mossy areas in woods and fields. It can be quite a brightly colored species, having an orange-brown to reddish-brown cap with a striate margin. The gills are decurrent and widely spaced, and a pale creamy orange. The stem is usually long and slender. Once again, there are a number of similar species best distinguished with specialist literature, but most are not as brightly colored as in this case.

Cantharellula umbonata (Gmelin ex Fries) Singer

Cap: 1–2in (2.5–5cm)
Spores: white, 7–11 x 3–4μm, smooth
Edibility: doubtful; best avoided

Found in mossy areas on acid soils, this species is rather uncommon in the USA, but is quite easy to recognize if close attention is paid to the gills, which are decurrent, thick, blunt-edged, and are all forked one or more times. They may also spot reddish-brown on handling. The cap and stem are a dull gray-brown to blackish-gray, often with a lilac flush. The spores are unusual, being long, bullet-shaped, and rather like those of a *Boletus* species in shape.

Omphalotus illudens (Schweinitz) Saccardo
"Jack o' Lantern"

Cap: 3–6in (7.5–15cm)

Spores: pale cream, 3.5–5µm, rounded, non-amyloid

Edibility: poisonous

This remarkable species well lives up to its common name. A fresh specimen, if taken into a very dark room, will be seen to glow bright greenish-yellow on the gills after about 5–10 minutes. All parts of the fungus are a bright orange, and it usually grows in clumps on stumps, but often also on buried roots in lawns and gardens. It is sometimes mistaken for the edible Chanterelle (*Cantharellus cibarius*) and causes a number of poisonings every year because of that resemblance. The two can be distinguished easily by the crowded, narrow gills of the Jack o' Lantern versus the blunt, shallow, and irregular "gills" of the Chanterelle. The Jack o' Lantern is sometimes grouped with the European species *O. olearius*, which is found on olive trees, but many authors prefer to keep them separate.

Armillaria mellea (Vahl ex Fries) Kummer – "Honey Mushroom"

Cap: 2–4in (5–10cm)

Spores: white, 7–10 x 5–6µm, smooth

Edibility: edible, but must be well cooked; considered a great delicacy

Formerly considered a very variable species, this has in recent years been split into a number of different species, some of which can be easily distinguished. This species is a serious parasite of woodland trees and plantations, and causes many million dollars' worth of damage every year the world over. It will also attack a very large array of other plants in woods and gardens, including many popular shrubs. The caps are almost smooth and vary from bright honey yellow to greenish-yellow, with a darker center where there may be minute brownish scales. The stems taper downward and are fused together to form large clumps. There is a well-developed wooly ring above, white to yellow. If the bark of the dead or dying tree on which it appears is peeled back, long, very tough black "bootlaces" may be found. These rhizomorphs are the Honey Mushroom's way of spreading long distances to infect other trees.

Armillaria bulbosa (Barla) Romagnesi
"Honey Mushroom"

Cap: 2–4in (5–10cm)

Spores: white, 7.5–8.5 x 4.5–5μm, smooth

Edibility: edible and excellent when well cooked

The name *bulbosa* is appropriate, as the stems are bulbous, never tapered. The caps are reddish-brown to pinkish-ocher with brown scales at the center. The gills are cream to pinkish-buff. The stems are pinkish-buff, often with a yellow coating at the base. A key feature is the white, cobwebby veil at the stem apex, unlike the thick wooly ring of *A. mellea*. This species rarely grows in clumps, but is scattered singly over a wide area, arising from buried wood or roots. It is common in the northeast. *A. cepaestipes*, in the northwest, is so similar that it needs microscopic study to distinguish clearly. The recently described *A. calvescens* is similar but grows in small clumps on stumps and living trees, has a thin, membranous veil, and an almost smooth cap. It is widespread in the north and east.

Armillaria ostoyae Romagnesi – "Honey Mushroom"

Cap: 2–4in (5–10cm)

Spores: white, 8–10 x 5–6μm, smooth

Edibility: edible when well cooked

This is the "scaliest" of the species with the dark reddish-brown caps and dark blackish-brown scales. The stems are club-shaped, and it grows in clumps on stumps and at the base of trees. The ring is white with blackish-brown scales on the edge and down the stem in many specimens. The black rhizomorphs are branching and flattened with blunt tips.

Armillaria tabescens (Scopoli ex Fries) – Emel "Honey Mushroom"

Cap: 2–3in (5–7.5cm)

Spores: white, 8–10 x 5–7μm, smooth

Edibility: edible and good when well cooked

This Honey Mushroom is the exception to the rule. Although it is very similar in general appearance to the other species, it is completely without any trace of a veil or ring on the stem. The yellow-brown caps are smooth with minute brown scales at the center. The gills are adnate to slightly decurrent and pale buff. The slender stems are fused at the base to form often huge clumps. It is erratic in appearance, seeming to prefer years with hot summers, but then may not be seen for some years. It grows at the base of various deciduous trees, especially oaks, and is a serious parasite in some areas.

Hygrophoropsis aurantiaca (von Wulfen ex Fries) Maire – "False Chanterelle"

Cap: 1–3in (2.5–7.5cm)
Spores: white, 5–8 x 3–4.5μm, smooth
Edibility: often thought to be poisonous, but apparently it is just tasteless

As the common name suggests, it can be confused with the genuine Chanterelle, *Cantharellus cibarius*, but it differs in a number of respects. The soft, slight velvety yellow-orange cap is thin-fleshed and has an inrolled margin. The gills (it has true gills, unlike the Chanterelle) are thick and blunt-edged, fork repeatedly, and are a bright yellow-orange. The stem is slender and yellow. The true affinities of this mushroom probably lie with *Paxillus* in the Paxillaceae, since they share many features except for the spore color, but it is placed here in its traditional position because most people will expect to look for it among other white-spored mushrooms. It is very common in mixed woods and heaths throughout North America.

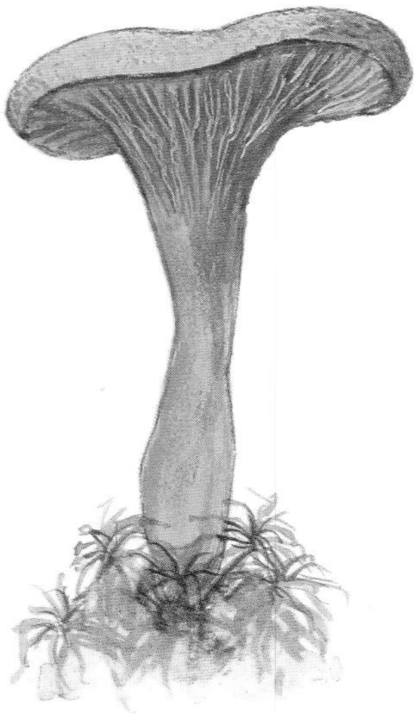

Clitocybe clavipes (Persoon ex Fries) Kummer

Cap: 2–3in (5–7.5cm)
Spores: white, 6–8.5 x 3–5μm, smooth
Edibility: doubtful, best avoided; has been reported to cause nausea when consumed with alcohol

This species is quite attractive, the domed, gray-brown to ocher-brown cap contrasting with the pale yellow-cream decurrent gills. The gray-brown stem swells out below, very much like a club (*clavipes* is Latin for club foot). There is a faint, delicate, but very sweet odor which has been likened to spice or flowers. The reported reaction with alcohol – palpitations, flushing, and nausea – is something that also turns up in other, unrelated mushrooms. In fact, it is similar to the effects of the chemical Antabuse, which is used to treat alcohol addiction. This mushroom is a common species of pine woods everywhere.

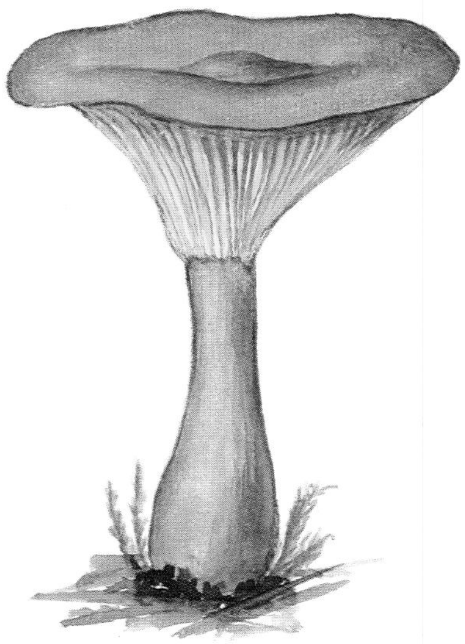

Clitocybe geotropa (Bulliard ex Fries) Quélet

Cap: 3–14in (7.5–35cm)
Spores: white, 6–7 x 5–6μm, smooth
Edibility: edible, but best avoided

This can be a very large and stately mushroom with a funnel-shaped cap, usually with a central umbo. The color ranges from white to ivory or pale buff. The decurrent gills are white and quite crowded. The stem is tall and firm. It often grows in small troops under deciduous trees, seems to prefer calcareous soils, and is fairly common in the Pacific northwest and Rocky Mountains. The similar *C. candida* is slightly smaller and usually remains whiter with age.

Clitocybe gibba (Persoon ex Fries) Kummer

[=*C. infundibuliformis*]

Cap: 2–4in (5–10cm)

Spores: white, 5–8 x 3.5–5μm, smooth

Edibility: edible, but best avoided

One of the commonest species of *Clitocybe,* the delicate pinkish-buff to tan cap is very thin-fleshed and soon funnel-shaped. The crowded gills are whitish and decurrent, and the stem is slender and whitish. There is a pleasant, fragrant odor a little like almond or anise. It grows in both conifer and deciduous woods, and is found throughout the USA. The similar *C. squamulosa* has a slightly roughened, darker cap with a concolorous stem, and occurs under conifers, especially in the spring and early summer.

Clitocybe nebularis (Batsch) Kummer

Cap: 2–6in (5–15cm)

Spores: pale buff, 6–7 x 3–4μm, smooth

Edibility: edible with caution; has caused upsets to some

Sometimes given the common name of "Clouded Agaric," this refers to the cap color, which is a smoky gray-brown. The cap is large and smooth with a central dome or boss, while the gills are slightly decurrent, crowded, and pale cream. The stout stem is rather short and fibrous, gray like the cap. It grows late in the year, often during the first frost, and may appear in large fairy rings. It prefers deep leaf litter or compost and frequently appears in gardens; it is commonest on the west coast.

Clitocybe odora (Bulliard ex Fries) Kummer

Cap: 1–3in (2.5–7.5cm)

Spores: pinkish–buff, 6–7 x 3–4μm, smooth

Edibility: edible

This species has one of the loveliest odors in the mushroom world, smelling exactly like fresh anise extract, and can often be detected in the woods from some distance away. Combined with the delicate blue-green to gray-green coloration of the slender fruit-body, it forms one of the most recognizable of species. Added to this is the rather unusual spore color, which serves to make it an easy species for the beginner to learn. In the eastern states, however, you should look out for *C. aeruginosa*, which is also blue-green but lacks the odor, is minutely hairy, and has white spores.

Clitocybe rivulosa (Persoon ex Fries) Kummer

Cap: 1–2in (2.5–5cm)
Spores: white, 4–5.5 x 2.5–3µm, smooth
Edibility: poisonous

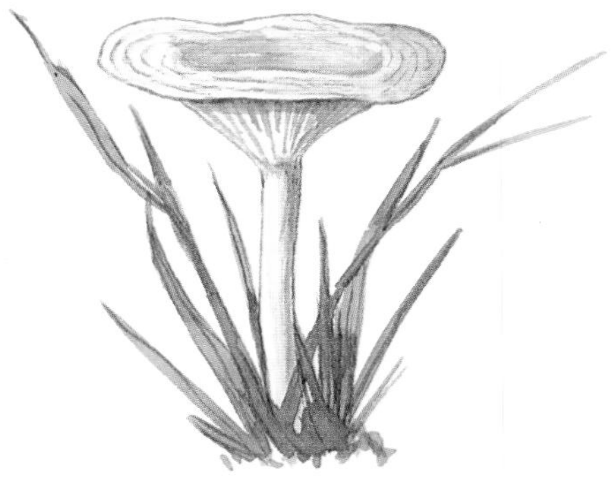

This is one of a number of small, white species of *Clitocybe*. They can be very difficult to distinguish accurately and should certainly all be avoided as far as eating is concerned. This one has a "frosty" coating, which is usually cracked in concentric zones, showing a browner undersurface. The gills are crowded, white, and adnate. It grows in open grass, often in circles, late in the year. It contains large amounts of the toxin muscarine, which can cause death in large quantities. There is some difference of opinion as to the correct name for this species and it may be that *C. dealbata* should be used.

Clitocybe nuda (Bulliard ex Fries) Bigelow & Smith – "Wood Blewit" [=*Lepista nuda*]

Cap: 2–6in (5–15cm)
Spores: pale pinkish-buff, 6–8 x 4–5µm, minutely roughened
Edibility: edible and good

This species is usually placed in the genus *Lepista,* characterized by its roughened, pinkish spores. However, many mycologists feel that the two genera merge gently into each other with no clear demarcation so they lump them all under *Clitocybe,* as is done here. This common species is to be found in large numbers, often in rings at the end of the year, and is very characteristic, with its deep violet cap, gills, and stem, although the cap soon fades to brownish-buff with age. It has a very pleasant, flowery-fruity odor and mild taste, and is widely collected for eating. It might be confused with some of the violet-purple *Cortinarius* species, but these all have rust-brown spores.

Clitocybe inversa Scopoli ex Fries

Cap: 2–4in (5–10cm)
Spores: pale creamy yellow, 4–5 x 3–4µm, minutely roughened
Edibility: edible, but best avoided

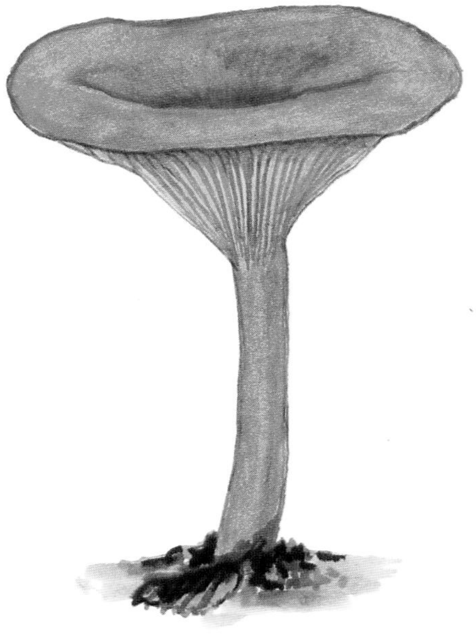

The funnel-shaped cap is a rich tawny to foxy red, fading to pale orange-brown with age and when dry. The gills are crowded and decurrent. The stem is slender and quite tall. It often grows in troops in deep leaf litter of both deciduous and coniferous trees from late summer onward. Because of the colored, roughened spores it is often placed in the genus *Lepista*, but that genus is here included under the concept of *Clitocybe*. It is particularly common in the western states.

Laccaria laccata (Scopoli ex Fries) Berkeley & Broom

Cap: ½–2in (1–5cm)
Spores: white, 7–8μm, subglobose with spines up to 1μm
Edibility: edible

One of the commonest of fungi everywhere, and distributed across most of the temperate parts of the world. It is also one of the most variable, with numerous varieties, subspecies or even species being separated out by different authors. The basic characteristics include the reddish-brown to pinkish-brown cap, which may be slightly scurfy at the center, and the thick, pale pinkish-brown gills, often dusted with the white spores. The stem is slender, fibrous, and reddish-brown. It grows in all sorts of woodlands, especially on paths and woodland edges, but also on open heaths with scattered trees.

Laccaria nobilis Mueller

Cap: 2–4in (5–10cm)
Spores: white, 7.5–10 x 6.5–8.5μm, with sharp spines up to 1μm
Edibility: edible

One of the largest and most striking species of *Laccaria*, it was only very recently described. The large cap is reddish-brown and scaly-fibrous, while the tall stem is coarsely scaly-fibrous and tough, and the flesh has a radishy odor. It has proved to be quite common in the northeastern and northern states in damp, boggy woods under pines. Although edible, it is rather tough in texture.

Laccaria amethystea (Bulliard) Murrill

Cap: 1–2in (2.5–5cm)
Spores: white, 8–10μm, globose with minute spines
Edibility: edible

One of the most beautiful of all fungi when fresh and moist, the entire fruiting body is a deep, intense amethyst-violet. As it dries, however, the cap fades to a dull grayish-lilac, although the gills usually retain their deep violet hue. This is a common species, but seems to prefer shadier, moister areas of woodland than such species as *L. laccata*, and is found throughout the east and north. In the west, however, it is replaced by the very similar *L. amethysteo-occidentalis*, which has elliptical spores.

Laccaria ochropurpurea (Berkeley) Peck

Cap: 2–8in (5–20cm)
Spores: white, 7.5–10 x 6.5–7µm, with spines up to 1.5µm
Edibility: edible

Our largest and most robust species of *Laccaria*, it seems to prefer more open, drier woods, especially oaks, in the eastern and southern states. The fleshy cap and stem are a pale gray-brown to slightly purplish-brown, while the very thick gills are deep purple to lilac. Both cap and stem can be very fibrous. Also large and robust is *L. trullisata*, found only in sandy soils, especially in coastal areas, which has a large, swollen stem, often completely buried in the sand.

Laccaria tortilis (Bolton) S.F. Gray

Cap: ¼–½ in (0.6–1cm)
Spores: white, globose, 11–16µm and spiny, with only two spores per basidium
Edibility: edible

Probably our smallest species, it is striking for its very thick and very sparse gills, and for the wavy-fluted cap, which is pale pinkish. This is a very uncommon species, although it is also probably overlooked because of its small size. It prefers very damp areas, often bare soil in deep shade such as stream sides and banks, or deep, shady tracks in woodlands.

Tricholoma sulphureum (Bulliard ex Fries) Kummer

Cap: 2–4in (5–10cm)
Spores: white, 9–12 x 5–6µm, smooth
Edibility: poisonous

This fungus gives off a strong, penetrating odor of coal gas, which can be smelled from some distance away. This, combined with the overall bright sulfur-yellow to ocher-yellow colors, makes it an easily recognizable mushroom. It is quite common, especially late in the season under oaks and beeches on acid soils in the Pacific northwest. In eastern states the very similar species *T. odorum* differs in its pallid, whitish gills.

Tricholoma saponaceum (Fries) Kummer

Cap: 2–4in (5–10cm)
Spores: white, 5–6 x 3.5–4μm, smooth
Edibility: poisonous? best avoided

A very variable mushroom, both in color and in smell (on which there is some disagreement), but the basic colors are greenish-gray to gray-brown, often with pink flushes in the stem base and gills. The cap is smooth to minutely scaly. The odor is fragrant, said to be of soap or flowers, or sour like sesame oil, or of green almonds. It is a common species in mixed woodlands, particularly on clay soils, and is found from the Pacific northwest to the northeastern states.

Tricholoma sulphurescens Bresadola

Cap: 2–4in (5–10cm)
Spores: white, 5–6 x 4–5μm, smooth
Edibility: inedible

A very rare species, it is nevertheless quite easy to identify. The entire fruiting body is white to cream, and all parts rapidly stain sulfur-yellow if handled or bruised. The odor is rank and unpleasant when old, but the taste is quite mild. The cap is smooth and silky to touch, and the gills are narrow and crowded with rather wavy edges. The stem is firm and fleshy, quite fibrous and rather rooting. Its distribution is uncertain because of its rarity, but it occurs under oaks and conifers, and has been found in the northeast.

Tricholoma terreum (Schaeffer) Kummer

Cap: 2–4in (5–10cm)
Spores: white, 5–7 x 4–5μm, smooth
Edibility: doubtful; best avoided

There are a number of gray *Tricholoma* species, not all easy to distinguish. Close attention must be paid to such characteristics as taste, texture of cap surface, color of gill edges, and so forth. The species shown here has a felty-tomentose gray to gray-brown cap. The gills are broad, gray-white, and notched where they join the stem. The short stem is white and smooth. It has a mild taste and is almost odorless. It often grows in large troops and is found under pines late in the season throughout the USA.

Tricholoma virgatum (Fries) Kummer

Cap: 2–4in (5–10cm)
Spores: white, 6–7 x 5–6µm, smooth
Edibility: inedible

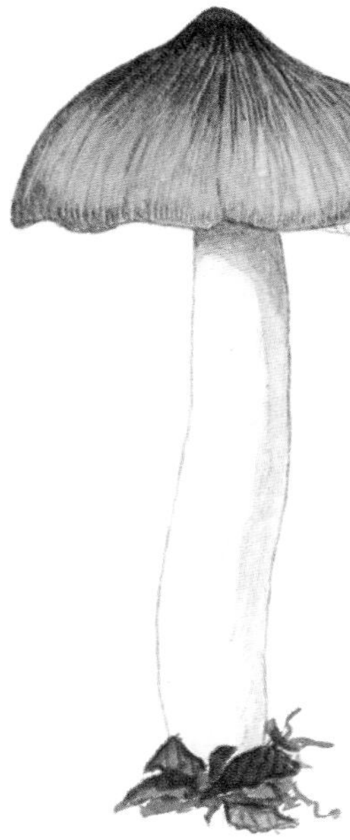

This is one of a few gray species with a peppery or burning taste to the gills and flesh. The cap is almost conical and is gray to gray-black with darker grayish fibers, and is almost smooth or silky to touch. The gills are broad, white, and notched next to the stem. The stem is white and rather tall, firm and smooth. It grows in small troops under conifers throughout the USA.

Tricholoma subresplendens Peck

Cap: 2–4in (5–10cm)
Spores: white, 5–7 x 3.5–4.5µm, smooth
Edibility: inedible

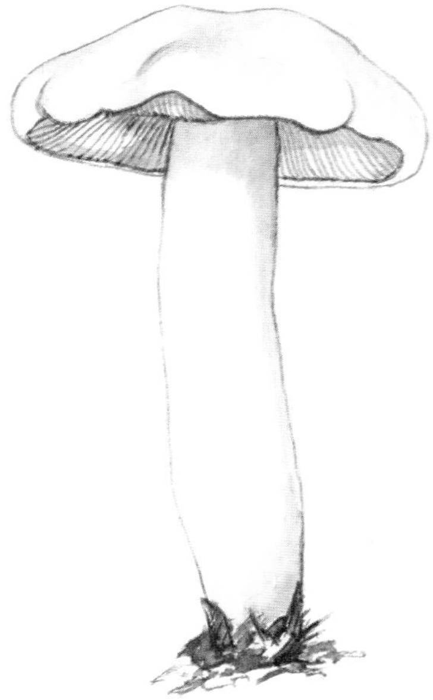

A striking, beautiful species, this is distinguished by its snow-white cap, gills, and stem becoming slightly buffy at the cap center with age. Other white species usually have a distinct, strong odor, or stain when bruised. This species grows under mixed deciduous trees and seems to prefer oaks on neutral soils in eastern North America. Some white species of *Clitocybe* might be mistaken for this fungus, but they have slightly to distinctly decurrent gills, not the notched or sinuate gills of *Tricholoma*.

Tricholoma sejunctum (Sowerby ex Fries) Quélet

Cap: 2–4in (5–10cm)
Spores: white, 5–6 x 4–5µm, smooth
Edibility: inedible

A very variable species, a number of different varieties having been described based mainly on color or habitat differences. The commonest forms are yellow-green to olive-gray in color, with darker radiating fibrils, browner at the center. Some forms are browner or greener, others are much paler, almost yellow. The gills are white to yellowish, broad and crowded, with a notch by the stem. The stem is firm, stout, and white to flushed slightly yellowish or green. The odor and taste are strongly mealy or floury, becoming rather bitter. It is a common species in both coniferous and deciduous woods throughout North America.

Tricholoma flavovirens (Persoon ex Fries) Lundell [=*T. equestre*]

Cap: 2–4in (5–10cm)
Spores: white, 6–8 x 3–5μm, smooth
Edibility: edible and good

An attractive species and quite variable, depending upon habitat. The cap is usually broadly bell-shaped with the top flattened, smooth, yellow-brown to brownish-olive, with darker brown squamules. The gills are bright yellow, crowded, and notched by the stem. The stocky stem is brownish-yellow, paler above, but the flesh inside is white. The odor is mealy, as is the taste. It is found mainly under pines on sandy soils, and is widely distributed. It is one of the few species considered a good edible.

Tricholoma portentosum (Fries) Quélet

Cap: 2–5in (5–12.5cm)
Spores: white, 5–6 x 3.5–5μm, smooth
Edibility: edible and good, but best avoided

The characteristic of this species is the yellow flush that spreads over the stem and gills, and the blunt, gray-brown cap which is streaked with darker fibrils. There may also be greenish or even violet tones present. The stem is usually large and stout, and the flesh has a mealy, cucumber-like taste. It appears very late in the season, often growing in rings or troops under pines or beech, throughout North America.

Tricholoma fulvum (A.P. de Candolle) Saccardo [= *T. flavobrunneum*]

Cap: 2–4in (5–10cm)
Spores: white, 5–7 x 3–4.5μm, smooth
Edibility: inedible

This is perhaps one of the easier species to identify once the key features are understood. Although there are other reddish-brown species, this one is unique in its yellowish, brown-spotted gills and yellow flesh in the stem, easily seen by gently splitting the stem with a fingernail. The cap is sticky when wet and has a grooved margin, but is otherwise smooth. It is a common species and grows exclusively under birch in boggy situations, appearing rather earlier than most other *Tricholoma* species. It has been reported from northern and western states.

Tricholoma aurantium (Schaeffer ex Fries) Ricken

Cap: 2–4in (5–10cm)
Spores: white, 4–5 x 3–3.5µm, smooth
Edibility: inedible

Rather brightly colored for a *Tricholoma*, this attractive species is a bright orange to orange-brown, with a viscid cap contrasting against the almost white gills. The latter are often spotted with reddish-brown. The stem is similarly colored, with irregular zones up to a distinct ring-zone; it is white above. The taste and odor are mealy and cucumber-like. It is a frequent species under conifers, late in the season, throughout much of North America.

Tricholoma caligatum (Viviani) Ricken
[=*Armillaria caligatum*]

Cap: 2–6in (5–15cm)
Spores: white, 6–7.5 x 4.5–5.5µm, smooth
Edibility: edible

There is a group of *Tricholoma* species where the veil is well developed and forms a ring and/or scaly zones on the stems. Because of this many of them were formerly placed in the genus *Armillaria*, but in other respects they are typical of *Tricholoma*. This species is large, rather dull in color, with darker scales on the pallid cap. The stem is white with a sheath of brown scales, patches, and zones over the lower half. There may be bluish-gray tones present in some forms. It is quite a common species found mainly under deciduous trees in the east, but apparently under conifers in the west.

Leucopaxillus albissimus (Peck) Singer

Cap: 2–4in (5–10cm)
Spores: cream, 5.5–8.5 x 4–6µm, with tiny amyloid warts
Edibility: edible

This all-white species often grows in large rings and has a number of distinguishing features. The gills are very crowded, adnate to slightly descending; the stem is swollen at the base and usually bound to the leaf litter by copious white masses of mycelium. It is found in conifer woods in northern North America across to the eastern states.

Melanoleuca alboflavida (Peck) Murrill

Cap: 2–4in (5–10cm)
Spores: white, 7–9 x 4–5.5μm, amyloid and and minutely warted
Edibility: edible

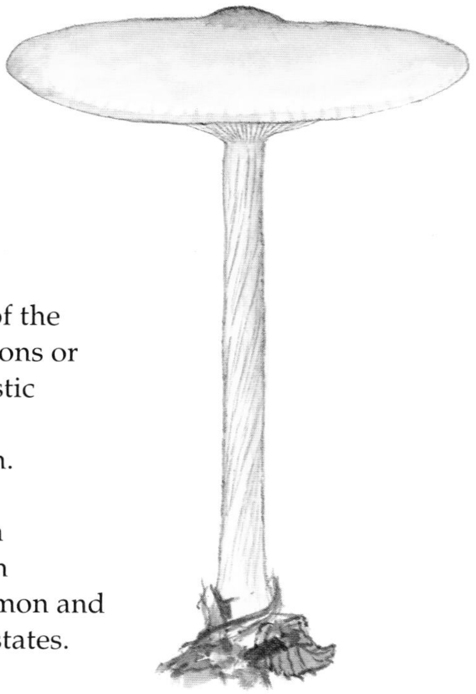

This group of fungi provides good reason to use a microscope since many of the species have fascinating cells on the gills, often strangely shaped like harpoons or clubs, and quite beautiful to examine. Most of the species have a characteristic bump or umbo at the center of the smooth cap, and a fibrous stem. The species are variable in their characteristics and rather difficult to distinguish. Certainly, there seem to be more names in the literature than there are good species. This one, however, is well characterized by the cream-buff cap with white, sinuate gills. The tall, slender stem is pallid and fibrous, and the flesh is often browner in the base. It has pointed, harpoon-like cystidia. It is common and grows in mixed woods and clearings throughout the eastern and northern states.

Melanoleuca cognata (Fries) Konrad & Maublanc

Cap: 2–4in (5–10cm)
Spores: unusual for the genus, deep creamy yellow, 9–10 x 6–7μm, with amyloid warts
Edibility: edible

This is one of the easier species to identify because of the bright ocher-yellow to yellow-brown colors of the cap, floury-rancid odor, rather short, stout stem, and the deep creamy yellow spores (most *Melanoleuca* spores are white to cream). It is fairly common, preferring open woodlands or even pastures, and is widely distributed. This may be one of a complex of very closely related forms since there are discrepancies in the literature regarding cap color and spore color, some being described as darker, others lighter.

Lyophyllum decastes (Fries) Singer

Cap: 2–4in (5–10cm)
Spores: white, globose, 4-6μm, smooth
Edibility: edible and good

Enormous clumps of this mushroom can be found bursting up through soil or gravel, or even through Tarmacadam. It seems to show a definite preference for roadsides, trackways or other disturbed areas. The caps vary greatly in color, from gray to brown, and are smooth and dry to touch. The stout, firm stems are white and smooth. A number of other forms (or species) have been described, but since many of the characteristics appear to intergrade, they seem of doubtful value. In the USA this is often called the Fried Chicken Mushroom because of the taste, and I would agree that it is one of the best mushrooms I have tried for both flavor and texture.

Catathelasma imperialis (Fries) Singer

Cap: 5–15in (12.5–38cm)
Spores: white, 10–15 x 4–5.5μm, smooth
Edibility: edible and good

One of the largest mushrooms you are likely to find, the specific name of imperialis is an apt one for it does form an imposing and regal sight. The huge cap is a dull brown, breaking into broad patches and scales. The thick, heavy stem has a double veil of pinkish-brown ending in a double ring at the top of the stem. The white flesh is very thick. It grows under spruce and fir in the Rocky Mountains and the Pacific northwest.

Tricholomopsis rutilans (Schaeffer ex Fries) Singer

Cap: 2–6in (5–15cm)
Spores: white, 7–8 x 5–6μm, smooth
Edibility: edible

This has the common name of Plums and Custard, which gives an accurate idea of the colors present in this species. It is a beautiful combination of wine-red tiny scales overlaying a yellow background, with bright golden yellow gills; only when old and rather faded might it be a little more deceptive. This is a good example of not trying to judge spore color by the color of the gills, since the spores are white, not yellow. It is found growing on or near conifer stumps or sawdust, and is very common throughout North America.

Calocybe carnea (Bull. ex Fries) Kuhn

Cap: ½–2in (1.5–5cm)
Spores: white, 4–6 x 2–3μm, smooth
Edibility: inedible

A rather uncommon species, it is nevertheless a very attractive and easily recognized one. The pale pink to reddish cap is smooth and dry, as is the stem. The gills are very contrasting, white, crowded, and attached to the stem, or slightly descending. The stem is fibrous in texture. This species is found throughout the temperate regions of the world, including North America, and prefers grassy clearings in woods, lawns, and roadsides.

Tricholomopsis platyphylla (Persoon ex Fries) Kotlaba & Pouzar [=*Megacollybia platyphylla*]

Cap: 2–6in (5–15cm)
Spores: white, 7–9 x 5–7μm, smooth
Edibility: inedible

This is one of the earliest mushrooms to appear following late spring rains, and continues to fruit throughout the summer and early fall. Its cap is a dull gray to gray-brown, smooth, with fine radiating fibers. The gills are the most recognizable feature, being white, very broad, and widely spaced, with the edges often split or jagged, and with a notch where they join the stem. The stem is white and firm, then hollow and very fibrous; if carefully traced down into the wood or soil, it will be seen to form long, white mycelial strands at the base. Extremely common, it is sometimes the only species fruiting in summer woodland, growing from logs, stumps, or from buried wood.

Asterophora lycoperdoides (Bulliard ex Mérat) Ditmar
Cap: ¼–¾ in (0.6–2cm)
Spores: basidiospores white, 3.2–5.8 x 2.0–4.2μm, chlamydospores 13–20 x 10–20μm, strongly warted and bluntly spiny
Edibility: unknown; too small

Here is a fungus attacking a fungus. This strange organism is found only on mushrooms of the genera *Russula* and *Lactarius*, and they have to be old and rotting specimens at that. The small caps are squat and misshapen, and are soon covered in a thick, brownish powder. This is a layer of thick-walled asexual spores, called chlamydospores, which are completely separate from the normal basidiospores produced on the rudimentary gills. It is widespread, although rarely common, and seems to prefer very wet years. The similar *A. parasitica* also grows on rotting *Russula* and *Lactarius*, but differs in the more perfect caps, well-formed gills, and lack of brown chlamydospores.

Flammulina velutipes (Fries) Karsten
Cap: 1–3in (2.5–7.5cm)
Spores: white, 7–9 x 3–6μm, smooth
Edibility: edible and good

Very few mushrooms can withstand frosts or even cold weather for a prolonged period, but this species is actually stimulated into growth and fruiting by low temperatures. It starts to fruit around October, goes right through to the early spring, and can often be picked in December and January. The bright orange-yellow to orange-brown caps are smooth and sticky, while the gills are pale creamy yellow. The slender stems are velvety and yellow, becoming deep blackish-brown below. It grows in clumps on dead or dying deciduous timber throughout North America. It is often particularly common in the east in May when the Morels are fruiting.

Cystoderma terrei (Berkeley & Broom) Harmaja [=*C. cinnabarinum*]
Cap: 1-3in (2.5–7.5cm)
Spores: white, 3.5–5 x 2.5–3μm, smooth
Edibility: inedible

An uncommon species, but quite beautiful, with its rich brick-red to orange cap and stem, and powdery-granular surface. The gills are white, as is the apex of the stem above a distinct ring zone. It grows in mixed woods, often under conifers, and is widespread in North America. There is some uncertainty about the placing of *Cystoderma*; some mycologists put it close to *Tricholoma*, as here, while others believe it to be related to *Lepiota*.

Cystoderma amianthinum (Scopoli) Fayod

Cap: 1–2in (2.5–5cm)
Spores: white, 4–6 x 3–4µm, smooth
Edibility: inedible

The powdery-granular cap is bright yellow-ocher and usually wrinkled at the center. The stem has a yellow, granular coating up to a slight ring zone near the apex. The gills are white to cream. This is the commonest species in the genus and grows in conifer woods throughout North America, especially in the northern states.

Xerula furfuracea Redhead

[=*Oudemansiella radicata* of some authors]
Cap: 2–5in (5–12.5cm)
Spores: white, 12–18 x 9–12µm, smooth
Edibility: inedible

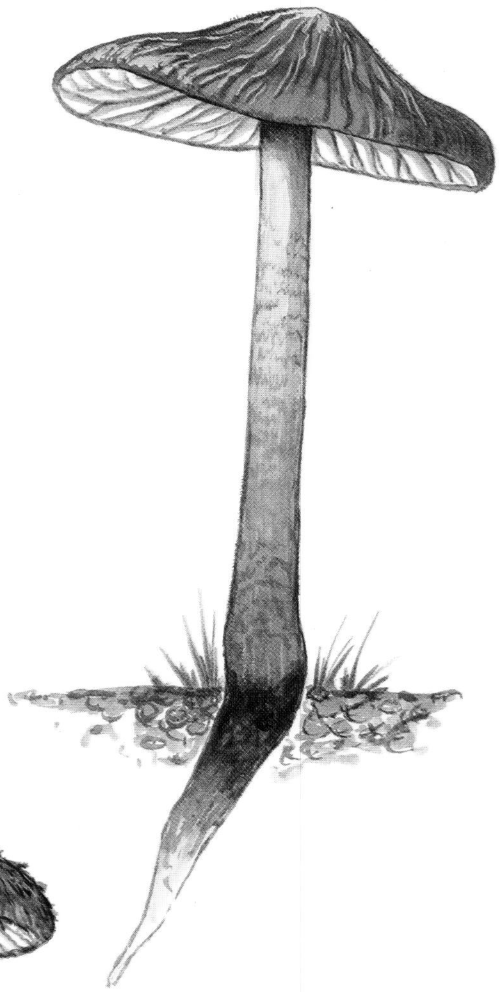

Many fungi seem to prefer growing from buried wood or tree roots rather than on wood lying on the surface, and these species often develop long mycelial strands to penetrate the soil. Nowhere is this more developed or so spectacular as in this species. The stem is prolonged into a long, deeply rooting "taproot" which can be traced down to 8in (20cm) or more in some specimens. The ocher-brown to buff cap is viscid in wet weather, and often extremely wrinkled and veined. The gills are white, very broad, and widely spaced. The stem is tough, smooth, and white to finely brown, scurfy-floccose below. The similar *X. rubrobrunneus* differs in developing reddish-brown stains on the stem.

Squamanita odorata (Sumstine) Bas

Cap: 1–3in (2.5–7.5cm)
Spores: white, 6.5–9 x 4–6µm, smooth
Edibility: inedible

A rare mushroom – indeed, all the species in this small genus are uncommon – but easily recognized. The stem has a large tuberous base buried in the soil. This species has a lilac-brown conical cap which is fibrous, while the stem is also lilac and fibrous up to a ring zone at the apex. The gills are white. A strong, aromatic or fruity odor is present. It grows in poor, sandy soils, especially in the east, but also across to Washington.

Marasmius androsaceus (Linnaeus ex Fries) Fries – "Horsehair Fungus"

Cap: ¼–½in (0.6–1cm)

Spores: white, 6–9 x 2.5–4.5μm, smooth

Edibility: inedible

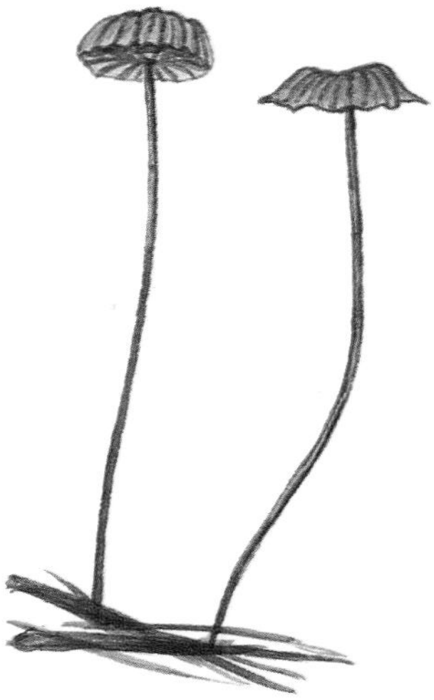

The common name refers to the extremely thin, hair-like, blackish-brown stems of this species, which are very long and on which the tiny, elegantly fluted brown caps are uplifted. The gills are very widely spaced and dull flesh-brown. It can be very common, growing in large numbers on the needle and cone litter of conifer woods throughout North America. Unlike many species of *Marasmius,* there is no particular odor.

Marasmius rotula (Scopoli ex Fries) Fries

Cap: 1/16–½ in (0.15–1cm)

Spores: white, 6–10 x 3–5μm, smooth

Edibility: inedible

This tiny, pretty mushroom is one of the commonest species of *Marasmius* and can be found dotting the woodland floor on fallen twigs and wood almost anywhere. The bell-shaped cap is white, pleated, and sunken at the center. The white gills are widely spaced, attached to the stem, or separated by a narrow collar. The cap has been likened to an open parachute and this is a very good description. The threadlike stem is dark brown and shiny. There is no special odor present. It can be found throughout North America.

Marasmius oreades (Bolton) Fries – "Fairy Ring Mushroom"

Cap: 1–3in (2.5–7.5cm)

Spores: white, 7–10 x 4–6μm, smooth

Edibility: edible and excellent

Although many other species of fungi form fairy rings, this is the most well known the world over since it "disfigures" lawns and golf courses everywhere. Of course, to mushroom lovers it is a wonderful sight to see the often enormous rings of dark green grass with the mushrooms fruiting on the outer edge. The expansion of the ring can be traced year after year, and some truly gigantic rings many hundreds of yards across are thought to be well over a thousand years old. Indeed, it has even been suggested that some rings may be among the oldest inhabitants of this planet. The tough, pale buff caps are smooth. and the gills are thick and widely spaced. The stems are tough and fibrous, not usually eaten.

Marasmius siccus (Schweinitz) Fries

Cap: ⅛–¼in (0.3–0.6cm)
Spores: pale cream, 7–11 x 6–8μm, smooth
Edibility: inedible

Some of the smallest mushrooms are also the prettiest, and this is no exception. The bright orange-rust caps are bell-shaped and deeply fluted with a sunken center. The gills are pale creamy yellow, while the slender stem is yellow-brown, smooth, and brittle. It is common on fallen twigs and leaves in mixed woods, especially in eastern states. The similar *M. fulvoferrugineus* is deeper rust-brown in color.

Marasmius nigrodiscus (Peck) Halling

Cap: 2–4in (5–10cm)
Spores: white, 8.5–10 x 3.5–4μm, smooth
Edibility: doubtful; best avoided

This is a little-known species, but not particularly uncommon; it is just one of many distinctive species which have rarely been included in field guides. The ivory-buff caps have a darker brown disc and are translucent when wet, becoming opaque when dry. The widely spaced gills are thick and pale cream. The very tough, fibrous stem is pale cream. It often grows in large troops under the shade of pinewoods in the southern and eastern states. The similar *M. oreades* (see page 77) grows in open grass.

Collybia maculata (Albertini & Schweinitz ex Fries) Kummer

Cap: 2–4in (5–10cm)
Spores: pale pinkish-buff, 5–6 x 4–5μm, smooth
Edibility: inedible

This is sometimes given the common name of Cocoa-caps because of the cocoa-colored spots and stains which soon spread over the initially white cap and gills. The whole mushroom is very tough and sinewy, and the cap is very rounded with an incurved margin. The white gills are very shallow and crowded. The thick stem can be rather spindle-shaped and rooting, and has rather bitter-tasting flesh. It is a common species and can form fairy rings in the litter of the beech or conifer woods in which it likes to grow.

Collybia butyracea (Bulliard ex Fries) Quélet

Cap: 2–3in (5–7.5cm)
Spores: cream-buff, 6–8 x 3–4µm, smooth
Edibility: edible

The name *butyracea* means buttery or greasy, and this refers to the texture of the cap surface which in humid conditions is very slippery and greasy without actually being glutinous or viscid. The cap varies from the dark brown shown to grayish forms referred to as variety *asema,* and is hygrophanous. The gills are broad, cream, and often rather serrated on the margins. The stem is characteristically tapered upward from a swollen base. It is a common species growing in troops across the needle litter under pines and occasionally deciduous trees too.

Collybia dryophila (Bulliard ex Fries) Kummer

Cap: 1–3in (2.5–7.5cm)
Spores: pale cream, 5–6 x 2–3µm, smooth
Edibility: edible

A contender for the title of commonest mushroom, this species is found all over the temperate regions of the world in a wide variety of habitats. The thin, flattened caps are smooth and dry, and vary with age from reddish-brown to pale yellow-ocher. The crowded gills are thin, narrow, and pale cream. The smooth stem is slender and pale orange-brown, with white hairs at the base. It grows singly but in groups in both coniferous and deciduous woods, and has a particular preference for oak and pine.

Collybia alkalivirens Singer

Cap: ½–1½in (1–3cm)
Spores: white, 4–6 x 3–4.5µm, smooth
Edibility: edible

This is not an easy species to place at first sight, being exceptionally dark for a *Collybia*. The cap is deep blackish-brown and is radially furrowed; the gills and stem are similarly colored. The most distinctive feature is the deep green reaction of the mushroom if a drop of caustic soda (KOH) is applied. It is an occasional to frequent species and grows in mixed woods throughout North America.

Collybia confluens (Persoon ex Fries) Kummer

Cap: (1–2in) 2.5–5cm
Spores: white, 7–10 x 2–4μm, smooth
Edibility: inedible

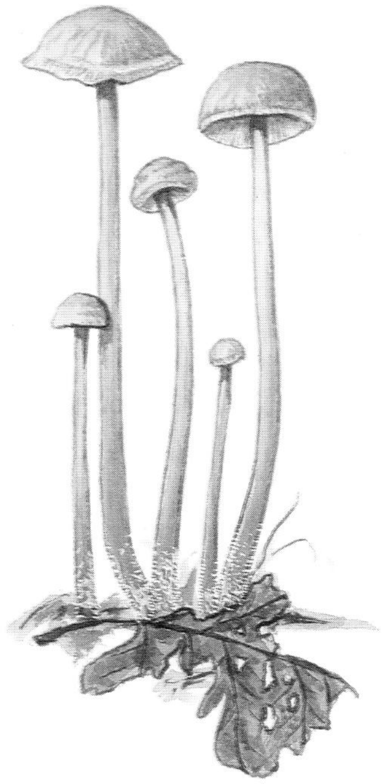

The densely clustered groups with the hairy pale brown stems fused together are very distinctive. Also the top of the stem widens to form a small "button" which is easily separable from the cap. The rounded, thin caps are gray-brown to pinkish and dry, while the gills are narrow, very crowded and cream.There is a curious aromatic odor which is quite pleasant. It is a common species and grows in fallen leaf or needle litter in mixed woods throughout North America.

Mycena galopus (Persoon ex Fries) Kummer

Cap: (¼–½ in) 0.6–1cm
Spores: white, 10–14 x 5–7μm, smooth
Edibility: inedible

This is one of a series of species which will exude a "milk" or latex when broken and quite fresh. In this species the milk is white while in others it may be red or orange. The tiny bell-shaped cap is gray-brown to beige fading with age. The gills are pale grayish-white and the stem is gray-brown to reddish-brown with a hairy base. When snapped the hollow stem drips white latex. It is very common growing singly, scattered over the leaf litter of coniferous and mixed woods everywhere. *M. leucogala* is gray-black, but otherwise similar, except for some minor microscopic differences; it is sometimes referred to as a variety (*nigra*) of the species described here.

Mycena galericulata (Scopoli ex Fries) S. F. Gray

Cap: (1–2in) 2.5–5cm
Spores: white, 8–11 x 5.5–7μm, smooth
Edibility: edible

This very common species is quite variable in color, size and shape and causes most beginners a lot of difficulty in recognition. The features to look for are the rather bluntly conical cap which is dull gray-brown and radially wrinkled. The gills are white to grayish or even pinkish when mature and are noticeably interveined with cross-veins. The smooth stem is shiny, grayish, fused into clumps and often deeply rooting into the wood on which it grows.

Mycena inclinata (Fries) Quélet

Cap: (1–2in) 2.5–5cm
Spores: white, 8–10 x 5.5–7μm, smooth
Edibility: doubtful; best avoided

Often confused with the previous species and vice versa, this species has a gray-brown bell-shaped cap which is minutely but distinctly toothed along the margin when young. The gills are gray-white to pinkish. The stem is smooth, becoming strongly reddish-brown to orange-brown in the lower half, and the surface is flecked with minute tufts of white cottony hairs (use a hand lens for this). There is a distinct odor, difficult to define, but suggestive of cheap soap or even cucumber. It grows in small tufts on fallen logs and stumps, especially oaks, everywhere.

Mycena haematopus (Persoon ex Fries) Kummer

Cap: ½–2in (1–5cm)
Spores: white, 9–10 x 6.5–7μm, smooth
Edibility: inedible

Sometimes called the Bleeding Mycena, this name refers to the dark reddish-brown juice that "bleeds" from the stem when broken. The small, bell-shaped caps are dark reddish-brown to wine-red with small teeth along the margin. The stems are slender, smooth, and colored like the cap. This species is usually found in clusters on fallen timber and is a common species throughout North America. The juice will stain the fingers for some time.

Mycena pura (Persoon ex Fries) Kummer

Cap: 1–2in (2.5–5cm)
Spores: white, 5–9 x 3–4μm, smooth
Edibility: doubtful; best avoided

A common odor in many mushrooms is that of radish – referred to as raphanoid – and nowhere is this better demonstrated than in this species, which both smells and tastes radishy. The rather robust cap and stem are a delicate lilac-pink to purplish-gray or even blue-gray. Although the colors seem to vary considerably, depending on the habitat, the smell nevertheless remains constant. It is a common species in both deciduous and coniferous woodlands throughout North America.

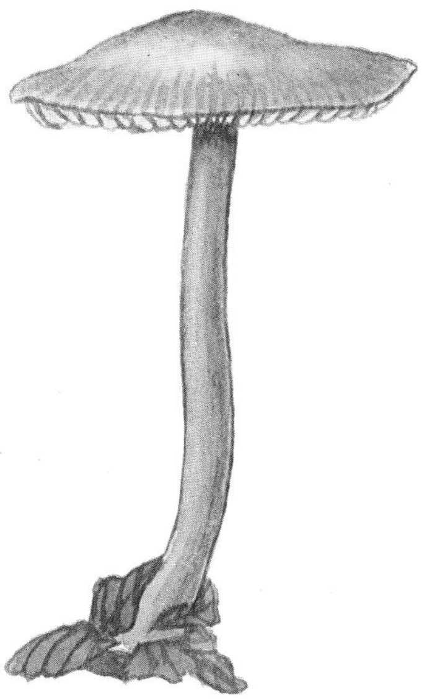

Mycena subcaerulea (Peck)

Cap: ¼–½in (0.5–1cm)
Spores: white, 6–8µm, globose smooth
Edibility: inedible

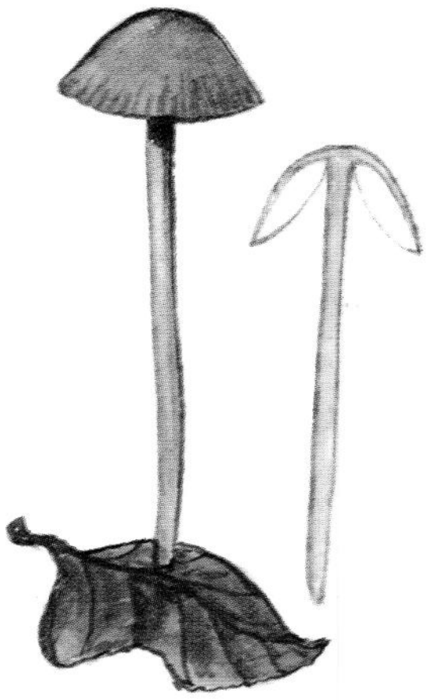

Truly blue mushrooms are very rare; this is one of the few, and even here the color can vary to a blue-green. The tiny caps are bell-shaped, and when old the color will fade to brown at the center. The gills are whitish. The stem is blue like the cap. Quite a common species, it grows singly on decaying leaf litter in deciduous woods east of the Great Plains. *M. amicta*, also blue, is found in the northwestern states growing under conifers.

Mycena leiana (Berkeley) Saccardo

Cap: ½–2in (1–5cm)
Spores: white, 7–10 x 5–6µm, smooth
Edibility: doubtful; best avoided

This is a difficult mushroom to mistake. All parts of this small, clustered species are a vivid, almost fluorescent orange and quite sticky to touch. The edges of the orange gills are a darker reddish-orange. It can be found quite commonly pushing out of cracks in the bark of fallen deciduous trees and stumps in both the northern and eastern states.

Mycena sanguinolenta (Albertini & Schweinitz ex Fries) Kummer

Cap: ¼–½in (0.5–1cm)
Spores: white, 8–11 x 4–6µm, smooth
Edibility: inedible

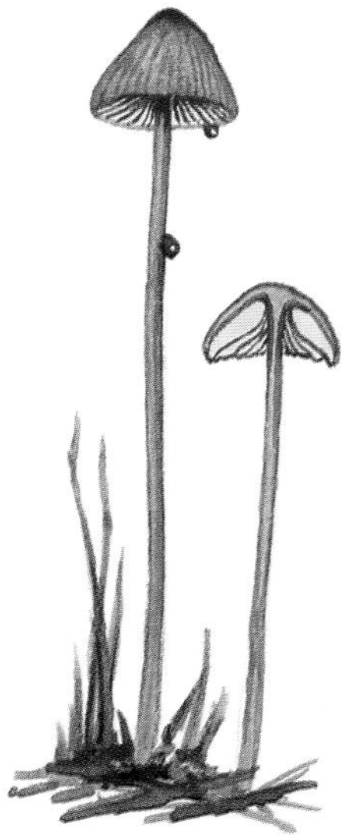

This very delicate, slender species is another of those mushrooms that "bleed" when broken, this time a reddish juice from the stem. The small bell-shaped cap is reddish-brown to purplish-brown, while the gills are whitish. The slender stem is pale reddish-brown. Unlike *M. haematopus*, which also bleeds when cut, it grows singly in small troops on decaying leaf or needle litter and is widespread throughout North America.

Mycena luteopallens (Peck) Saccardo

Cap: ¼–½ in (0.5–1cm)
Spores: white, 7–9 x 4–5µm, smooth
Edibility: inedible

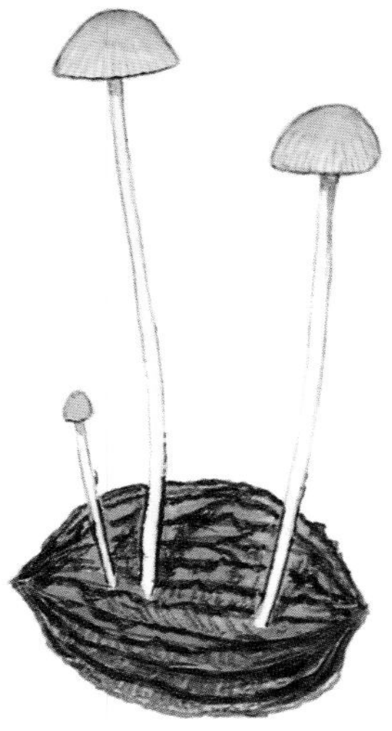

Many mushrooms are very specific in their choice of habitat, and this can be an important clue when it comes to identification. Some are so singular in their choice as to be easily distinguished by anyone. In this instance, the choice of fallen hickory nuts or walnuts, and the tiny, pale yellow caps with whitish stem combine to make it unmistakable. The nut is usually buried in the soil, so the stem must be carefully traced down through the soil to find it. Often abundant, but easily overlooked, throughout the eastern states.

AMANITACEAE
Amanita Family

There are over 120 species of *Amanita* in North America, and the genus contains some of the most beautiful, and the most deadly, mushrooms in the world. Features to look for are the white, smooth spores, and the universal veil, which may be left as a sac-like volva at the stem base or as mere warty remnants on the cap and stem base. A partial veil may also be present as a skirt-like ring or annulus at the top of the stem. Always make sure to collect the entire stem base from under the ground so that any volva can be seen. Some *Amanita* species have distinctive odors. The gills are free from the stem, as seen in the cross-section below.

A second genus usually included in this family is *Limacella*, which has a slimy veil.

Amanita phalloides (Fries) Saccardo – "Death Cap"

Cap: 2–6in (5–15cm)

Spores: white, 8–10.5 x 7–8μm, amyloid

Edibility: deadly poisonous; kills many people every year in Europe

This deadly species causes severe illness and death in both Europe and North America, where it has been accidentally introduced and is spreading rapidly. It contains complex chemicals called amatoxins and phallotoxins, which soon cause severe liver damage, preceded by painful and intensive vomiting and diarrhea, muscle cramps, and general debilitation. Unfortunately, the symptoms rarely appear until several hours after the meal, making prompt recognition and treatment difficult. The yellowish-green to olive cap may also be brownish, or even completely white in some forms. The ring and large, bulbous volva are distinctive, as is the sweet, sickly odor that develops with age – rather like old honey. In its white form it may be mistaken for a Horse Mushroom (*Agaricus* species), but, unlike that genus, the gills and spores are pure white. It grows under oaks and pines in the western states and in the northeast.

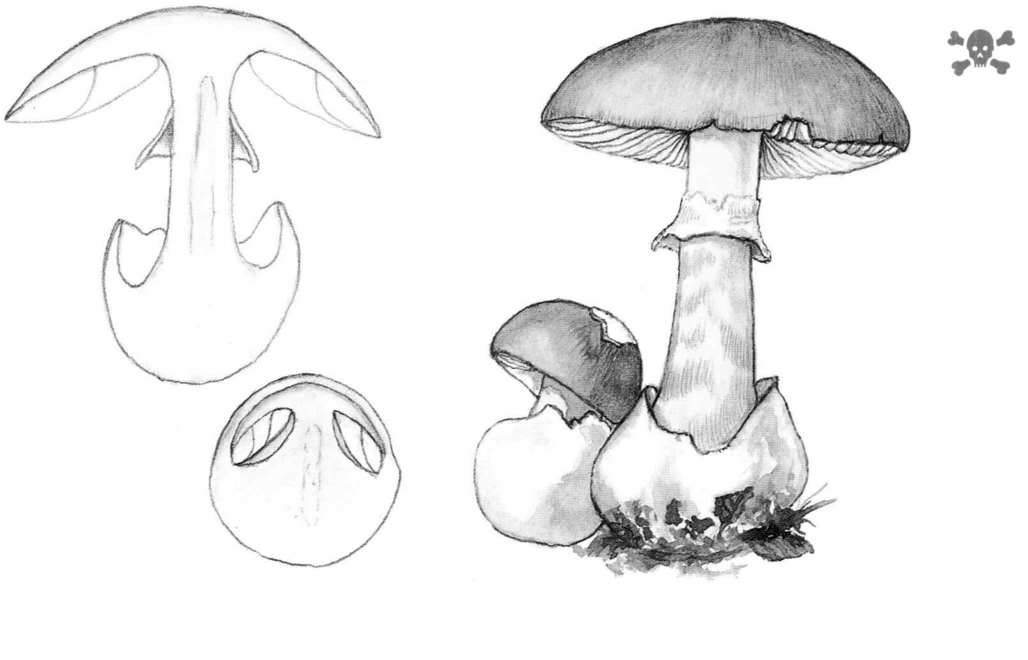

Amanita virosa Secretan –
"Destroying Angel"

Cap: 2–6in (5–15cm)
Spores: 8–10 μm globose, amyloid
Edibility: deadly poisonous; contains similar toxins to the Death Cap (page 83)

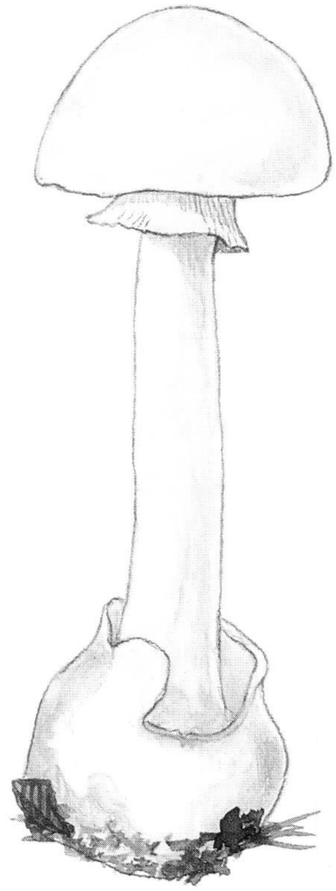

As beautiful as it is deadly, this species well deserves its common name. All parts of the mushroom are pure white, and the cap is smooth and sometimes slightly sticky. The stem may be slightly wooly-scaly to completely smooth, and has a large volval sac at the base. The odor is faint, sickly sweet, like honey. A good test for this species is to place a drop of caustic soda (KOH) on the cap, which will turn bright golden yellow. It is a very common species in many parts of North America, in woods and gardens under mixed trees. A number of other white species with volvas are also found, differing mainly in their microscopic characteristics and negative KOH reaction.

Amanita caesarea (Scopoli ex Fries) Persoon –
"Caesar's Mushroom"

Cap: 3–6in (7.5–15cm)
Spores: 8–10μm globose, amyloid
Edibility: highly regarded as an edible, but, like all *Amanita* species, not recommended

The true *A. caesarea* has been found under pines in Arizona and New Mexico, and was originally described from the Mediterranean regions of Europe. The bright orange cap is rounded, often with thick patches of white veil adhering, and the gills and stem are bright yellow-orange. The volva is large, thick, and white. This species should be carefully compared with the eastern Caesar's Amanita, shown opposite, which is much more slender and umbonate.

Amanita calyptrata (Peck)
"Coccora Mushroom"

Cap: 2–10in (5–25cm)
Spores: 8–11 x 5–6μm, non-amyloid
Edibility: edible, but best avoided

Looking rather like the Caesar's Amanita, this species is much duller, more yellow-brown to bronze in color, although it too often has large flakes of veil left on the cap. The stem, gills, and ring are all white to creamy yellow, while the very thick volva is white. It is quite common in northern California, Oregon, Washington, and Vancouver Island, and grows under oaks, pines, and madrones (*Arbutus* species).

Amanita hemibapha Berkeley & Broome –
"Eastern Caesar" [= *A.caesarea* of some authors]

Cap: 2–4in (5–10cm)
Spores: white, 8–10μm, globose, non-amyloid
Edibility: edible, but best avoided

This is a sadly localized species, being common in some areas of the northeast and south, but totally absent in others; for example, it is frequent in Massachusetts, but apparently absent in New Jersey. The bright red to reddish-orange cap contrasts with the yellow-orange gills, banded stem, and the white volva. The cap is distinctly umbonate and may have white patches of volva attached, although not as commonly as in *A. caesarea* in the west. The mushroom is also taller and more slender compared with that species. It grows under oaks and pines. A similar but undescribed species is common in the northeast, but differs in its even more slender stature, brassy yellow cap, and yellowish stem with thin, narrow white volva.

Amanita brunnescens Atkinson
"Cleft-foot Amanita"

Cap: 2–6in (5–15cm)
Spores: white, 7–10μm, globose, amyloid
Edibility: doubtful; best avoided

This common species varies a great deal in cap color, although the brownish to yellow-brown cap is usually streaked irregularly with darker fibers or sometimes decolored patches. The stem is the most distinctive feature, however, since it has no volva but instead has a swollen base with an abrupt upper edge which splits or fissures vertically in an easy-to-recognize manner. The flesh often stains pinkish-red in the stem base. It can be found under various trees, but especially oaks, throughout the eastern and many southern states. An all-white variety, *pallida*, is common and shares the cleft foot.

Amanita citrina Schaeffer ex S.F. Gray

Cap:2–4in (5–10cm)
Spores: white, 7–10μm, rounded, amyloid
Edibility: inedible

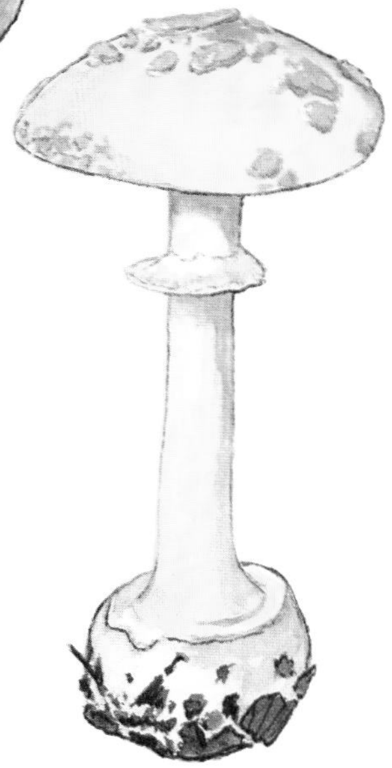

The lovely pale lemon-yellow cap is frequently patterned with patches of whitish veil, while the stem and ring are also tinted pale yellow. The stem has a large, rounded bulb with a gutter-like upper margin. A strong odor of freshly dug potatoes is present in the gills and flesh, and helps to distinguish it from the similar Death Cap (*A. phalloides*). A fairly common species, it grows in mixed woods in eastern North America. A form with a faint lavender flush (var. *lavendula*) in the veil remnants and bulb is probably best considered an independent species.

Amanita porphyria (Albertini & Schweinitz ex Fries) Secretan

Cap: 1–3in (2.5–7.5cm)
Spores: white, 7–9µm, globose, amyloid
Edibility: doubtful; best avoided

A close relative of the previous species and rather similar in its shape, particularly in its bulbous base. Its coloration, however, is very different, being gray-brown with distinct hints of lilac, especially in the ring and stem. The odor is weaker than in *A. citrina,* and may be of potato or radish. This is a rather uncommon species in North America. It grows in both coniferous and deciduous woods in the Pacific northwest and in the east, but may be widely distributed elsewhere.

Amanita vaginata (Bulliard ex Fries) Vittadini

Cap: 2–4in (5–10cm)
Spores: white, 9–12µm, globose, non-amyloid
Edibility: edible, but best avoided

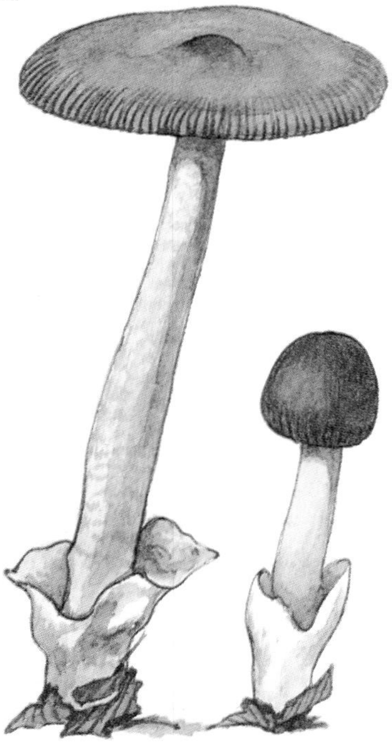

This elegant species is one of the "ringless'" *Amanita* species, sometimes called *Amanitopsis* in older literature. The cap is a pale gray to steel-gray with a deeply grooved margin, while the gills are white. The slender stem is pale gray with faint, darker bands, and has a white volva at the base. Found in mixed woods throughout North America, it is just one member of a large complex of species difficult to distinguish accurately.

Amanita fulva (Schaeffer ex Fries) Persoon – "Tawny Grisette"

Cap: 2–4in (5–10cm)
Spores: white, 8–10µm, globose, non-amyloid
Edibility: edible, but best avoided

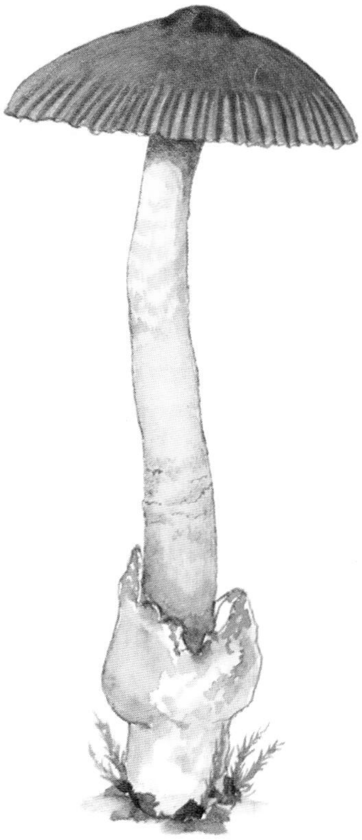

One of the commoner species in North America, it can be found in almost any woodland anywhere and is quite variable in color. Usually it is a rich orange-brown to reddish-brown, but may be paler or darker. The gills are crowded, cream, and often have minutely jagged edges. The stem is cream with faint brownish bands and has a white volval sac with the inner surface pale brown. There is no ring present on the stem. The common name is of European origin.

Amanita ceciliae (Berkeley & Broome) Bas [= *A. inaurata*]

Cap: 2–4in (5–10cm)
Spores: white, 11.5–14µm, globose, non-amyloid
Edibility: doubtful; best avoided

A rather common species, the cap is dark gray-brown, smooth, and usually has fragments of grayish veil left on the surface as lumpy warts. The gills are grayish-white and crowded. The tall, rather slender stem is pale grayish with darker bands of wooly gray. At the base the volval remnants form broken, constricted fragments and these are often left behind in the soil when it is picked. There is no ring present on the upper stem. It grows in mixed woods throughout North America, and until recently has been more widely known under the synonym *A. inaurata*.

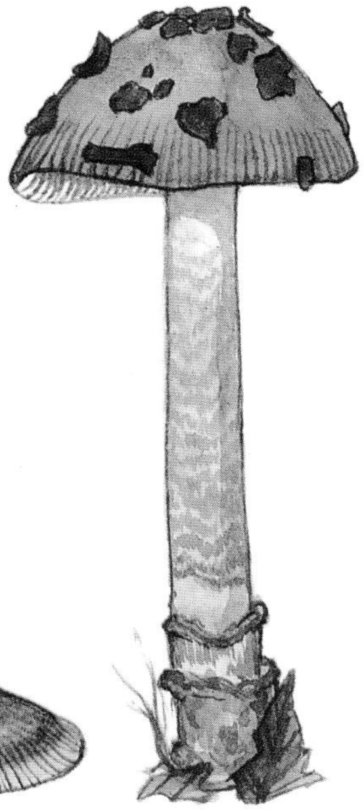

Amanita pachycolea Stuntz

Cap: 2–8in (5–20cm)
Spores: white, 11–14.5 x 10–12.5µm, non-amyloid
Edibility: edible, but best avoided

This western species can reach large sizes and is distinctive for its very dark, almost black cap when young, becoming paler as it ages but with a darker center and usually a dark zone just inside the broadly lined margin. The stout stem is grayish-brown with a thick white volval sac. Unusually, the gills are soon a pale orange-buff. It is quite common under oak and pine in the Pacific northwest.

Amanita sinicoflava Tulloss

Cap: 2–4in (5–10cm)
Spores: white, 7–10 x 6–8.5µm, non-amyloid
Edibility: unknown; best avoided

This is a good example of how a common and quite distinctive species can remain officially undescribed for many years. Described only a few years ago, it has an odd yellow-ocher to olive-ocher cap (the specific name *sinicoflava* means Chinese yellow, an artist's pigment that matches the cap color), usually with a central umbo and grooved margin. The slender stem is paler yellow-buff with some slight banding. The volva and any fragments left on the cap are pale gray, forming an easily recognized contrast of colors. It grows mainly under conifers and is found in many northeastern states.

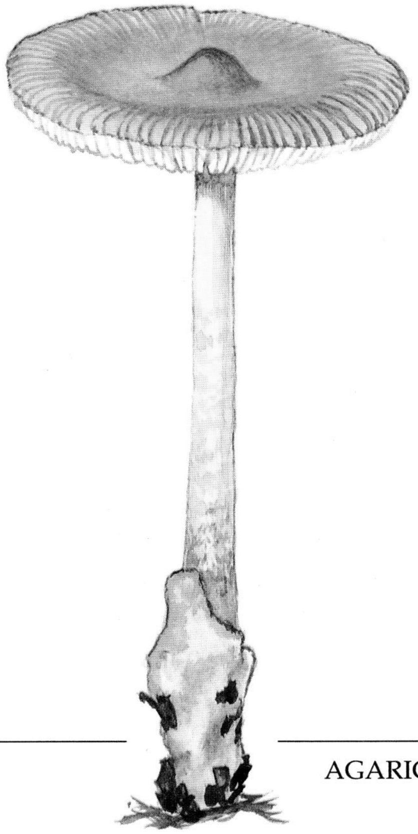

Amanita muscaria (Linnaeus ex Fries) Hooker
"Fly Agaric"

Cap: 3–10in (7.5–25cm)
Spores: white, 9.5–13 x 6.5–8.5µm, non-amyloid
Edibility: poisonous, but rarely dangerous

There can be few people who do not recognize the traditional fairy-tale mushroom with the red cap and white spots, although many are surprised to find that it really exists outside of children's books. The large, scarlet cap is smooth and slightly sticky at first, enclosed in a white or yellowish veil which breaks up into warty fragments. The stem is bulbous with bands of warty veil around the top of the bulb, and there is a large, floppy ring hanging down. The common name refers to its use in country districts of Europe as a remedy against houseflies.The skin of the cap is peeled off and placed in a saucer of milk, which both attracts and then poisons the flies. It is a common species, often found in rings in birch and occasionally pine woods in the western states. Curiously, in the east this red form is replaced by a yellow to yellow-orange-capped form found under pines.

Amanita pantherina (A.P. de Candolle ex Fries) Secretan – "Panther Cap"

Cap: 2–4in (5–10cm)
Spores: white, 8–14 x 6.5–10µm, non-amyloid
Edibility: poisonous and dangerous

The pale gray-brown to dark brown cap is strikingly spotted with pure white warty fragments of veil. The gills, stem, and ring are all white. The stem has a round bulb with a gutter-like margin, and usually one or more narrow rings of white veil immediately above it. This species is common in the west, but rather rare in the eastern and southern states, and is usually found under pines. It is a very poisonous species, causing delirium, vomiting, and a coma-like sleep, and, rarely, even death.

Amanita gemmata (Fries) Gillet
[=*A. junquillea*]

Cap: 2–4in (5–10cm)
Spores: white, 8.5–11 x 5.5–8.5µm, non-amyloid
Edibility: possibly poisonous

Commonest in the west, it is nevertheless widely distributed; it is one of a group of species that has a rounded bulb with a gutter-like upper margin, including the dangerous *A. pantherina*. The extent of the toxicity of this species is uncertain and debated. There may be localized varieties which are more poisonous than others or perhaps it is a complex of species which remains to be sorted out and distinguished; certainly, there seem to be cases of quite severe poisoning on record. This species is distinguished by its pale butter-yellow to ocher cap with white veil patches and fragile ring on the stem.

Amanita rubescens (Persoon ex Fries) S.F. Gray – "Blusher"

Cap: 2–6in (5–15cm)
Spores: white, 8–10 x 5–6µm, amyloid
Edibility: edible, but best avoided

This very common fungus has the common name of Blusher. This refers to the flush of pinkish-red which appears in the flesh, especially at the stem base, either when injured or with age. All parts of the mushroom will eventually become a dull reddish, which can make it difficult for the unpracticed eye to recognize. When young the cap may be almost white, pale yellowish-brown to almost pink, usually with numerous small groups of whitish veil remnants like warts. The stem base is rounded, but without a volva, and there is a well-formed ring above. It grows in almost any woodland throughout the USA.

Amanita flavorubens Atkinson

Cap: 2–3in (5–7.5cm)
Spores: white, 8–10 x 5–6µm, amyloid
Edibility: doubtful; best avoided

Often confused with the Blusher (*A. rubescens*) with which it shares the reddening flush in the flesh. The cap is, however, much brighter yellow to yellow-brown, particularly when young, and has small fragments of dull yellowish veil adhering. When old it is entirely yellowish-brown. It is quite common under oaks from Canada down through the eastern states and south into Florida.

Amanita spissa (Fries) Kummer [= *A. excelsa*]

Cap: 2–6in (5–15cm)
Spores: white, 9–10 x 7–8µm, amyloid
Edibility: doubtful; best avoided

An uncommon and very variable species, usually rather squat and robust, with gray-brown colors and a bulbous, rooting stem which is gray wooly-scaly and has a white ring. A distinctive odor of potato or radish is present. Several variants have been given names, in particular a large pearly gray form with a long, slender, deeply rooting stem and a pleasant fruity odor, but this is often regarded as a separate species, *A. excelsa*. Other authors regard it as just a variety. *A. spissa* grows in mixed woods throughout the USA, but its exact distribution is uncertain.

Amanita francheti (Boudier) Fayod

[=*A. aspera*]

Cap: 2–6in (5–15cm)

Spores: white, 8–10 x 6–7µm, amyloid

Edibility: doubtful; best avoided

An unusual species which is quite attractive, being essentially a dark brown-capped species with bright yellow veil remnants on the cap, ring edge, and upper edge of the stem bulb. The flesh is white and hardly discolors, unlike that of *A. rubescens*, which it may perhaps resemble. It seems to be rather rare almost everywhere, but is perhaps commonest in the Pacific northwest and California.

Amanita abrupta Peck

Cap: 2–4in (5–10cm)

Spores: 6.5–9.5 x 5.5–8.5µm, amyloid.

Edibility: unknown; best avoided

One of a large group of white to grayish species in a section known as Lepidella, many of which are quite difficult to distinguish accurately. This species, however, has some distinctive characteristics: the cap is white with small, firm, pointed warts, while the stem is slender with a large, very abruptly bulbous base. A ring is present, which has small warty "teeth" on the margin. It is commonest in the southeastern states, but has been found as far north as Vermont, growing in mixed woods.

Amanita onusta (Howe) Saccardo

Cap: 1–4in (2.5–10cm)

Spores: 8–11.5 x 5–8.5µm, amyloid

Edibility: doubtful; best avoided

A strange species not easily recognized as an *Amanita* by beginners, this small mushroom often grows deeply buried in the sandy or loose soil which it prefers. The cap is grayish with small, conical to irregular warts, powdery at the margin. The gills are white and crowded. The stem is whitish-gray with wooly-warty veil remnants and has a rooting base. An odd odor of bleach or even old ham is present (quite common in this group of species). It is widespread throughout eastern and southeastern states.

Amanita longipes Bas

Cap: 1–3in (2.5–7.5cm)
Spores: white, 8.5–17.5 x 4–7.5µm, amyloid
Edibility: doubtful; best avoided

An all-white species best distinguished by its long, slender, deeply rooting stem. Both the cap and stem have a loose, powdery covering of veil remnants. There is no true ring present, just a faint ring zone. The odor is completely absent or of weak bleach. Quite uncommon, it is widely distributed in mixed woods in the northeast and southeast.

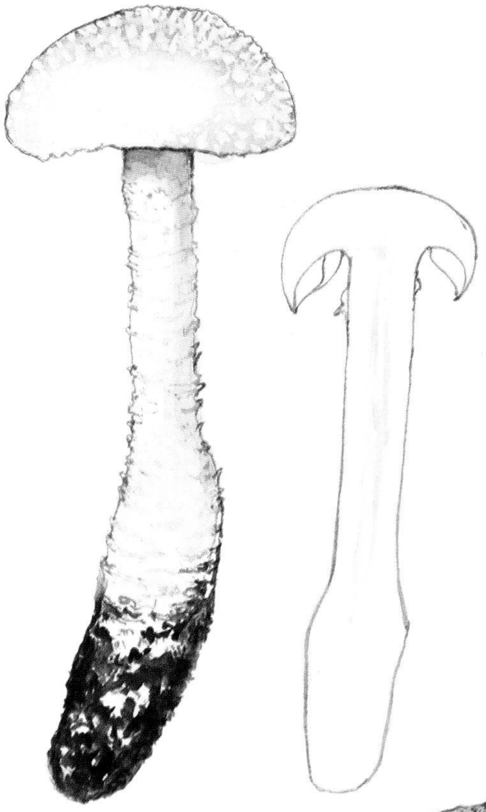

Amanita daucipes (Montagne) Lloyd

Cap: 3–10in (7.5–25cm)
Spores: white, 8.5–11.5 x 5–7.5µm, amyloid
Edibility: unknown; best avoided

A magnificent species, quite easy to recognize, the large cap is a pale salmon-pink to salmon-buff and is covered with soft wooly fragments of veil. The margin is also often festooned with veil fragments. The gills are white and crowded. The robust stem is whitish with a strange, turnip-like tuberous base, at the upper edge of which there are usually small, teeth-like fragments of veil. There is a large, floppy white ring present, which is very soft and rather like cream cheese in texture. The odor of old ham is strong. It is quite common in some regions, growing under beech and oak in late summer and fall.

Amanita cokeri (Gilbert & Kuhner) Gilbert

Cap: 3–6in (7.5–15cm)
Spores: white, 3–4µm, amyloid
Edibility: doubtful; best avoided

Another all-white species, this has soft, blunt warts on the cap. The stem is the most distinguishing feature: at the base is a large bulb which has 2 or 3 rings of large recurved scales at the top. A large white ring is present which has warts on the margin, and sometimes there is a secondary ring of tissue below the first. No special odor is present. It is quite common in mixed woods in the eastern and southeastern states.

Amanita volvata (Peck) Lloyd

Cap: 2–4in (5–10cm)
Spores: white, 8.5–10 x 5.5–7μm, amyloid.
Edibility: doubtful; best avoided

This striking species is only one of a complex of 3 or 4 very similar species best distinguished microscopically, but is typical of the basic form and coloration. The white cap soon develops pinkish tints and is decorated with numerous, mosaic-like fragments of veil. The ringless stem is rough or wooly with bands, and emerges from a thick, whitish volva. Other species in this group may have narrower volvas. It is quite a common species, often in loose sandy soils in mixed woods throughout the eastern and southeastern states.

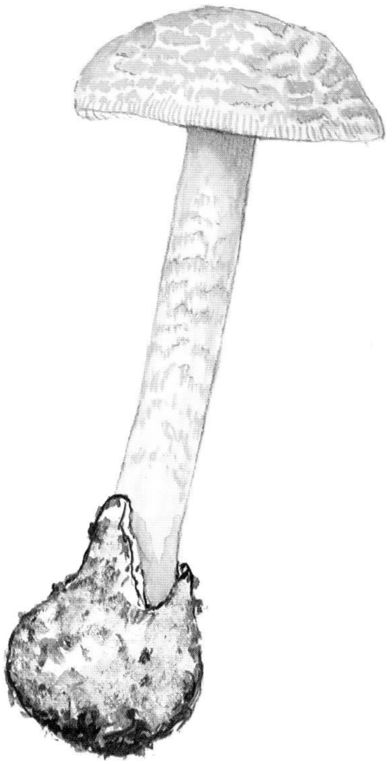

Amanita crenulata Peck

Cap: 1–4in (2.5–10cm)
Spores: white, 7.5–10 x 6–8.5μm, non-amyloid.
Edibility: poisonous; causes delirium, sweating, violent fits, and finally a coma-like sleep

This is a little-known species that has only recently been redescribed and identified as the cause of a serious poisoning. It is rather nondescript in appearance, but nevertheless has some key features to look out for. The pale ocher cap has small patches of veil, while the bulbous stem has a narrow rim of small, granular veil fragments. The thin ring is easily torn and soon collapses. It grows under pines in the northeast, and is quite common.

Amanita flavoconia Atkinson

Cap: 1–3in (2.5–7.5cm)
Spores: white, 7–9.5 x 4.5–5μm, amyloid
Edibility: doubtful; best avoided

One of the commonest and most attractive species in the woods of eastern North America, it varies in color from deep orange to yellow, usually with thin, flattened patches of yellow veil. The gills are white to yellowish, while the bulbous stem is white or yellow, often with bright yellow, crumbly fragments of veil adhering to the base or left behind in the soil when it is picked. The almost identical *A. frostiana* differs in the edge of the cap being radially grooved, the marginate bulb, and non-amyloid spores; it is much rarer.

Amanita parcivolvata (Peck) Gilbert

Cap: 1–4in (2.5–10cm)
Spores: white, 10–14 x 6.5–8µm, non-amyloid
Edibility: doubtful; best avoided

This vividly colored, elegant species is sometimes mistaken for the eastern Caesar's Amanita, *A. hemibapha,* but there are clear differences. This species, although red like the Caesar, does not have a white volva and the cap has numerous small fragments of flattened, yellowish veil. The bulbous stem has a powdery yellow coating and there is no ring present. It is quite uncommon to rare and grows mainly under oaks from New Jersey down to Florida and west to Ohio.

Amanita wellsii Murrill

Cap: 2–5in (5–12.5cm)
Spores: white, 11–14.5 x6. 5–8µm, non-amyloid
Edibility: doubtful; best avoided

This species is one of the most subtly and beautifully colored of all the *Amanita* mushrooms. The cap is a pale salmon-pink to yellowish-salmon, with dull yellowish patches of veil, often with the margin draped with wooly fragments of yellowish veil. The gills are white and the stem is pale yellow with a very fragile yellowish ring which tears and mostly clings to the edge of the cap. It grows in mixed woods from New York up into Canada, and also in the mountains of North Carolina.

Limacella glioderma (Fries) Maire

Cap: 1–3in (2.5–7.5cm)
Spores: white, 3–4µm, globose, non-amyloid
Edibility: unknown; best avoided

A strange genus thought to be closely related to the genus *Amanita* by some authors, but placed closer to *Lepiota* by others. It differs from both genera in the extremely slimy, viscid cap and stem. In this species the cap is dark reddish-brown to pinkish at the margin, with a granular center under the gluten. The gills are white and free from the stem. The latter is also brown and viscid up to a distinct ring zone. There is a strong odor of new meal. A rare species, it grows under hemlock and birch, and is widespread in the USA.

LEPIOTACEAE
Lepiota Family

A large family of mushrooms ranging from tiny, delicate species to some of the largest mushrooms in the world. A number are considered good edibles, while others are dangerously poisonous and are known to contain similar toxins to those found in the infamous and deadly *Amanita* mushrooms. The family is characterized by free gills, white to pale pinkish-cream or green spores, and usually a more or less obvious ring on the stem. It is related to the black-brown-spored *Agaricus* mushrooms.

Lepiota cristata (Fries) Kummer –
"Stinking Lepiota"
Cap: ½–2in (1.5–5cm)
Spores: white, 5–7 x 3–4µm, bullet-shaped with the apiculus offset
Edibility: possibly poisonous

Sometimes called the Stinking Lepiota, this refers to the strong, unpleasant odor of rubber or of the common Earthball (*Scleroderma citrinum*), which is present in the gills and flesh. This is probably one of the commonest small *Lepiota* species and is recognized by the white cap marked with dark reddish-brown scales, and the white, smooth stem which has a tiny ring near the top. It can be found in grassy areas in mixed woods, gardens, and along roadsides.

Lepiota clypeolaria (Bulliard ex Fries) Kummer
Cap: 1–3in (2.5–7.5cm)
Spores: white, 12–16 x 4–5µm, spindle-shaped, dextrinoid
Edibility: poisonous

A rather attractive, wooly-scaly species, the specific name means shield-like, which is a good description of the cap with its pale brown, scaly surface and darker, smooth central umbo. The stem is distinctive as it is clothed in wooly-shaggy scales up to an apical ring zone. The flesh is nearly odorless. It grows in mixed woods, especially under conifers, and is widespread in North America.

Lepiota rubrotincta Peck
Cap: 1–2in (2.5–5cm)
Spores: white, 6–10 x 4–6µm, elliptical, dextrinoid
Edibility: doubtful; best avoided

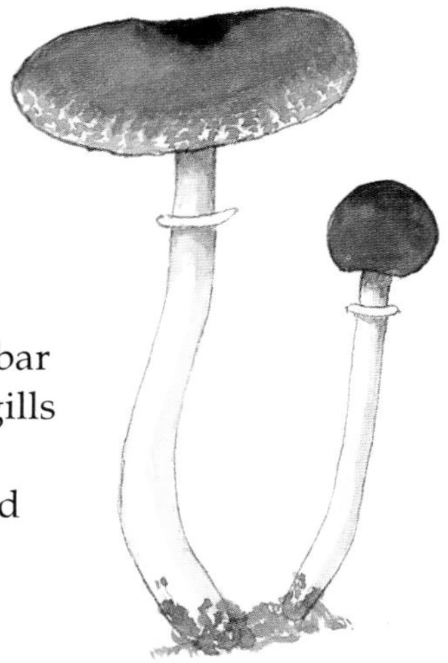

A slender, delicate species with a bright coral-red to cinnabar cap with a darker center and minutely scaly margin. The gills and smooth stem are white. There is a narrow ring at the stem apex. It is widespread throughout North America and grows in deciduous woods, but is never very common.

Lepiota josserandii Bonorden & Boiffard

Cap: 1–2in (2.5–5cm)
Spores: white, 6–8 x 2.5–4.5µm, elliptical, dextrinoid
Edibility: deadly poisonous

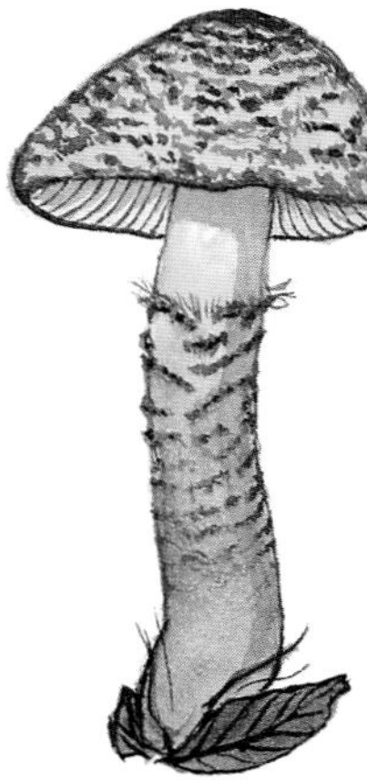

It is only comparatively recently that it has been realized that some of the small *Lepiota* species can be as deadly as the infamous *Amanita* mushrooms. This species has already been implicated in a number of poisonings. The cap has bands of concentric brown to purple-brown scales, and the stout stem has bands of scales up to a small ring zone. There is often an unpleasant musty odor present. It grows in deciduous woods and gardens, and is reported most commonly in western North America.

Lepiota americana Peck

Cap: 2–6in (5–15cm)
Spores: white, 8–14 x 5–10µm, elliptical, dextrinoid
Edibility: edible, but best avoided

This common species is found on or around old stumps or on woodchips, so is becoming increasingly common in gardens where woodchip mulching is used. The whitish cap is overlaid with dark reddish-brown scales radiating out from the brown bump at the center. The margin of the cap is deeply grooved when mature. The large, spindle-shaped stem is white with a distinct ring at the apex. All parts of the mushroom bruise bright yellow-orange, then quickly reddish-brown. This fungus is almost certainly better placed in the next genus, *Leucocoprinus*, with which it shares many characteristics.

Leucocoprinus birnbaumi (Corda) Singer

[=*Lepiota lutea*]
Cap: ½–1in (1.5–2.5cm)
Spores: white, 8–13 x 5–8µm, smooth
Edibility: unknown

Leucocoprinus species share the common features of a fragile, sometimes small body with a strongly striated-pleated cap margin and spores with a germ-pore at the end. This species is known from all over the world, but is almost certainly an introduction from some tropical region since in cooler regions it occurs only in glasshouses or in potted houseplants. The brilliant yellow coloration of all its parts, its finely granular-scaly surface, and its extreme fragility are all unmistakable.

Macrolepiota procera (Scopoli) Singer – "Parasol Mushroom" [=*Lepiota procera*]

Cap: 4–10in (10–25cm)
Spores: white to cream, 15–20 x 10–13μm, elliptical
Edibility: edible and delicious

One of the most magnificent species, the common name is a good description of its general appearance – it stands in grassy clearings and fields and looks very much like a tall parasol. It can reach heights of up to 18in (45cm). The cap is whitish-brown with thick, almost concentric scales formed by the break-up of the outer cuticle. At the center the cap has a darker brown blunt umbo. The broad, crowded gills are white. The tall stem is very stiff and cross-banded with darker brown zones, and has a bulbous base. There is a thick, whitish double-layered ring, which can be slid up and down the stem when loose. This is a delicious and much sought-after species; one cap can fill a frying-pan. Closely related species differ in their size, scaliness, and lack of banding on the stem, as well as their darker spores.

Macrolepiota prominens (Fries) Moser [=*Lepiota prominens*]

Cap: 4–8in (10–20cm)
Spores: pinkish-cream, 9–10 x 6–7μm, elliptical
Edibility: edible and good

This strikingly tall and graceful species is usually mistaken for the common Parasol Mushroom, *M. procera*, but differs in a number of features. All parts of it are much paler, almost white, and the scales of the cap are much finer. The tall stem has no prominent cross-bands, just fine, almost concolorous markings. The ring is double-edged and thick. If a spore print is taken, you will see that it is darker and pinker, as well as the spores being smaller. It is fairly common in woodland clearings and pastures in the northeast.

Macrolepiota gracilenta (Fries) Wasser [=*Lepiota gracilenta*]

Cap: 3–4in (7.5–10cm)
Spores: cream, 10–13 x 7–8μm, elliptical
Edibility: edible and good

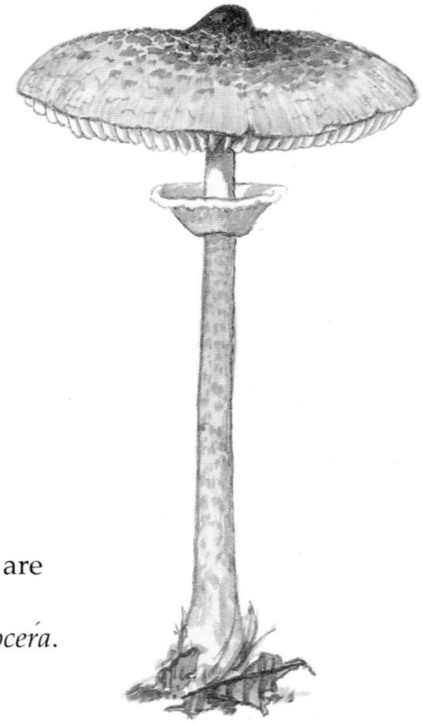

This slender, graceful species is often mistaken for the Parasol Mushroom, *M. procera*, but may be distinguished by its much less robust stature, very finely scaly stem without the prominent cross-bands of that species, and by the smaller spores. The ring on the stem is also thinner and usually funnel-shaped when young. Its colors are pale brown to gray-brown, and the cap scales are small and pulled back from the cap margin. It can be quite common and seems to grow more often in woodlands and grassy clearings, less often in open pastures, unlike *M. procera*.

Macrolepiota rhacodes (Vittadini) Singer

[=*Lepiota rhacodes*]

Cap: 3–6in (7.5–15cm)

Spores: white, 6–10 x 5–7µm, elliptical

Edibility: edible and good

This species (sometimes spelled *rachodes*) comes in two varieties, sometimes regarded as two species. Illustrated here is the typical variety to be found in woodlands on deep leaf litter or needle beds in conifer woods. It has a dull or dirty brown cap, which is finely to coarsely scaly, and a whitish, bulbous stem with a prominent two-layered ring. The flesh bruises reddish-brown. A much larger, more robust variety is more often found in gardens on compost heaps and leaf beds, and this has an almost white and very coarsely scaly cap, brown at the center, and with an extremely bulbous stem. This may be referred to as the variety *hortensis*, but is often considered a species, *L. bohemica*.

Leucoagaricus naucinus (Fries) Singer

[=*Lepiota naucina* of some authors]

Cap: 2–4in (5–10cm)

Spores: at first white, but later deposits pink

Edibility: best avoided; has caused some upsets

This all-white species is often mistaken for a field mushroom (*Agaricus*), especially since the gills are pinkish when mature, but careful examination will show that, unlike *Agaricus*, the gills never proceed to darken to blackish-brown. This species exhibits an unusual phenomenon in that if a series of spore deposits are taken from a single cap over a period of time, each print will be darker and pinker than the preceding one. The cap and stem discolor to dull gray-brown with handling or aging. It can be quite common in open fields and woodland edges throughout North America.

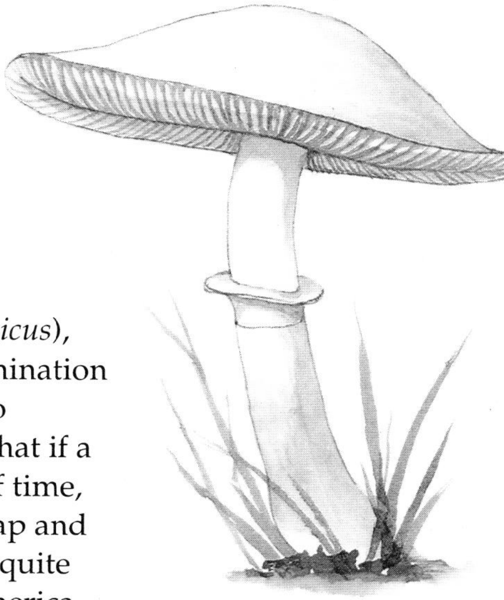

Chlorophyllum molybdites Massee

[= *Lepiota morgani*]

Cap: 4–12in (10–30cm)

Spores: green, 8-13 x 6.5-8µm, elliptical.

Edibility: poisonous; frequent accidental poisonings

This species is sometimes mistaken for the Parasol Mushroom, *Lepiota procera*, with unfortunate consequences. Although not deadly, it certainly makes you feel as if you are dying. It causes intense nausea, stomach cramps, and general debilitation. The large caps are very white and strikingly marked with dark brown scales. The gills are white at first, but soon take on a pale greenish-gray hue as the spores mature. A prominent ring is present. A spore print will be a clear pale green, eventually aging to grayish-brown. It often grows in large fairy rings many yards across in open fields and lawns from the southern states up through New Jersey and parts of New York.

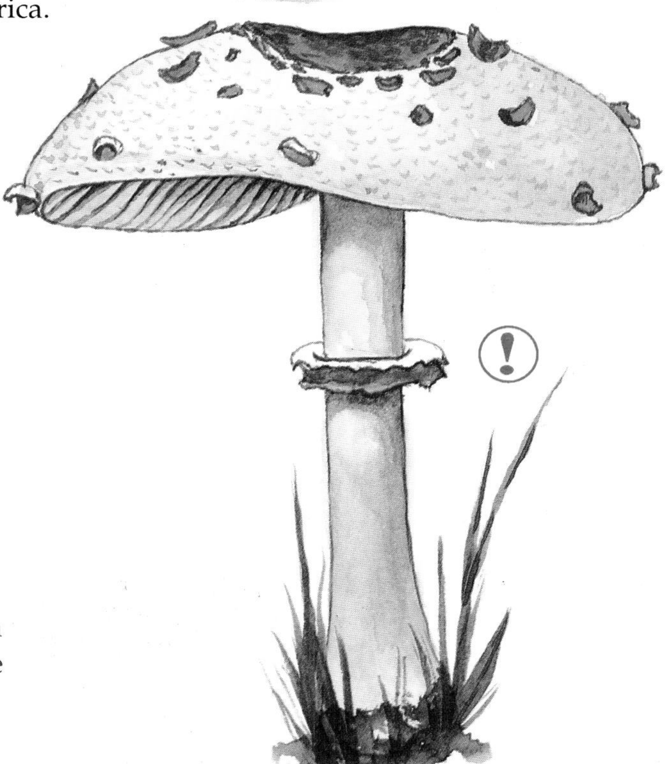

GOMPHIDIACEAE
Gomphidius Family

These mushrooms actually appear closer to the boletes than to other gilled mushrooms because of their very similar spores, body chemistry, and other microscopic characteristics. For convenience, however, they are grouped here with other gilled mushrooms. Most species have a veil which may be dry or glutinous. The two genera – *Gomphidius* and *Chroogomphus* – are divided by their respective reactions to Melzer's iodine solution placed on the flesh. The first genus has a negative reaction (dull yellow), while the second is positive (blue-black). *Gomphidius* are usually slimier than *Chroogomphus*.

Gomphidius subroseus Kauffman

Cap: 2–4in (5–10cm)
Spores: almost black, 15–21 x 4–7.5µm, spindle-shaped
Edibility: edible

This can be an extraordinarily beautiful species with its bright coral-pink, glutinous cap shining out against the dark needle litter in which it grows. The thick, widely spaced gills are whitish-gray and deeply decurrent. The stem is white, tapered below, with a yellowish base and glutinous veil up to a faint ring zone. The thick flesh is white and slightly reddish below. Frequent throughout North America, it is found under conifers, especially spruce.

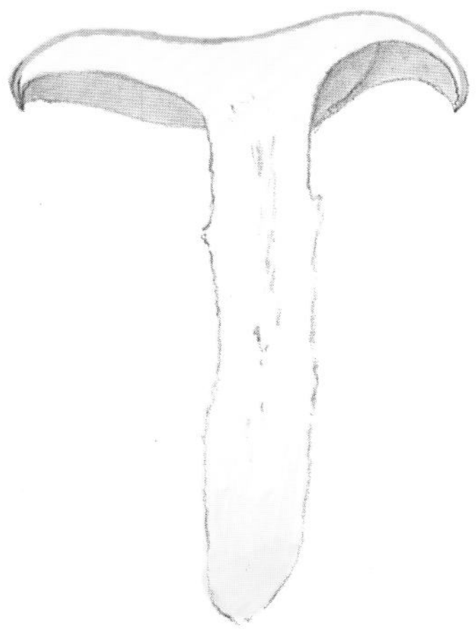

Gomphidius glutinosus

(Schaeffer ex Fries) Fries

Cap: 2–4in (5–10cm)
Spores: black, 15–21 x 4–7.5µm, spindle-shaped
Edibility: edible

Another very slimy species, but nevertheless very attractive, the top-shaped cap is a pale grayish-brown to purplish-brown, with decurrent, thick gray-white gills. The stem is white with a glutinous ring zone, and is bright yellow at the base both within and without. It grows under conifers, especially spruce, and is widespread through North America. The closely related *G. maculatus* is a much more uncommon species, which is found in the northern and northwestern United States. It differs in having a more slender stature, all parts tending to bruise or spot reddish then black with age, particularly the gills and stem base.

Chroogomphus vinicolor (Peck) O.K. Miller

Cap: 1–3in (2.5–7cm)
Spores: blackish, 17–23 x 4.5–7.5µm, spindle-shaped
Edibility: edible

The genus *Chroogomphus* is separated from *Gomphidius* by the ochraceous colors of its gills and flesh, and by the reaction of many of the fruit-body's cells to Melzer's iodine, becoming a deep blue-black. The cap of this species is frequently sharply umbonate and is viscid when wet, but then soon dry, and is orange-brown to wine-reddish. The decurrent gills are ocher, then purplish-gray when mature. The stout stem is ocher-orange flushed pale wine-red, and has faint wooly zones below a ring zone. The solid flesh is ocher-orange. This is a common species and grows under pines throughout North America.

AGARICACEAE
Agaricus Family

Agaricus provides us with the well-known white mushroom we purchase in stores, as well as the popular Field Mushroom and Horse Mushroom. All species have deep blackish-brown to chocolate spores, free gills, and a veil that usually forms a ring on the stem.

Agaricus campestris Linnaeus ex Fries – "Field Mushroom"

Cap: 2–4in (5–10cm)

Spores: deep brown, 6–9 x 4–6µm, smooth

Edibility: edible and delicious; gathered the world over for food

One of the most famous edible mushrooms in the world with many common names, including Field Mushroom, Pink-bottoms, and Champignons, this delicious wild mushroom is to be found in large fairy rings in open grass all over the world in temperate regions. The white cap may be smooth to scaly, and the crowded gills start bright pink and slowly turn deep brown. The short, stout stem is white with a delicate ring. The white flesh flushes slightly reddish-pink to brown when cut, *not bright yellow* (see *A. xanthodermus*, page 104). The explanations in folklore for fairy rings are quite fascinating and range from fairies dancing to lightning strikes, animals running in circles, witches' cauldrons, and buried bodies. In reality they are the natural result of the steady outward growth and expansion of the fungal mycelium, which radiates outward in a circular fashion and fruits on the actively growing leading edge. *A. andrewi* is a similar species, except for specialized cells on the gill margins, so the two may be considered as if one species; in some parts. *A. andrewi* is the commoner of the two.

Agaricus cupreobrunneus (Møller) Pilat

Cap: 1–3in (2.5–7.5cm)

Spores: deep brown, 7–9 x 4–6.5µm, smooth

Edibility: edible and good

Although less well known than the common Field Mushroom, *A. campestris*, this is nevertheless quite common and equally delicious. It is a short, squat species, much like the Field Mushroom, but the cap is marked with fine copper-brown to wine-colored fibers and scales. The young gills start bright pink and soon mature to a deep brown. It likes short grass in open pastures and meadows, and may prefer sandy soils.

Agaricus bitorquis (Quélet) Saccardo

Cap: 2–6in (5–15cm)

Spores: deep brown, 5–6 x 4–5µm, smooth

Edibility: edible and good

The way in which mushrooms often push their way up through the hardest of soils is quite remarkable. This species more than any other can be found bursting through hard-packed soil, tarmac or even concrete. Specimens have been seen to push up entire paving slabs through the relentless pressure of osmosis, as fluids expand their fruit-bodies upward. The flattened white cap of this species has extremely thick flesh and only very narrow gills. The stem is thick and heavy, and has a curious double ring which leaves a volva-like veil at the base. The flesh slowly stains reddish-brown when cut. Usually found along roadsides, tracks, and other disturbed urban areas.

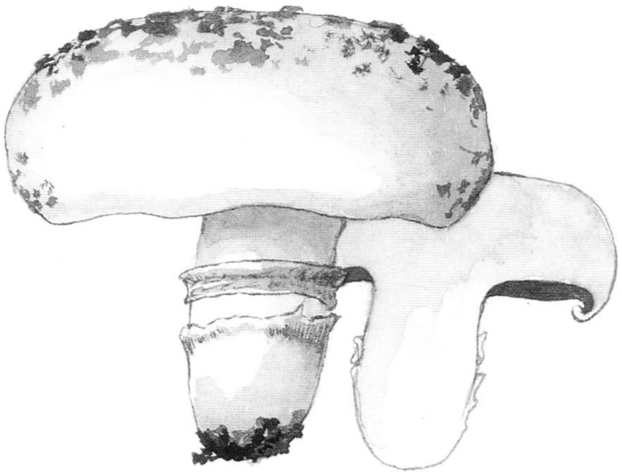

Agaricus subrutilescens (Kauffman) Hot & Stuntz

Cap: 2–6in (5–15cm)

Spores: deep brown, 5–6 x 3–4µm, smooth

Edibility: doubtful; best avoided

An attractive species, it has a wine-red to purplish-brown cap which is fibrillose and scaly. The stem is tall and club-shaped, and wooly fibrous below the ring. The gills begin white before maturing to pinkish-brown and finally deep brown. An odor of fruit is present. It grows in small groups in conifer woods along the west coast.

Agaricus augustus Fries – "The Prince"

Cap: 4–10in (10–25cm)
Spores: deep brown, 8–11 x 5–6µm, smooth
Edibility: edible and excellent

In the USA this has the common name of Prince, and it is indeed a princely mushroom with its large, golden-tawny cap with fine scales and fibers. The gills are pale pink, then mature to a deep brown. The tall stem is club-shaped and finely wooly-scaly below the large, floppy ring at the top. The mushroom has a pleasant odor of anise or almonds, and is considered one of the very best edible fungi. It often grows in large numbers in woodlands, parks, and gardens, usually under shrubs or hedgerows, and is one of the most distinctive and easily recognizable species. It is particularly common in the western states and the Pacific northwest.

Agaricus arvensis Schaeffer ex Secretan – "Horse Mushroom"

Cap: 4–6in (10–15cm)
Spores: deep brown, 7–9 x 4.5–6µm, smooth
Edibility: edible and excellent

The common name refers to its preference for fields manured with horse dung, and to the old practice of cultivating it in trenches filled with soil and horse manure. It is a large, striking species with a white, smooth to scaly cap which ages brassy yellow. The gills are pale pink, then deep brown. The club-shaped stem is white with a slightly wooly surface below the ring. The latter is thick and well formed with cog-wheel-like scales on the underside. The flesh is white, has a pleasant odor of anise, and bruises slightly ocher-yellow. If brilliant yellow stains develop, be careful: check the description of *A. xanthodermus* (page 104). A common species, it grows in fields and woodland clearings throughout North America.

Agaricus abruptibulbus Peck

Cap: 3–6in (7.5–15cm)
Spores: deep brown, 6–8 x 4–5µm, smooth
Edibility: edible and good

This is an elegant and rather uncommon species, often confused with the Horse Mushroom, above. The beautiful white cap bruises brassy yellow and is quite smooth. The gills are very pale pink, then mature to a deep brown. The stem is the key feature, since it has a large and very abrupt bulb at the base and is quite smooth overall. There is a large, floppy ring present. The flesh smells pleasantly of anise. It grows in mixed woods, but especially under spruce, and is widespread.

Agaricus silvaticus Schaeffer ex Secretan – "Red-staining Mushroom"

Cap: 2–4in (5–10cm)
Spores: deep brown, 4.5–6 x 3–3.5µm, smooth
Edibility: edible and quite good

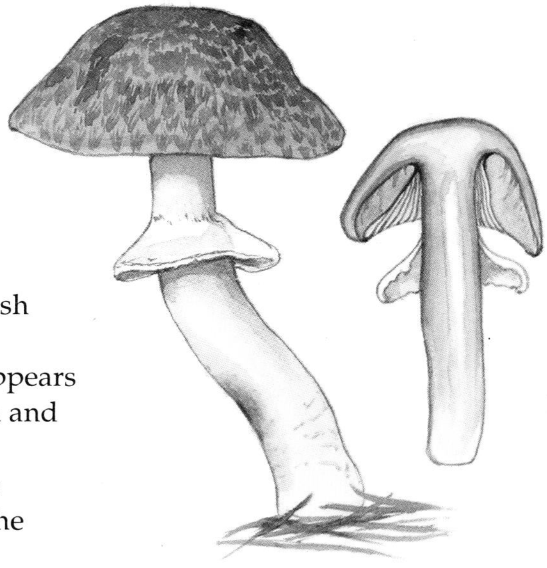

Most species of *Agaricus* stain to some degree, either yellowish or reddish, but in some species this reaches an extreme where the flesh turns either bright red or bright yellow. This species is one of the former, and if the cap or stem is scratched, a bright scarlet stain appears in a few minutes. The cap is a light yellow-brown to russet-brown and covered with fine scales. The gills are pink, then dark brown. The slender stem is slightly bulbous and white, and smooth below the fragile ring. It is quite common in coniferous woods throughout the USA. Other red stainers include *A. fuscofibrillosus,* with fibrillose (not scaly) reddish-brown cap, and *A. benesi,* an all-white species.

Agaricus placomyces Peck

Cap: 2–4in (5–10cm)
Spores: deep brown, 5–7 x 3–4µm, smooth
Edibility: inedible and poisonous to many

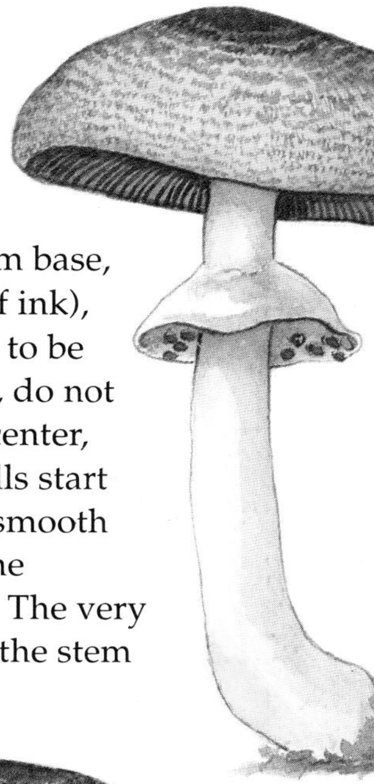

One of a number of species which bruise bright yellow, especially in the stem base, and which have an unpleasant phenolic odor (rather like iodine or bottles of ink), this can cause painful stomach upsets to many people, although some seem to be unaffected. If you see any bright yellow stains at the stem base after cutting, do not risk eating the mushroom. This species has a rounded cap with a flattened center, and is covered with extremely fine, gray-black or gray-brown scales. The gills start whitish, then mature brown. The elegant stem is bulbous and white with a smooth surface. A floppy ring is present and frequently has brownish droplets on the underside. It grows in woods, hedgerows, and gardens, but is not common. The very similar *A. pocillator* is even slimmer and has a prominent bulb with a rim at the stem base; it is equally common in southern and eastern states.

Agaricus praeclaresquamosus Freeman

[= *A. meleagris* of many American authors]

Cap: 2–6in (5–15cm)
Spores: deep brown, 4–6.5 x 3–4.5µm
Edibility: poisonous; causes nausea and vomiting

Similar to the previous cap, the dark gray-brown scales are perhaps a little larger. The gills begin a pale whitish-pink, then mature to dark brown. The stem is smooth below the prominent ring, which is thick, felt-like, and often split at the margin. When crushed, the flesh has an unpleasantly strong odor of phenol or iodine. Quite a common species, it grows along roadsides and paths under trees in the western states.

Agaricus xanthodermus Genevier – "Yellow Stainer"

Cap: 3–5in (7.5–12.5cm)
Spores: deep brown, 5–7 x 3–4μm, smooth
Edibility: poisonous to many, causing nausea and headaches

An infamous mushroom because it is often confused with either the Field Mushroom or the Horse Mushroom, it can be easily distinguished from both of these if certain key characteristics are observed. First, the white cap soon ages grayish and becomes fibrous or scaly. When scratched, the cap or stem cuticle, and especially the flesh in the stem base, turn a brilliant chrome yellow. The flesh has an unpleasant phenolic odor like iodine or old-fashioned school ink. The stem is stout and bulbous, and has a well-developed ring with cottony patches on the underside. It seems to frequent urban environments, such as hedges, gardens, and garbage dumps, but also occurs in woodlands, and is quite common, especially in western states.

Agaricus micromegathus Peck

Cap: 1–2in (2.5–5cm)
Spores: deep brown, 4.5–5.5 x 3.5–4μm
Edibility: unknown; best avoided

A small and inconspicuous species, it can be quite common in some areas in very short turf, usually on sandy soils. The pale yellowish-brown cap is faintly marked with purplish scales at the center, and may flush completely purplish-brown. The broad gills are pink, then turn pale brown. The short, sturdy stem has a faint ring zone, but is otherwise smooth. All parts bruise a dull yellow-ocher. The smell is pleasant, faintly of anise.

STROPHARIACEAE
Strophoria Family

A large family with smooth spores of a purplish-brown, and gills which are sinuate to adnate and purplish-brown. A veil is often present, leaving a ring on the stem, and the cap may be dry to glutinous.

Stropharia rugosoannulata Farlow ex Murrill

Cap: 4–6in (10–15cm)
Spores: deep purple-brown, 10–13 x 7.5–9μm, smooth
Edibility: edible and excellent

A large species, now widely cultivated for food by commercial growers and amateurs. When fresh and growing in shade, the large caps are a deep wine-red to reddish-brown with a fibrous, dry surface, but when exposed to the sun, they soon decolor to a pale buff-yellow and often crack. The margin frequently has fragments of veil. The gills are sinuate and pale grayish-lilac before turning purple-black. The stem is white, firm, smooth, and fibrous, and has a thick ring which is toothed or segmented on the underside. A common species, it first appears in the late spring and early summer on woodchips, and is widespread in parks and gardens on mulched flowerbeds where woodchips are laid.

Stropharia thrausta (Schulzer) Saccardo

Cap: 1–2in (2.5–5cm)
Spores: purplish-black, 12–14 x 6–7μm, smooth
Edibility: doubtful; best avoided

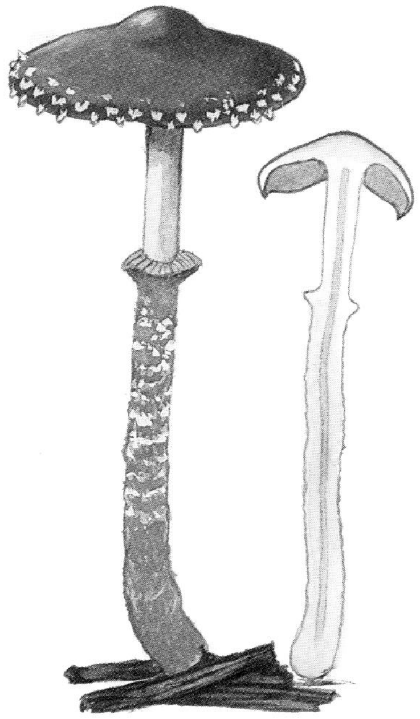

This rather rare species is one of the most striking and attractive to be seen in woods during the fall. The umbonate cap is a bright fox-red to orange with small white scales around the margin. The sinuate gills are purplish-black. The long, elegant stem is reddish-orange below the narrow ring, and whitish above. It grows in small groups on fallen twigs and branches of deciduous trees, and is widely distributed.

Stropharia semiglobata (Batsch) Quélet

Cap: 1–2in (2.5–5cm)
Spores: purple-brown, 15–19 x 8–10μm, smooth
Edibility: doubtful; best avoided

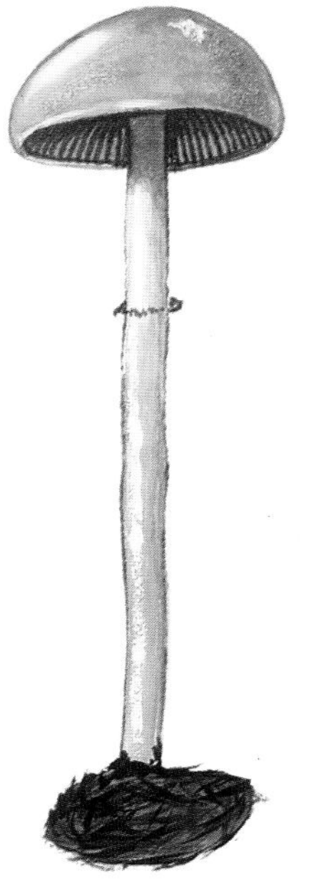

This is sometimes called the "Dung Roundhead", and this is a good description of both its preferred habitat and its appearance. The small cap is rounded, smooth, and very sticky when wet, and a pale to bright yellow-ocher. The adnate gills are broad and a pale lilac-brown. The slender, tall stem is sticky below the narrow ring and colored like the cap. It grows on horse, sheep, and cattle dung everywhere.

Stropharia aeruginosa (Curtis) Quélet

Cap: 1–3in (2.5–7.5cm)
Spores: violet-brown, 7–9 x 4–5μm, smooth
Edibility: doubtful; best avoided

This could be the archetypal toadstool, with its slimy cap and strange, poisonous-looking colors. However, it does not seem to be particularly poisonous or psychoactive, as is often suggested, but it certainly appears strange. The viscid cap is a bright blue-green with white flecks of veil at the margin. The sinuate gills are a deep violet-brown. The greenish stem is clothed in white scales up to a distinct, well-formed ring. It is a fairly common species late in the season, mostly in the western states, and grows on rich soil or in grass at the edge of woods. The very similar *S. cyanea* differs in having very little white veil, a paler green cap, a thin transient ring, and paler gills, and grows in nettle beds, garden borders, and woods.

Psilocybe cubensis (Earl) Singer

Cap: 1–3in (2.5–7.5cm)
Spores: dark purple-brown, 11.5–17 x 8–11μm, smooth
Edibility: strongly psychoactive and poisonous

A notorious species often collected or even cultured for so-called "recreational" purposes. The bell-shaped caps are sticky and whitish with a darker brownish-yellow center; there are often bluish stains along the margin. The stem is whitish, fibrous, and grooved at the top, and often stained bluish below. A ring is present at the top. This mushroom grows on cow and horse dung in pastures in the south and southeastern states.

Psilocybe semilanceata (Fries ex Secretan) Kummer – "Liberty Cap"

Cap: ¼–1in (0.6–2.5cm)
Spores: purple-brown, 11–14 x 7–8μm, smooth
Edibility: psychoactive and toxic

The common name of Liberty Caps refers back to the days of the French Revolution and the tall hats that were in vogue with the revolutionaries at the time. The tall, narrow, and sharply pointed caps are pale yellow-buff and sticky in wet weather. The gills are deep gray-brown, then violet-brown. The slender stem is smooth, often twisted, and pale yellow, bruising blue. It grows in the depths of old grass tussocks in fields, as well as in lawns, parks, and gardens in the Pacific northwest. It is widely known because of its hallucinogenic properties.

Hypholoma fasciculare (Hudson ex Fries) Kummer – "Sulfur Tuft" (= *Naematoloma fasciculare*)

Cap: 1–3in (2.5–7.5cm)
Spores: purple-brown, 6.5–8 x 3.5–4μm, smooth
Edibility: inedible; often regarded as poisonous

The clustered caps of this species are smooth and bright yellow-orange when young, becoming pale sulfur-yellow with age. The narrow gills are a distinct greenish-yellow when young, but mature to a dull violet-brown. The stems are yellow with a cobwebby veil at the apex. The taste of the flesh is extremely bitter and unpleasant. It grows in large tufts on fallen logs and stumps everywhere.

Hypholoma sublateritium (Fries) Quélet – "Brick Caps"

Cap: 2–4in (5–10cm)
Spores: purple-brown, 6–7 x 4–4.5μm, smooth
Edibility: edible, but best avoided

Appearing at the end of the year as the weather turns cooler, the robust caps are indeed a brick-red, with paler veil remnants at the margin. The gills are whitish-yellow, then gray-violet. The thick stems are pale brick-red with a cobwebby veil at the apex. It grows in tufts on fallen timber and is quite common throughout eastern North America.

COPRINACEAE
Coprinus Family

Usually thin, delicate mushrooms (there are exceptions), *Coprinus* species all have black spores, and many have a veil and/or a ring. These fungi are often called Ink Caps because they dissolve away into an inky liquid as they disperse their spores.

Panaeolus sphinctrinus (Fries) Quélet

Cap: 1–2in (2.5–5cm)
Spores: blackish, 13–16 x 8–11µm, smooth
Edibility: doubtful; best avoided

A relatively small group of species, the majority of which grow in grass, often on animal dung. This species has a silvery-gray to yellow-gray cap which is bell-shaped, and when young and fresh has tiny white "teeth", which are veil remnants, around the margin. The gills are grayish and, like all *Panaeolus* species, become mottled with black as the spores mature in irregular patches. The slender stem is smooth and pale gray. It grows on horse or cow dung everywhere.

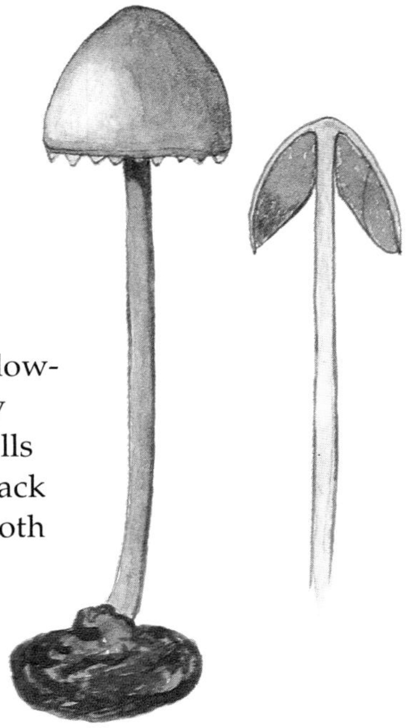

Panaeolus semiovatus (Sowerby ex Fries) Lundell & Nannfeldt

Cap: 1–3in (2.5–7.5cm)
Spores: blackish, 15–20 x 8–11µm, smooth
Edibility: doubtful; best avoided

One of the largest members of the group, although *very* variable in size, as are all fungi that grow on dung. The bell-shaped cap is pale buff to whitish, and slightly sticky when wet. It frequently cracks in dry weather. The gills are widely spaced, blackish-gray, and mottled. The tall stem is rigid, with a distinct ring at the apex which soon vanishes with age. It seems to prefer horse dung and is widespread throughout North America.

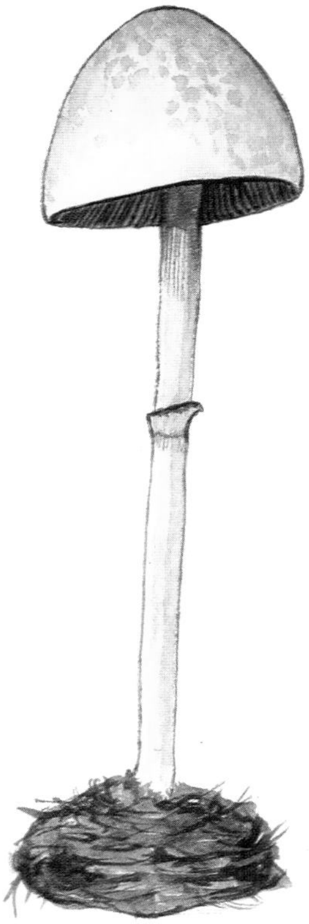

Panaeolus foenisecii (Persoon ex Fries) Maire

Cap: ½–1in (1–2.5cm)
Spores: purple-brown, 12–15 x 6.5–9µm, with minute warts
Edibility: doubtful; best avoided

An extremely common mushroom; indeed, there can hardly be a lawn anywhere that has not had this mushroom growing in it at one time or another. The rounded to flattened cap starts date-brown, but rapidly dries to a pale pinkish-buff. The widely spaced gills are dark brown. The slender stem is pale buff. There is debate about which genus this mushroom belongs to since it is atypical for a *Panaeolus* in having warty spores. You may see it listed as a *Panaeolina* or even a *Psathyrella*.

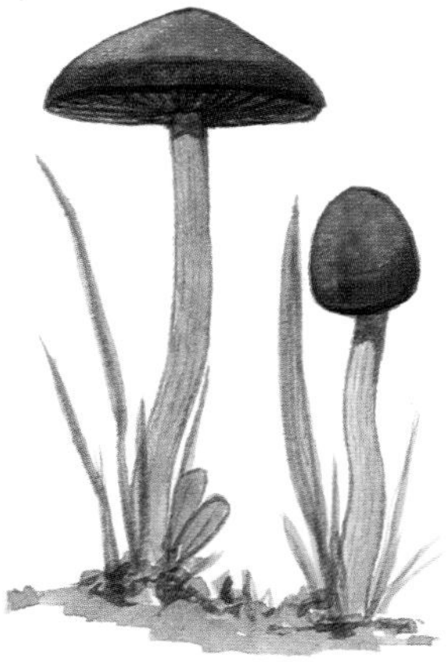

Psathyrella candolleana (Fries) R. Maire

Cap: 1–3in (2.5–7.5cm)
Spores: purplish-brown, 7–10 x 4–5µm, almost cylindrical, smooth
Edibility: inedible

Almost a "weed" species in some areas, this mushroom grows in small tufts close to stumps and buried wood everywhere. The extremely fragile caps are soon expanded and buff-brown, drying rapidly to ivory-white. The narrow gills are grayish-lilac. The slender stems are white. There is no obvious veil present, unlike some other closely related species such as *P. leucotephra*.

Psathyrella velutina (Persoon ex Fries) Singer [=*Lacrymaria lacrymabunda*]

Cap: 1–3in (2.5–7.5cm)
Spores: blackish-brown, 9–12 x 6–7µm, warty
Edibility: edible, but best avoided

Extremely common along tracks and paths in woodlands and wherever the soil has been disturbed. The pale reddish-brown cap is fibrous-hairy and frequently ragged at the margin. The gills are deep yellow, then black, with white edges and often weep droplets of liquid. The shaggy stem is also reddish-brown and has a ring zone at the top. Similar but poisonous species of *Inocybe* have a brown spore deposit (see pages 121–2).

Psathyrella delineata (Peck) Smith

Cap: 2–4in (5–10cm)
Spores: purplish-brown, 7–9 x 4–6µm
Edibility: inedible

A strange species with a curiously wrinkled and corrugated cap, and unusually large and fleshy for this genus of mushrooms. The cap is a deep watery brown, drying paler. The gills are attached, crowded, and purplish-brown. The stout stem is white with a faint ring zone at the apex. It is quite common on woody debris and leaf litter in the eastern and northern states.

Coprinus quadrifidus (Peck)

Cap: 1–3in (2.5–7.5cm)
Spores: black, 7.5–10 x 4–5µm
Edibility: edible

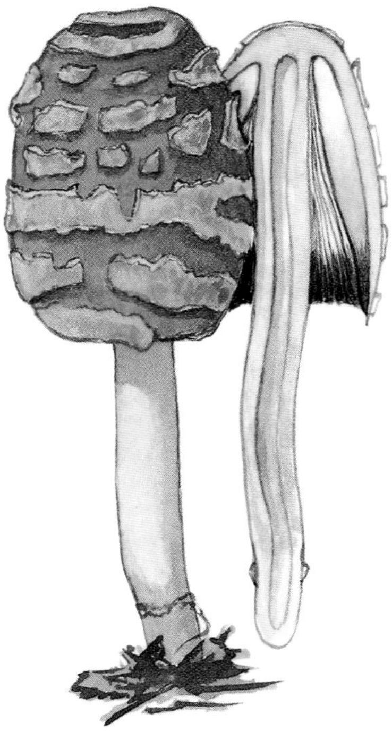

An uncommon but easily recognized species with large, coarse fragments of veil cracking apart on the brown cap. The cap barely opens, but instead dissolves away from the margin and continues this up to the top; this process is called deliquescence. The stem is white and slightly scaly with a faint ring zone below. It grows on woody debris, often in large clusters, in the eastern states. Some forms of this species (or perhaps developing with age) have a pronounced unpleasant odor and taste of garlic. When this is present the fungus has been reported as causing stomach upsets. It is possible that a complex of very closely related species is involved here, and further work needs to be done on the whole group.

Coprinus comatus (Müller ex Fries)

S.F. Gray – "Shaggy Mane"; "Lawyer's Wig"
Cap: 2–6in (5–15cm tall)
Spores: black, 11–15 x 6–8.5µm, smooth
Edibility: edible and delicious when young

This species is well known enough to have received several common names – very unusual for a mushroom. Both of the names given allude to the white, shaggy surface of the cap, where each scale recurves back to look very like the curls on an English lawyer's wig. As in the previous species, and indeed many *Coprinus* species, the cap rapidly dissolves away from the margin upward so as to release the spores. The tall white stem is smooth and has a thin white ring around the middle. It grows in grass and bare soil, wherever there has been disturbance, and is very common along roadsides and freshly laid lawns, as well as garbage dumps and landfills.

Coprinus atramentarius (Bulliard ex Fries) Fries

Cap: 1–3in (2.5–7.5cm)
Spores: black, 7–11 x 4–6μm, smooth
Edibility: edible, except with alcohol

A remarkable species which typifies a reaction known in only a very few mushrooms. If eaten alone, the mushroom generally causes no problems, but if consumed with alcohol, an unpleasant reaction of palpitations, nausea, tingling, and flushing of the extremities occurs. The chemical that causes this is very similar to "Antabuse", which is used in the treatment of alcoholism. This common species grows in large clumps near stumps and buried wood everywhere, and has a gray-brown, slightly scaly cap with a white, spindle-shaped stem with a distinct ring zone close to the base.

Coprinus micaceus (Bulliard ex Fries) Fries

Cap: 1–3in (2.5–7.5cm)
Spores: black, 7–10 x 4–5μm, smooth
Edibility: edible

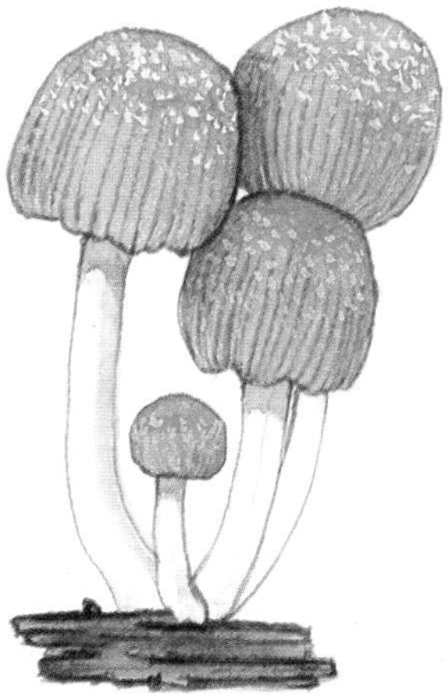

A beautiful species when young and viewed through a lens, for the entire cap is coated with a fine layer of reflective, mica-like cells over the reddish-brown surface. As it expands, the margin of the cap becomes strongly striate-pleated. The whitish stems are joined into large clusters, and it grows at the base of stumps and buried wood everywhere. There are a number of similar species best distinguished microscopically with the aid of specialist literature.

Coprinus plicatilis (Curtis ex Fries) Fries

Cap: ¼–1in (0.6–2.5cm)
Spores: black, 10–13 x 6.5–10μm, smooth
Edibility: inedible

A beautiful, tiny, and delicate species looking just like an oriental parasol. The cap flattens out and is deeply pleated and furrowed radially. The narrow gills are separated from the stem by a narrow collar. The extremely fragile stem is whitish. The entire mushroom lasts only a few hours, although it hardly dissolves (deliquesces) – it merely collapses with age. It is very common in fields and lawns everywhere.

PAXILLACEAE
Paxillus Family

These species, despite their gills, are thought to be closely related to the boletes. They share many microscopic and chemical features, and have similar spore colors.

Paxillus involutus (Bataille ex Fries) Fries

Cap: 2–6in (5–15cm)
Spores: ocher-brown, 7–9 x 4–6µm, smooth
Edibility: poisonous if eaten raw or inadequately cooked, and has proved deadly to some. It may have a cumulative toxic effect

Until recent years this was not suspected of being poisonous, and indeed many people in Europe ate it regularly. But then suspicion fell upon it in a number of deaths, and it now appears to be cumulative in its effects and deadly. The poisoning seems to be increased if it is eaten raw or incorrectly cooked. On no account should this now be eaten. The ocher-brown cap has a strongly inrolled, wooly margin when young, and can be quite viscid when wet. This soon flattens out, leaving a rather grooved margin. The soft, crowded gills are yellowish and bruise quickly rust-brown. The short stem is smooth and colored like the cap. It is abundant in mixed woods, especially birch, throughout the USA.

Paxillus atrotomentosus (Bataille ex Fries) Fries

Cap: 2–8in (5–20cm)
Spores: yellowish-brown, 5–6 x 3–4µm, smooth
Edibility: supposedly edible but best avoided in view of its relationship to *P. involutus*, described above

This often huge mushroom can hardly be mistaken if its habitat and velvety brown or black stem are both noted. The latter is usually offset to one side of the large cap. The gills are crowded, soft, and yellow. The flesh is yellow to pinkish and rather bitter. It grows on stumps of pine trees and is common throughout the USA.

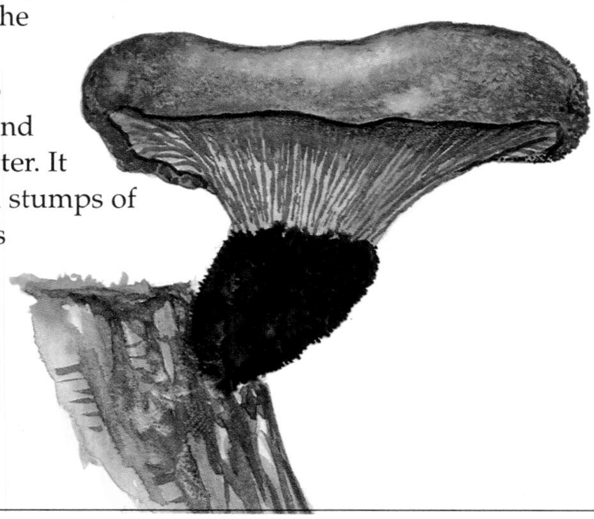

Phylloporus rhodoxanthus (Schweinitz) Bresadola

Cap: 1–4in (2.5–10cm)
Spores: olive-brown, 9–12 x 3–5µm, spindle-shaped
Edibility: edible

This looks remarkably like some of the boletes, such as *B. spadiceus*, until you turn it over and realize that it has gills. In almost all characteristics it shows relationships with the boletes. The velvety reddish-yellow to brown cap gives a brilliant green reaction with ammonia, just like some of the boletes. The gills are bright yellow and thick with strong cross-veins, and are easily separated from the cap. It is very common in mixed woods throughout the USA. *P. foliiporus* differs in its whitish-gray gills, which bruise deep blue, and its shorter spores; it grows in the south in sandy soils, such as the New Jersey Pine Barrens.

CORTINARIACEAE
Cortinarius Family

This is the largest family of mushrooms in the world, particularly the genus *Cortinarius*, and they grow in a bewildering number of forms, colors, and sizes. The spores vary from rust-brown to dull, cigar-brown and may be smooth, warty, or even angular-lumpy. A cobwebby veil is often present. Some *Cortinarius* species are now known to be deadly poisonous; all should be avoided for culinary purposes.

Cortinarius trivialis Lange

Cap: 2–4in (5–10cm)
Spores: rust-brown, 10–15 x 7–8µm, warty
Edibility: doubtful; best avoided

Swamps and bogs are wonderful places to hunt for mushrooms, and many *Cortinarius* species, including this one, prefer to grow in such habitats. It particularly likes willow bogs. The very viscid cap is yellow-brown, while the gills are pale lilac before turning rust-brown from the mature spores. The stem is peculiarly banded and zoned, with viscid rings of whitish-yellow veil over a darker brown background. The flesh is white with pale lilac in the stem apex.

Cortinarius muscigenus Peck

[=*C. collinitus* of some authors]
Cap: 2–4in (5–10cm)
Spores: rust-brown, 12–15 x 7–8µm, warty
Edibility: doubtful; best avoided

Many *Cortinarius* species have some blue or violet colors in the stem or gills, and in this species the entire stem is flushed violet and banded with thicker rings of viscid veil. The viscid cap is a rich orange to tawny brown, while the gills are white at first, then rust-brown. It also likes boggy situations, and is quite common and widespread. It usually grows under spruce in wet woods in the northern and eastern states, and up into Canada.

Cortinarius pseudosalor Lange

Cap: 2–4in (5–10cm)
Spores: rust-brown, 12–15.5 x 6.5–9μm
Edibility: doubtful; best avoided

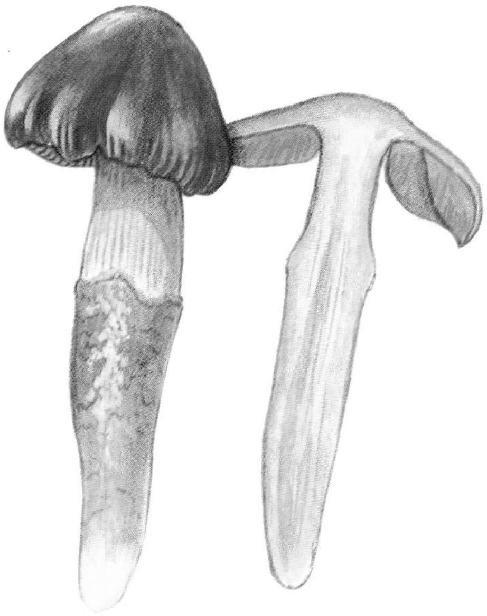

This species can be found in beech woods in the northern and eastern states, and at times may be the commonest species present. The viscid cap is strangely wrinkled and radially ridged, and is a pale ocher-brown. The gills are a pale clay-buff when young, then rust-brown, and their surfaces are also wrinkled. The spindle-shaped stem is often rooted into the soil and is usually bluish-lilac and viscid up to a distinct ring zone, and white above. The flesh has a honey-like odor when rubbed.

Cortinarius delibutus Fries

Cap: 2–4in (5–10cm)
Spores: rust-brown, 7–8 x 5–6μm, warty
Edibility: doubtful; best avoided

Another species which prefers boggy, mossy areas, especially under birch and willow. The sticky, rounded cap is a bright yellow-ocher, while the young gills and apex of the stem are a pale lavender. The lower half of the stem is also sticky, and is a pale yellow with darker yellow bands. The stickiness is actually a complete veil (the universal veil), which enveloped the young mushroom. There is also a cobwebby partial veil present at the top of the stem. This species is distinctive for its almost globose spores.

Cortinarius iodes Berkeley & Curtis

Cap: 1–3in (2.5–7.5cm)
Spores: rust-brown, 8–12 x 5–6.5μm, warty
Edibility: doubtful; best avoided

A rather small species in this group of species, with both sticky caps and stems, and very attractive with its bright bluish-violet colors. The cap color is unusual in that it is frequently blotched and spotted with whitish areas. It is probably the commonest of the *Cortinarius* species in the northeastern woods from summer through fall. The similar but rarer *C. iodeoides* differs in the bitter taste of the cap surface and the smaller spores.

Cortinarius volvatus A.H. Smith

Cap: 2–4in (5–10cm)
Spores: rust-brown, 8–10.5 x 5–6µm, warty
Edibility: doubtful; best avoided

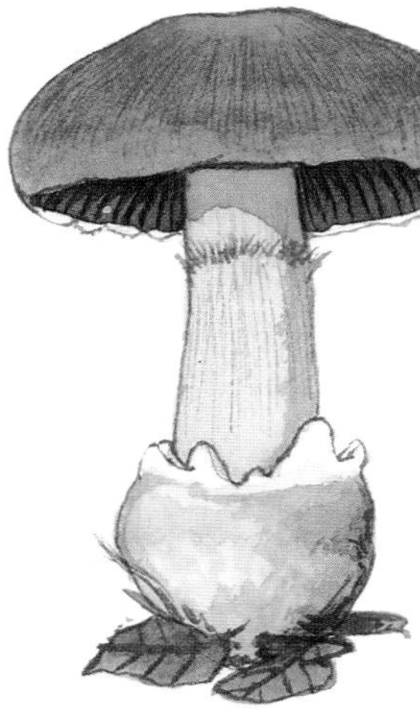

Although all *Cortinarius* species have a universal veil of sorts, it is rarely well developed, so it is all the more striking when it occurs, as in this species, in the form of a volva-like structure on the stem. The cap is bluish when young, and viscid then browner and dry with age, while the young gills are deep blue-violet. The stem is bluish and very bulbous, but the edge of the bulb has thick, soft remnants of an enveloping white veil, which stand up to form a volva or sac. The taste is bitter. It grows in mixed woods on calcareous soils, and is quite rare in the north and northeast.

Cortinarius calyptrodermus Smith

Cap: 2–4in (5–10cm)
Spores: rust-brown, 10–12 x 5.5–6.5µm, warty
Edibility: doubtful; best avoided

One of the most beautiful of all mushrooms; in fact, many people never imagine that such colors can be present in "lowly" fungi. The cap, stem, and gills are all of the brightest and most intense violet. As it ages the violet slowly fades to brown. The stem is very bulbous with a distinct gutter-like upper margin. The universal veil in this species is unusually thick and tough, and breaks up to leave thick platelets on the cap and bulb. It is apparently widely distributed in the north and east, but is unfortunately rare.

Cortinarius elegantiodes Peck

Cap: 1–3in (2.5–7.5cm)
Spores: rust-brown, 14–19 x 8–10µm, very warty
Edibility: doubtful; best avoided

There are a number of brilliant yellow or orange species in this section, often difficult to separate, of which this species is perhaps the most common. The rounded cap is a bright golden yellow, flushing more tawny-orange with age. The gills are bright yellow when young, then soon rust-brown. The bulbous stem is whitish-yellow with a prominent cobwebby veil when young. It is a rather small species, but has enormous spores and is easily identified by this feature. It grows in beech woods on calcareous soils in the northeast.

Cortinarius purpurascens Fries

Cap: 2–4in (5–10cm)
Spores: rust-brown, 8–10 x 4–5.5μm, warty
Edibility: doubtful; best avoided

Color changes in the flesh are not as common in species of *Cortinarius* as in some other mushroom groups, but in this species the change is very noticeable and diagnostic. All parts of the mushroom bruise a deep purple-violet, especially the gills and stem. The slightly sticky cap is dark brown streaked with darker fibers, and can show violet flushes at the margin. The gills and stem are pale violet, and the stem has a distinctly bulbous base. It is a fairly common species in conifer woods.

Cortinarius torvus (Fries) Fries

Cap: 2–4in (5–10cm)
Spores: rust-brown, 8–10 x 5–6μm, warty
Edibility: doubtful; best avoided

There are enormous numbers of small to medium-sized species with brown colors differing in minor macroscopic and microscopic characteristics, and for the most part very specialized literature is required to identify them. This is one of the few that stands out by means of some distinctive features. It might be given the common name of "Stocking Cortinarius" because the club-shaped stem really does look as if it has a whitish stocking pulled half way up; this is the remains of the universal veil. The widely spaced gills and the apex of the stem are violet when young. It is a common species in beech woods throughout the northern and eastern states.

Cortinarius armillatus (Fries) Fries

Cap: 2–4in (5–10cm)
Spores: rust-brown, 9–12 x 5.5–7.5μm, warty
Edibility: doubtful; best avoided

This may be the easiest of all *Cortinarius* to identify, and even complete beginners quickly learn to recognize it. The very bulbous stem has between one and three bright cinnabar-red bands of veil circling the stem, which is otherwise smooth and pale whitish-brown. The cap is a rich brick-red, dry, and fibrous. When very young, it can look very strange, with tiny button cap perched upon an enormous rounded bulb. It can grow in large circles in beech and birch woods, and is often very common. In the west *C. haematochelis* has a darker cap, reddish-brown belts, and smaller, rounder spores.

Cortinarius evernius (Fries) Fries

Cap: 2–4in (5–10cm)
Spores: rust-brown, 9–11 x 5–6μm, warty
Edibility: doubtful; best avoided

This mushroom can be extremely beautiful, particularly when young and the colors are at their most intense. The entire mushroom is a clear blue-violet with bands of white veil on the tall, elegant stem. The cap gradually darkens to a deep reddish-brown. It grows in sphagnum moss in pine woods, and, like all species that grow in such deep mosses, the stems can elongate enormously in a bid to push through the moss. The size, therefore, can vary considerably, and allowance must be made for this when trying to identify it.

Cortinarius alboviolaceus (Persoon ex Fries) Fries

Cap: 2–4in (5–10cm)
Spores: rust-brown, 8–10 x 5–6μm, warty
Edibility: doubtful; best avoided

The Latin name means whitish-violet, and is a good description of the overall colors of this species. The entire mushroom is silvery-white with a flush of lavender or violet. The bulbous stem is ringed or booted with a white veil over the lower half. The flesh is violet above, fading to pale ocher below. It is one of the commoner species and grows in beech woods throughout the USA.

Cortinarius argentatus (Persoon ex Fries) Fries

Cap: 2–4in (5–10cm)
Spores: rust-brown, 8–10 x 5–6μm, warty
Edibility: doubtful; best avoided

Another silvery-white to lavender species, this differs from the previous one in its almost total lack of a veil and the distinctly bulbous stem base. With age the lavender colors fade from the cap to be replaced by pale ocher, and old specimens may be completely ocher. It is not a common species, but in some years may appear in large numbers in beech woods in the northeast, often in summer before other *Cortinarius* species appear.

Cortinarius violaceus (Fries) S.F. Gray

Cap: 2–4in (5–10cm)
Spores: rust-brown, 13–17 x 8–10µm, warty
Edibility: doubtful; best avoided

Sadly, this fungus, one of the most intensely colored, is a rather uncommon mushroom in the USA. The entire body is the deepest violet, so dark it is almost black. The cap is dry and minutely scaly, while the stem is fibrous. It seems to prefer beech or birch woods, and has been reported as fruiting for only a very short time each year, which may account for its being seen so rarely. The subspecies *hercynicus* is found in conifer woods and has rounder, smaller spores.

Cortinarius bolaris (Persoon ex Fries) Fries

Cap: 2–3in (5–7.5cm)
Spores: rust-brown, 6–7 x 5–6µm, warty
Edibility: poisonous; suspected of being deadly

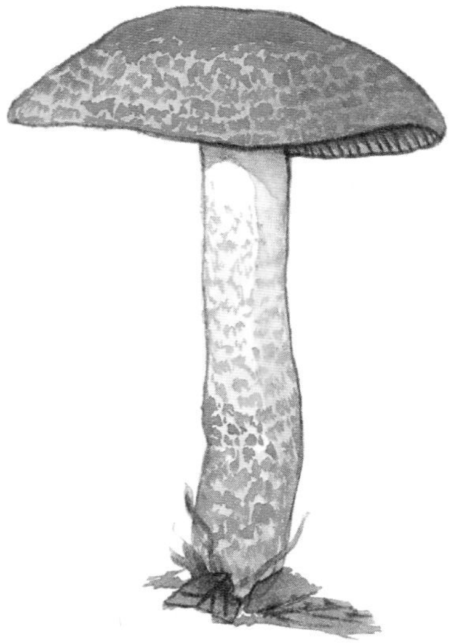

One of the relatively few species of *Cortinarius* that stains with age or handling, the pale yellowish cap and stem become spotted with copper-red scales. Eventually the entire mushroom will turn a dull copper-red to brick-red. It is a fairly common species in beech woods throughout the USA. Like a number of other species, it is now suspected of being a dangerously poisonous mushroom, and, as with all other members of this genus, must be avoided as an edible.

Cortinarius rubellus Cooke

[=*C. speciosissimus*]
Cap: 1–3in (2.5–7.5cm)
Spores: rust-brown, 8–11 x 6.5–8.5µm, warty
Edibility: deadly poisonous; causes severe kidney damage and possible death

For many years *Cortinarius* were considered to be "safe", if not particularly exciting, edibles. But a series of poisonings in Europe led to the implication of this and other species, particularly *C. orellanus*, in a number of poisonings and deaths. It is now known that they contain a series of complex toxins grouped together under the name orellanin. They are particularly dangerous in that many days may pass before symptoms become evident, by which time great damage to the system may already have occurred. This species is rare in the USA, being found mostly in the north under conifers, often in moss. It has bands of veil remnants on the stem and a smell of radish. Similar species include *C. raineriensis* and *C. callisteus*, best distinguished microscopically.

Cortinarius pyriodorus Peck

Cap: 2–4in (5–10cm)
Spores: rust-brown, 7–10 x 5–6μm, warty
Edibility: doubtful; best avoided

This beautiful fungus has a most penetrating and usually pleasant odor. The entire mushroom is a clear lilac-lavender, with whitish veil remnants spread over the cap and stem. The flesh is a bright yellow-brown and usually marbled irregularly. All parts of the mushroom emit a penetrating odor described as like over-ripe pears. It is common in conifer woods, and is widely distributed. The very similar *C. traganus*, which tends to be more coarsely scaly, has a strong, unpleasant odor, variously described as like goats or acetylene gas. That species grows mainly in the west.

Cortinarius sanguineus (von Wulfen) Fries

Cap: 1–2in (2.5–5cm)
Spores: rust-brown, 6–9 x 4–6μm, warty
Edibility: doubtful; possibly poisonous

Such an intense blood-red to carmine-red is very rare in mushrooms, only commonly being seen in the caps of *Russula* species. Here, however, the entire mushroom is colored both inside and out. This is quite a common species under conifers in the USA. A form with traces of golden veil and perhaps more purple-red colors is found under deciduous trees and is often called *C. puniceus* Orton. Owing to their bright colors, either reds or greenish-yellows, and their unusual chemistry, this and the following species are placed, along with a number of other species, in a separate subgenus called *Dermocybe*. The similar orange-red to rust-red *C. marylandensis* is common in the deciduous woods of the northeast.

Cortinarius semisanguineus (Fries) Gillet

Cap: 1–2in (2.5–5cm)
Spores: rust-brown, 6–8 x 4–5μm, warty
Edibility: doubtful; possibly poisonous

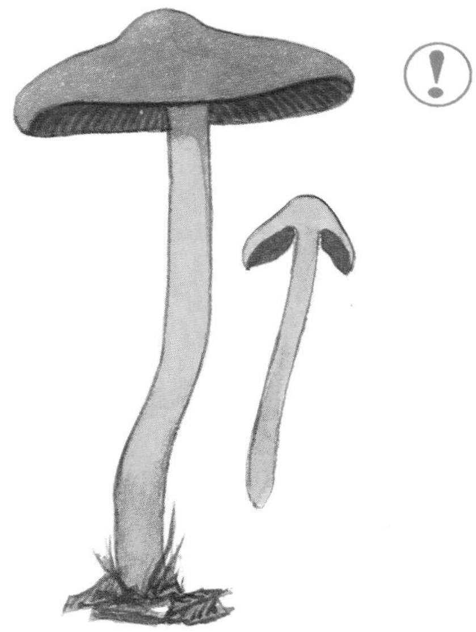

One of the commonest members in this group; the cap is a rather dull ocher-brown, as is the stem, but turn it over and the vivid blood-red to cinnabar-red gills are revealed. This and other species in the same group are greatly valued for use in the dyeing of wool, yielding beautiful yellow, gold, and reddish pigments. Many other fungi can also be used for dyeing, and give colors ranging from palest lavender to violet, browns, greens, and even blue. Several books are now available on this fascinating hobby.

Hebeloma crustuliniforme
(Bulliard ex St Amans) Quélet – "Poison Pie"

Cap: 2–4in (5–10cm)
Spores: dull cinnamon-brown, 9–13 x 5.5–7μm, minutely warty
Edibility: poisonous; causes severe stomach upsets

The cap of this and related species does indeed look rather like a pie, although the pastry is apparently uncooked. The entire mushroom is a pale ivory-buff, like uncooked dough. The gills are pale gray-brown to tan, and the edges are often beaded with tiny droplets. There is a strong odor of radish and the taste is slightly bitter. It is a common species late in the year in mixed woods everywhere. The entire genus *Hebeloma* appears to be more or less poisonous.

Hebeloma edurum Metrod ex Bon

Cap: 2–6in (5–15cm)
Spores: dull cinnamon-brown, 9–12 x 5–7μm, minutely warty
Edibility: poisonous; causes severe stomach upsets

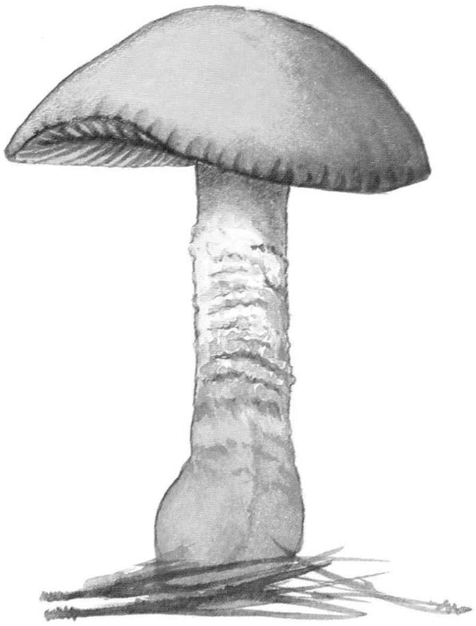

Rather a large species, its cap is a dull ocher-brown to beige with a slightly furrowed margin. The gills are pale buff and do not weep droplets, unlike some other species. The stout stem is fibrous-scaly with a slight ring zone, and tends to stain brown at the base. The odor is pleasant, of fruit or chocolate, then slowly unpleasant. It prefers conifer woods on chalky soils and is uncommon.

Hebeloma syriense Karst – "Corpse Finder", "Ghoul Fungus"

Cap: 1–2in (2.5–5cm)
Spores: pale brown, 11–14 x 7–9μm, minutely warty
Edibility: poisonous

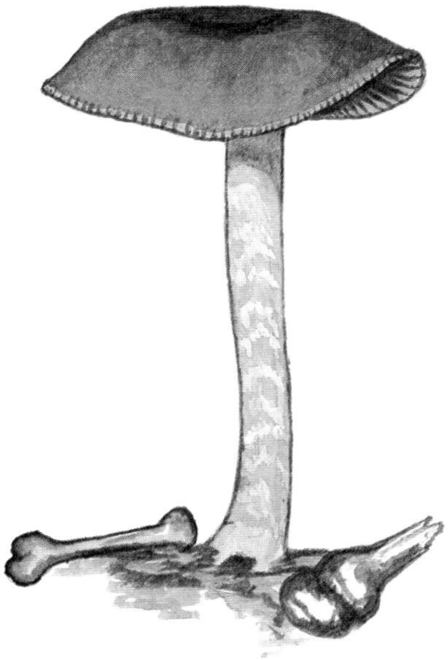

This fascinating species has a unique lifestyle. Like a small number of other closely related species, it seems to require soil with a high nitrogen or urea content in order to grow. In this instance, it obtains this supplement to its diet by growing next to the decaying remains of dead animals in woodlands in the northeast. The cap is brick-red to dull brown, fading to ocher-brown, and is sticky when wet. The stem is whitish to pale brown, slightly fibrous-scaly above. Similar species specialize in less gory habitats, such as animal burrows or wasp nests, again using the chemicals available in the waste produced by the tenants.

Rozites caperata (Persoon) Karsten

Cap: 2–5in (5–12.5cm)
Spores: rust-brown, 12–14 x 7–9μm
Edibility: edible and good

This species is sometimes given the common name of "Gypsy"; this is in reference to the fine, frost-like traces of white veil which are left on the cap as it expands. When very young, this white veil may be tinted with lavender. The cap has a finely radially wrinkled surface, and the gills are pale buff and join the stem. The stem is cylindrical, fibrous, and has a white ring around the center, often stained brown from fallen spores. It is quite common in the northeast and northern states, and grows under conifers.

Inocybe calamistrata (Fries) Gillet

Cap: 1–2in (2.5–5cm)
Spores: dull cigar-brown, 9–12 x 4.5–6.5μm, elliptical
Edibility: poisonous

The genus *Inocybe* is closely related to *Cortinarius*, shown earlier, but has a much darker, duller brown spore color, and the mushrooms themselves tend to be rather dull and featureless for the most part (although rich in features under the microscope). There are numerous species and most are difficult to distinguish without a microscope. Most *Inocybe* species have very well-developed cystidia on the gill margin, and some of these have strange crystals at the apex. This species has a rounded, scaly, dark brown cap and stem, but usually dark blue-green stains at the stem base. It grows in wet, mossy areas under conifers and is not uncommon. The spores are smooth and elliptical, whereas some *Inocybe* species have strange, knobbly or irregular-shaped spores. The marginal cystidia are short and club-shaped.

Inocybe tahquamenonensis Smith

Cap: ½–1in (1.2–2.5cm)
Spores: dull brown, 9–12.5 x 5–7μm, strongly angular, warted
Edibility: poisonous

Not only one of the strangest named mushrooms, but also one of the darkest colored species. The entire mushroom is a deep purple-black and is minutely scaly on both the cap and stem. The gills are nearly chocolate-brown with age. It is an uncommon species, growing under mixed woods in the northeastern and northern states.

Inocybe caesariata (Fries) Karsten

Cap: 1–2in (2.5–5cm)
Spores: deep brown, 9–12 x 5–7µm, elliptical
Edibility: poisonous

Perhaps the commonest species of *Inocybe* in many of the eastern and northern states, this is also rather brightly colored compared to many other species. The rounded to flattened cap is a bright tawny orange to golden yellow, and is densely scaly. The gills are dull ocher and crowded, while the stem is densely fibrous-scaly up to a ring zone. It is common along woodland paths and tracks, growing in grass or leaf litter.

Inocybe pyriodora (Persoon ex Fries) Quélet

Cap: 2–3in (5–7.5cm)
Spores: dull brown, 7–10 x 5–7.5µm, elliptical
Edibility: poisonous

Inocybe is rich in species with unusual odors, and a number of them have strong fruit smells of one kind or another. In this instance the smell of pears is very strong. It is otherwise distinguished by its pinkish-ocher or yellow-brown, fibrous, domed cap which bruises slightly pinkish-red. The stem is pale brown and fibrous to slightly shaggy. It is quite common in deciduous woods and widespread, especially in the western states.

Inocybe geophylla (Bulliard) Karsten

Cap: ½–1in (1–2.5cm)
Spores: dull brown, 7–9 x 4–5.5µm, elliptical
Edibility: poisonous

A pretty little species that comes in a number of distinct color forms, from white through pink to pale lavender, each of which has been given its own varietal name by various authors. The cap and stem are both smooth and silky, and the mushroom has a strong earthy odor. It can be very common and grows in small troops in mixed woods throughout North America.

Gymnopilus spectabilis (Fries) A.H. Smith
[=*G. junonius*]

Cap: 3–6in (7.5–15cm)
Spores: bright orange-brown, 8–10 x 5–6µm, coarsely warty
Edibility: inedible; very bitter

A spectacular species growing in large clumps, the cap is bright orange-tawny and varies from almost smooth to coarsely fibrous and scaly as it ages. The gills are crowded, shallow, pale straw, then amber to rust-brown, and often speckled. The tough, large stem is swollen, spindle-shaped to club-shaped, and has a well-developed membranous ring. The flesh is yellowish and extremely bitter to taste. It grows attached to buried wood or on fallen logs and stumps of deciduous trees.

Kuehneromyces mutabilis (Schaeffer) Singer & Smith [=*Galerina mutabilis*]

Cap: 1–3in (2.5–7.5cm)
Spores: ocher-brown, 6–7 x 3–4.5µm, smooth to slightly warty
Edibility: edible and good

This is a species which has undergone several name changes because authors are undecided which genus it belongs to; it has also been placed in *Pholiota*. Whatever its name, it is an attractive and delicious species, with a sticky cap when wet, which characteristically fades at the center as it dries. The scaly stem has a distinct ring at the top, and the gills are rust-brown. It grows in large clumps on dead deciduous wood and is quite common late in the year. Although it is an excellent edible, care must be taken not to confuse it with some *Galerina* species, such as that which follows, and one or two others which are deadly poisonous. They usually become paler from the edge inward, are more fragile, usually striate, and their spores are distinctly warted. Their stems do not have small, recurved scales.

Galerina autumnalis (Peck) Smith & Singer

Cap: 1–2in (2.5–5cm)
Spores: rust-brown, 8–9 x 5–6µm
Edibility: deadly poisonous

There have, fortunately, been very few cases of poisoning by this species, probably because it is rather small and not particularly attractive or appetizing in appearance. The flattened cap is dark tawny-brown, slightly sticky when wet but soon dry, and often has a striate margin. The gills are adnate, crowded, and rust-brown. The stem is smooth, minutely lined, and has a delicate ring above. It grows in small clumps on fallen logs, especially conifers, and is locally common. It contains similar toxins to those found in the Death Cap, *Amanita phalloides*, and causes severe liver damage with vomiting, diarrhea, hypothermia, and eventual death if not treated rapidly.

Phaeocollybia olivacea Smith

Cap: 2–4in (5–10cm)
Spores: dull brown, 8–11 x 5–6µm, warty
Edibility: doubtful; best avoided

Mushrooms which are entirely green are very rare, and when they are as distinctive as this one are very easy to recognize. The cap and deeply rooting stem are sticky to slimy; the gills join the stem and are pale buff. It is quite a rare species and grows in western conifer woods.

STROPHARIACEAE
Stropharia Family

Most species grow on or near wood and may have glutinous, dry, or scaly caps. The gills are sinuate-adnate and the spores are yellow-brown to rust-brown and smooth. Usually a veil and/or ring is present.

Pholiota lenta (Persoon) Singer

Cap: 2–4in (5–10cm)
Spores: ocher-brown, 6–7 x 3–4μm, smooth
Edibility: inedible

Unlike most *Pholiota* species, this one prefers to grow on the ground in woody debris in leaf litter. The pallid, yellow-beige cap is very viscid and has tiny white veil flakes floating in the slime. The gills are pale cinnamon to rust. The stem is whitish with wooly scales up to a faint ring zone. There is a slight odor of straw, and the taste is mild. It is a fairly common species in beech woods,usually appearing rather late in the year, especially in the north and west.

Pholiota squarrosa (Müller) Kummer

Cap: 2–6in (5–15cm)
Spores: ocher-brown, 6–8 x 3–4μm, smooth
Edibility: doubtful; best avoided

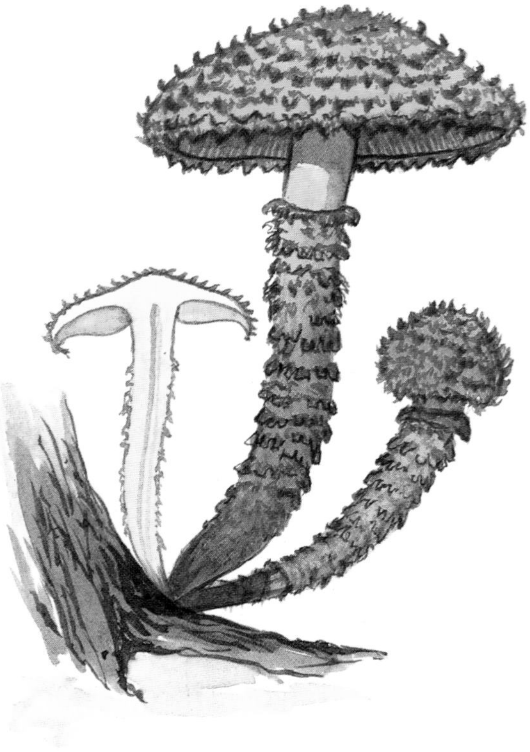

Certainly one of the scaliest mushrooms around, a large clump of this species in good condition can be quite spectacular. Both the cap and the stem, which are dry, are covered in small, pointed and recurved scales. The color varies from tawny yellow to russet on a paler background. The crowded gills are yellow to slightly olive, then rust-brown. The flesh is yellowish with a strong straw-like odor, and tastes rather bitter. It is a common species, growing at the base of deciduous trees and stumps. The very similar *P. squarrosoides* differs in the cap being paler, whitish-yellow, and distinctly sticky below the pointed, dry scales, and it has spores which measure 4–6 x 2.5–3.5μm. It is equally common.

Pholiota flammans (Fries) Kummer

Cap: 1–3in (2.5–7.5cm)
Spores: ocher-brown, 4–5 x 2.5–3µm, smooth
Edibility: doubtful; best avoided

The specific name, meaning "flame-colored" Pholiota, describes this fungus well. It is perhaps the brightest of all the species, its cap being a brilliant golden-yellow to orange with paler yellow, pointed scales. The cap cuticle is sticky below the scales. The stem is densely scaly up to the ring zone, and is dry. The flesh is bright yellow with a fruity odor and a rather acrid, unpleasant flavor. It is quite common , growing in small clusters on fallen conifer logs and stumps, and is widespread.

Pholiota aurivella (Fries) Kummer

Cap: 2–5in (5–15cm)
Spores: ocher-brown, 7–10 x 4.5–6µm, smooth
Edibility: doubtful; best avoided

This very glutinous species usually grows on standing trees, occasionally on fallen logs, and is often to be seen emerging from an old knothole or wound in the trunk of a beech tree. The bright orange cap is viscid, with small, dark brown glutinous scales that can wash off in rainy weather. The gills are crowded and pale yellow to tawny. The stem, in contrast to the cap, is dry, with small, yellowish, recurved scales.The flesh is yellowish and mild to taste. It is found mainly in the west and north, and there are a number of similar species best distinguished microscopically.

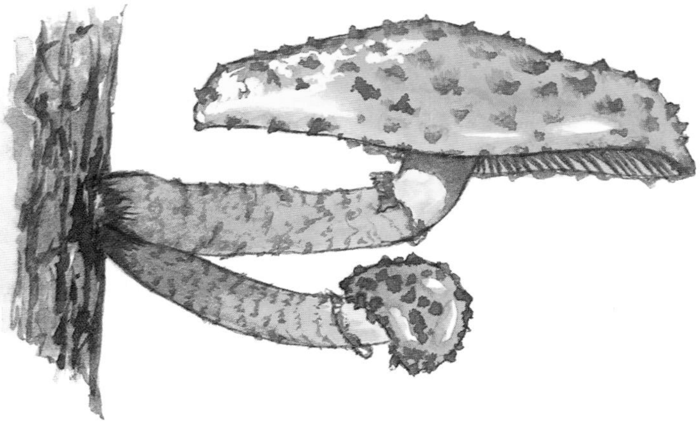

Pholiota highlandensis (Peck) Smith & Hesler

Cap: 1–2in (2.5–5cm)
Spores: ocher-brown, 5–8 x 3.5–4.5µm, smooth
Edibility: doubtful; best avoided

This is one of a number of fungi that specialize in old burn sites around dead stumps and suchlike, rapidly colonizing the area for a couple of years before the site is eventually grown over and returns to normal. This species has a tawny-brown, sticky cap, which is smooth and without scales. The gills are yellowish to rust and slightly adnate-decurrent. The stem is tawny and slightly fibrous up to a whitish-yellow ring zone. Wherever a forest fire has occurred, this species may be found a year or two after.

Pholiota malicola (Kauffman)

Cap: 2–4in (5–10cm)
Spores: ocher-brown, 7.5–11 x 4.5–5.5μm, smooth
Edibility: doubtful; best avoided

With its smooth yellow cap and elegant stature, this fungus can be mistaken for the Sulfur Tuft Mushroom, *Hypholoma fasciculare,* but that species has purple-brown spores and is much more fragile. This mushroom has a whitish veil, which leaves tiny remnants hanging on the cap margin, and has a ring zone at the stem apex. It grows in clumps, usually around the base of dead trees, especially birch and alder, and is quite common in some western states. There is a strong, fragrant odor present, which is another useful identifying characteristic. This is one of a complex of related species, best distinguished microposcopically. Once separated as the genus *Flammula*, they are now united with the scaly species of *Pholiota*.

Pholiota albocrenulata Peck

Cap: 2–4in (5–10cm)
Spores: rust-brown, 10–15 x 5–8μm, smooth
Edibility: doubtful; best avoided

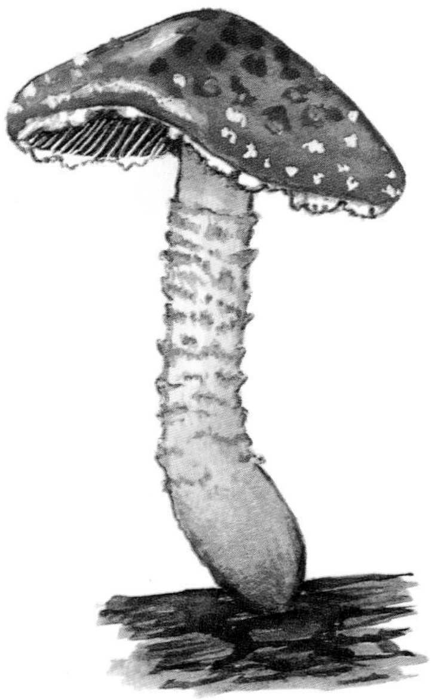

A somber but rather beautiful species, and quite easy to recognize. The glutinous cap is rather conical and a deep reddish-brown, with large brownish-yellow veil remnants and paler fragments around the margin. The gills are dark grayish-brown with finely toothed white edges, often beaded with droplets of liquid. The stem is reddish-brown with rings of darker scales up to a ring zone. It usually grows in ones or twos on logs and living trees of maple and elm, and is widely distributed in North America.

BOLBITIACEAE
Bolbitius Family

These fungi have their cap cuticle made up of rounded, rather than thread-like, cells, and all have pale brown spores.

Bolbitius vitellinus (Persoon ex Fries) Fries
Cap: ¾–2in (2–5cm)
Spores: rust-ocher, 10–15 x 6–9μm, smooth
Edibility: inedible

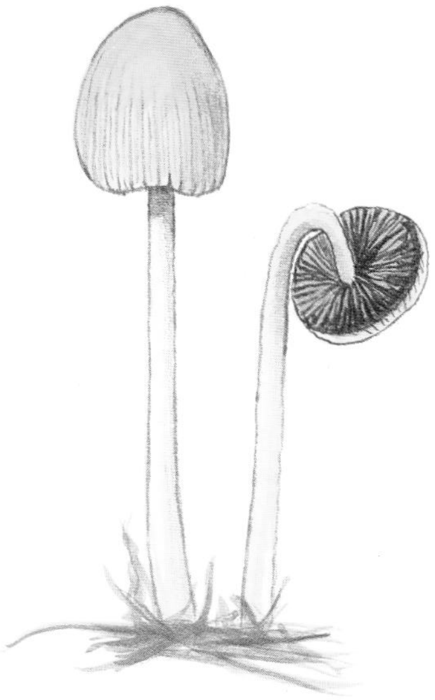

Some fungi are so fragile that they are almost impossible to collect without damage, and this species falls into that category. The beautiful lemon-yellow cap is very viscid and deeply grooved when old. The thin, elegant stem is white with a minutely hairy surface, and snaps very easily. The mushroom tends to collapse and partially dissolve with age, and rarely lasts much more than a few hours. It grows on rich soil wherever there is dung, manure or rotted straw, and is common everywhere.

Agrocybe praecox (Persoon) Fayod
Cap: 1–3in (2.5–7.5cm)
Spores: dull, tobacco-brown, 8–11 x 5–6μm, smooth
Edibility: inedible

The name praecox means "early" and refers to the time of year when this and some related species prefer to grow. They appear around April and continue through the early summer. This species is rather slender and elegant, and has a pale beige to tan cap which may crack slightly when dry. The gills are adnate and pale buff-brown. The slender stem has a distinct membranous ring at the top. It grows in woods, along roadsides and in open grassy areas everywhere.

Agrocybe molesta (Lasch) Singer [=*A. dura*]

Cap: 2–3in (5–7.5cm)
Spores: dull tobacco-brown, 10–14 x 6.5–8μm, smooth
Edibility: edible

The whitish to pale tan cap frequently becomes very cracked with exposure and age. The gills are crowded, adnate, and pale buff to brown. The sturdy stem is white, smooth to fibrous, and has a narrow ring above. This species, like the previous one, grows principally in the spring and prefers open, cultivated areas or waste places such as roadsides, and is quite common. The similar *A. sororia* can reach even larger sizes, and is common on woodchips in gardens. *A. acericola* prefers to grow on fallen timber, and has a particularly well-developed ring. The cap color of the last species is decidedly yellow and is a good key characteristic. The cap of *A. sororia* is similar to that of *A. molesta*, but the habitat preferences should separate them.

Conocybe tenera (Schaeffer) Fayod

Cap: ½–1in (1–2.5cm)
Spores: reddish-brown, 11–12 x 6–7μm, smooth
Edibility: inedible

This is one of a number of difficult-to-distinguish species, but is typical of the group. The bell-shaped cap is smooth, dry, and a rich yellow-brown to reddish-brown, fading with age. The narrow gills are almost free and cinnamon-brown. The tall, thin, straight stem is very fragile, pale brown, and finely lined from top to bottom. It is very common in lawns and open grasslands everywhere.

TRICHOLOMATACEAE
Tricholoma Family

Although the majority of species in this family are white-spored, there are some exceptions, of which this is an example. As the spores have a distinct pinkish hue, it is placed here in the guide, with other pink-spored genera, where one might expect to look first.

Rhodotus palmatus (Bulliard ex Fries) Maire
Cap: 1–3in (2.5–7.5cm)
Spores: pink, 6–8μm, globose and warty
Edibility: inedible

A strange but beautiful species, the lovely pink cap has a thick, rubbery-gelatinous cuticle, which is strangely wrinkled and pitted. The gills are attached to the stem and pale pink. The stout stem is pink and fibrous, rather tough, and usually set off-center. A pleasant odor of fruit is present. It is a rather uncommon species, growing on deciduous stumps and logs, but is quite widespread.

ENTOLOMATACEAE
Entoloma Family

The Entoloma mushrooms and their relatives all have strange, angular pink spores, or long spores with angular ridges.

Clitopilus prunulus (Scopoli ex Fries) Kummer

Cap: 1–3in (2.5–7.5cm)
Spores: pink, 10–12 x 5–7μm, with longitudinal ridges, appearing angular in end view
Edibility: edible and quite good

Although this mushroom is variable in shape and size, its odor is usually the first clue to its identity. It has a strong, almost pungent scent of cucumber or freshly ground meal. The white cap has the texture of kid leather, and starts inrolled at the margin. The gills are narrow, decurrent, white then pink, while the short stem is often offset from the center. It can be a very common species, and grows on soil in mixed woods everywhere.

Entoloma velutinum Hesler

Cap: 1–3in (2.5–5cm)
Spores: pink, 8–11 x 6–8μm, angular, 5-sided
Edibility: inedible

Many *Entoloma* species have beautiful colors, especially blues and violets, and this species has the entire fruit-body colored deep violet-blue to blue-black. The rounded cap becomes depressed at the center and has a texture like plush velvet. The gills are very distinctive, being bluish-pink with their edges minutely roughened and deep violet-black. The stem is slender and smooth, fading to white below. It is found in damp, mossy areas in mixed woods in the eastern and southeastern states, and is uncommon.

Entoloma abortivum (Berkeley & Curtis) Donk

Cap: 2–4in (5–10cm)
Spores: pink, 8–10 x 5–6µm, angular, 5–6 sided
Edibility: edible and considered a delicacy by many

In its normal form this species is a typical mushroom of a rather dull slate-gray color, finely fibrous or silky. In the aborted form, however, it develops strange, rounded white masses, with a soft mass of pinkish tissue inside. It is now known that these forms result from attacks by the Honey Mushroom, *Armillaria mellea,* whose mycelium infiltrates the *Entoloma* and stimulates these oddly deformed bodies. They are very common and widespread everywhere.

Entoloma salmoneum (Peck) Saccardo

Cap: ⅜–1⅝in (1–4cm)
Spores: pink, 10–12 x 10–12µm, angular, 4-sided
Edibility: inedible

A beautiful species in a soft, delicate shade of coral pink or salmon-orange. The sharply pointed cap has a distinct nipple at the center. The slender stem is similarly colored. It grows, often in large troops, in wet, mossy areas under conifers, and is common from the north down into the southern states. The related *E. luteum* has a similar shape and stature, but has a duller greenish-yellow cap and yellowish stem. Also in this group is *E. alboumbonatum*, with pale gray-pink or buff colors and a white umbo.

Entoloma murraii (Berkeley & Curtis) Saccardo

Cap: ⅜–1¼in (1–3cm)
Spores: pink, 9–12 x 8–10µm, angular, 4-sided
Edibility: inedible

A very easy species to recognize, with its clear, soft yellow cap and stem, the cap having a distinct nipple at the center. The stem is finely fibrous and often twisted. It grows in wet, boggy areas and is common from the north down into the southern states.

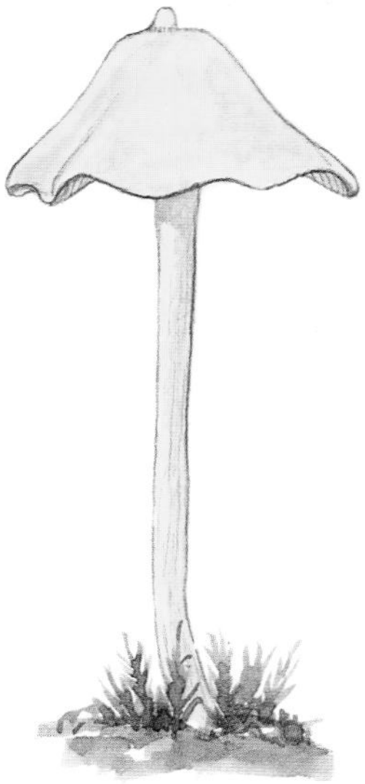

Entoloma luteum Peck

Cap: ⅜–1in (1–2.5cm)
Spores: pink, 9–13 x 8–12μm, angular and 4-sided
Edibility: inedible

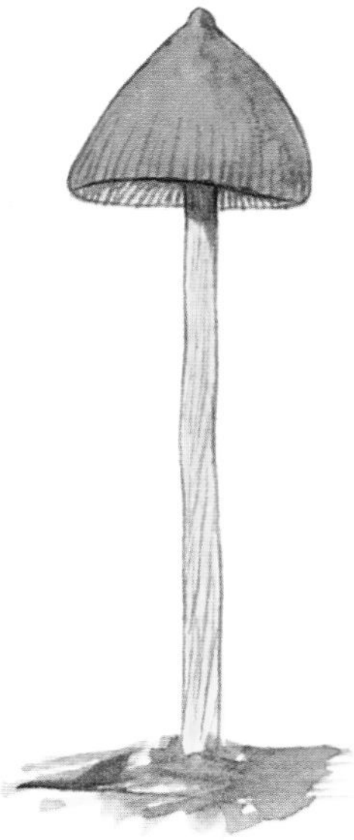

A close relative of the two preceding species, this mushroom differs in its greenish-yellow to yellow-buff colors in the cap, yellowish then pink gills, and greenish-yellow stem, white above. It grows in mossy areas in mixed woods, less often in bogs (unlike the previous species), and is widespread from the north down through the southeastern states. This and the previous two species have been placed in the genus *Nolanea*, but many mycologists now reduce this to a subdivision of the larger genus *Entoloma*.

Entoloma lividum Quélet

Cap: 2–6in (5–15cm)
Spores: pink, 8–10 x 7–9μm, angular, 5–7-sided
Edibility: poisonous; causes severe gastric upsets and can be quite dangerous

This rather uncommon species is quite infamous in Europe, where it is referred to as the "Grand Poisoner". It is less common in North America, but has been reported in several northeastern states. The large ivory-white to buff cap is umbonate to broadly rounded, smooth to slightly streaky, or mottled. The gills are sinuate, crowded, and an unusual shade of yellow when young, before turning pink. The stout, tough stem is white and fibrous. A strong odor and taste of meal or flour are present. It grows in open, grassy woodlands, especially on chalky soils.

Entoloma strictius (Peck) Saccardo

Cap: 1–3in (2.5–7.5cm)
Spores: pink, 10–13 x 7.5–9μm, angular
Edibility: doubtful; best avoided

There are a number of slender, brownish species of *Entoloma*, often difficult to identify, and this is perhaps the commonest and most distinctive. The silky gray-brown cap has a prominent central umbo, and the margin is often wavy. The gills are broad and pale pink. The stem is always long and very straight, whitish-gray with a silky-fibrous surface, and is often twisted. The base has a wooly covering of mycelium. It is common in leaf litter or on well-rotted wood in wet woodlands from Florida up to the extreme northern states and Canada.

PLUTEACEAE
Pluteus Family

These fungi all have gills completely free of the stem, and deep salmon-pink spores. One genus (*Volvariella*) has a volva at the base of the stem.

Pluteus cervinus (Schaeffer ex Fries) Kummer
Cap: 2–4in (5–10cm)
Spores: pink, 5.5–7 x 4–5μm, smooth
Edibility: edible

One of the commonest of fungi, this can appear at almost any time of year when conditions are suitable. Often when other fungi are scarce in dry weather, fallen logs act as a reservoir of moisture, and this fungus, along with other *Pluteus* species, will continue to fruit. The cap is very variable in color, ranging from dull gray-brown to deep chestnut or even pallid, always smooth, with fine fibers, and occasionally some tiny scales at the center. The broad gills are white, then soon pinkish. The stem is white, fibrous, and darker brown below. On the faces of the gills are special bottle-shaped cystidia with 2–3 hook-like projections.

Pluteus petasatus (Fries) Gillet
Cap: 2–6in (5–15cm)
Spores: pink, 6–10 x 4–6μm, smooth
Edibility: edible and good

Looking much like the previous species in overall appearance , this differs in its white cap with dark scales at the center. The gills are usually very broad and rounded at the margin, and are very slow to turn pink. The fibrous stem is white and hardly brown below. It is a fairly common species on old deciduous stumps and on woodchips, and is widely distributed. It too has large, bottle-like cystidia on the gills, with hook-like projections.

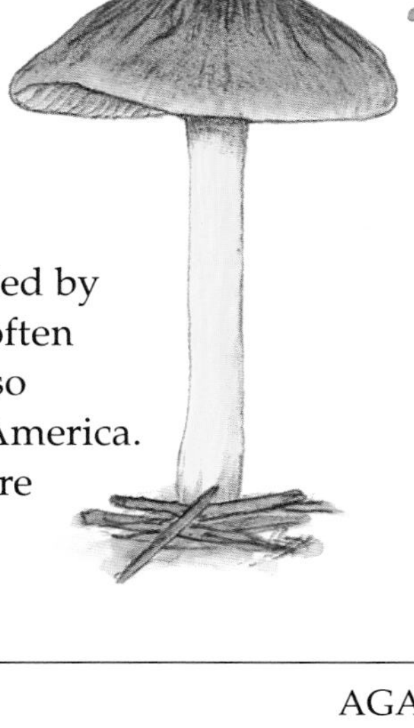

Pluteus romellii (Britzelmayr) Saccardo
Cap: 1–2in (2.5–5cm)
Spores: pink, 6–7 x 5–6μm, smooth
Edibility: doubtful; best avoided

Fairly common on old rotted logs, this species can be identified by its contrasting deep brown cap and yellow stem. The cap is often wrinkled or veined around the center. The young gills are also yellow before turning pink. It is quite widespread in North America. There are other yellowish species, but these usually have more yellow in the cap.

Pluteus aurantiorugosus (Trog) Saccardo

Cap: 1–2in (2.5–5cm)
Spores: pink, 5.5–6.5μm, smooth
Edibility: edible

A small but spectacular species, its cap when young is a vivid scarlet, but soon fades to bright orange as it expands. This is one of a group of species where the cap cuticle is composed of globose cells rather than the filamentous cells of the previous species. The gills are broad and yellow when young, then soon pinkish. The slender stem is whitish above, yellow-orange below. Sadly, it is rather an uncommon species, found on dead and dying elm trees and maples. It had something of a population explosion during the blight of dying elms due to Dutch elm disease.

Volvariella bombycina (Schaeffer ex Fries) Singer

Cap: 2–6in (5–15cm)
Spores: pink, 6.5–10.5 x 4.5–6.5μm, smooth
Edibility: edible and good

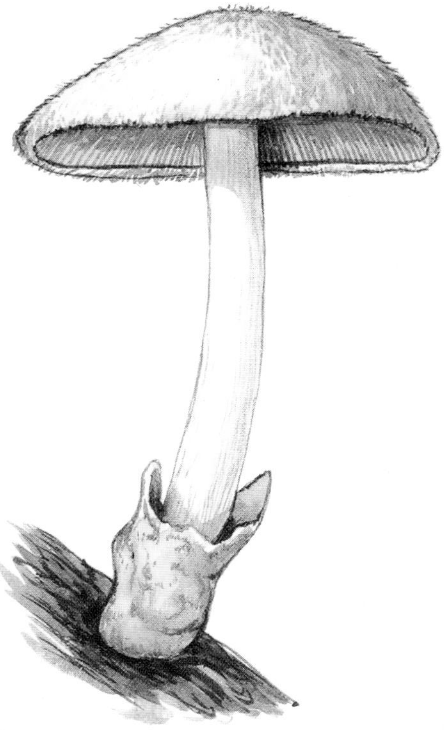

A large and magnificent species, although, sadly, a rare one. The entire mushroom begins enclosed in a thin, egg-like volval sac. This ruptures and the mushroom expands upward very rapidly. The cap is white to slightly yellowish and beautifully silky-hairy all over. The gills are free, broad, and white, then soon pink. The stem is white and fibrous. It grows in clusters, often appearing in old knotholes and wounds in old elms and maples. Like the previous species, it has been commoner in recent years because of Dutch elm disease killing off the elms.

Volvariella speciosa (Persoon ex Fries) Singer

Cap: 2–4in (5–10cm)
Spores: pink, 5.5–6.5 x 4–4.5μm, smooth
Edibility: edible

Probably the commonest species in this genus, it grows in old grass in fields, straw heaps, or around stables or middens. The silky, whitish-gray cap is often very viscid. The broad gills are white, then soon deep pink. The tall, elegant stem is white, fibrous, and emerges from a small, thick volval cup, usually buried in the grass. It is a well-known edible species and a very close relative of the Paddy-straw Mushroom popular in Chinese restaurants. If picking this, you must be sure you do not have a poisonous *Amanita,* which also has a volva. Remember, *Amanita* has white spores, never pink. It is safer to buy the canned Paddy-straw Mushroom (*V. volvacea*).

ORDER: APHYLLOPHORALES

These fungi all produce spores externally on basidia, but the spore-producing surface is not spread over gills like the gilled mushrooms, but on various other surfaces such as wrinkles, spines or fleshy tubes, or on simple clubs.

CANTHARELLACEAE
Chanterelle Family

These often delicious edible fungi include the well-known Chanterelle, which is eaten all over the world. They all lack true gills, forming their spores on either a smooth undersurface or on blunt-edged wrinkles or ridges.

Craterellus fallax A.H. Smith –
"Horn of Plenty", "Black Trumpet"

Cap: 1–3in (2.5–7.5cm)

Spores: pinkish-buff, 10–20 x 7–11μm, smooth

Edibility: edible and delicious; dries well as a spice

The twin species to this strange fungus (*C. cornucopiodes*) also has another, rather unfortunate, common name in France – "Trumpet of Death". This refers to its somber appearance only, since it is an excellent edible. The thin, black trumpet is hollow all the way down and has a slightly brownish, finely scaly inner surface. The outer surface is black with a finely ridged and wrinkled texture, which becomes pinkish with age. It is common, although difficult to spot, and grows in moist, mossy spots, often on stream banks, and sometimes in very large numbers. *C. cornucopiodes* is also found in the USA, although it is much rarer and differs in having pure white spores.

Cantharellus cibarius Fries – "Chanterelle", "Girolles"

Cap: 1–6in (2.5–15cm)
Spores: pale buff, 8–11 x 4–6μm, smooth
Edibility: edible and delicious

This has almost as many common names as the famous *Boletus edulis,* and almost every country has its own name for it. A delicious edible with a strange fruity flavour, it is collected by the thousand every year all over the world. The yellow-orange caps are thick and fleshy, and begin with an inrolled margin. The undersurface is formed of numerous wrinkled, gill-like ridges, often cross-veined, and descending the short stem. The flesh is thick, pale buff, and has a wonderful aroma resembling apricots. It grows all over the USA in woods of pine and oak, and reaches especially large sizes in the Pacific northwest. The similar *C. lateritius*, common in the northeast, differs in having a completely smooth undersurface, but is otherwise similar in color.

Cantharellus tubaeformis Fries

Cap: 1–3in (2.5–7.5cm)
Spores: cream, 8–12 x 6–10μm, smooth
Edibility: edible and good

Not as well known as the Chanterelle, this is nevertheless almost as good an edible and is equally common. It is found in much wetter, boggy situations, usually in sphagnum moss in mixed woods. The thin, trumpet-shaped caps are yellow-brown, while the wrinkled undersurface is yellow, then grayish-violet, and runs down the stem. The stem is pale yellow to yellow-orange. This species is widespread throughout North America.

Cantharellus cinnabarinus Schweinitz
"Cinnabar Chanterelle"

Cap: 1–2in (2.5–5cm)
Spores: pinkish-cream, 6–11 x 4–6μm, smooth
Edibility: edible

That such a common species should be so startling in color is one of the delights of mushrooming. These "miniature" chanterelles are a vivid coral-red to pinkish-red, fading when old, and are quite unmistakable. They can grow in large numbers, forming drifts across the leaf litter of the woodland floor, like exotic flowers. They are a good edible and worth collecting. They are common throughout the northern and eastern states, and extend down through Florida.

Cantharellus cinereus Persoon

Cap: 1–3in (2.5–7.5cm)
Spores: white, 8–10 x 5–7µm, smooth
Edibility: edible and good

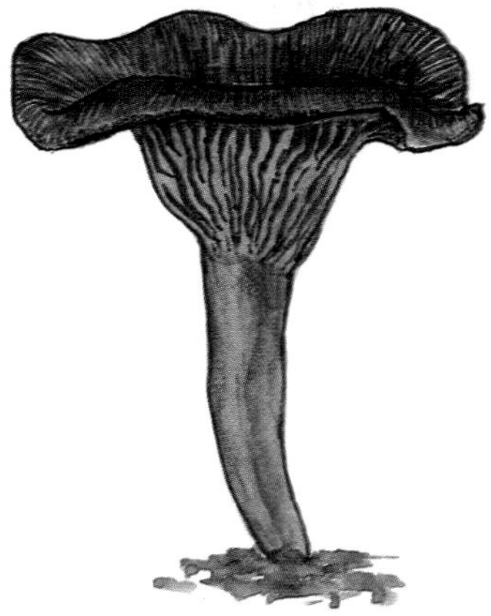

One of the rarer species of the Chanterelle family, this is a dark gray-black mushroom, thin-fleshed, with a very wrinkled-vein hymenium running down the stem. The stem is short, smooth, and also gray-black. Despite its somber appearance, it has a pleasant, fruity odor. Sometimes mistaken for the Horn of Plenty, *Craterellus cornucopiodes,* that species has an almost smooth hymenium and is completely hollow, trumpet-like. This species likes damp, mossy woods and is widely distributed.

Cantharellus ignicolor Petersen

Cap: 1–2in (2.5–5cm)
Spores: pale salmon-ocher, 9–13 x 6–9µm, smooth
Edibility: edible and good

This brilliant yellow-orange species is thin-fleshed with a sunken center to the cap. The undersurface has well-developed ridges, and wrinkles running down the stem, which is hollow with age. This is quite a common species in mixed woods of the northeastern and northern states.

Cantharellus minor Peck

Cap: 1–2in (0.6–2.5cm)
Spores: pale yellow-orange, 6–11.5 x 4–6.5µm, smooth
Edibility: edible

This is the smallest of the chanterelles and seems to show a decided preference for tracksides on bare soil, or in moss by streams. The tiny caps are perfectly formed in miniature, even to the narrow wrinkled ridges on the undersurface. It is very common throughout much of North America.

Cantharellus subalbidus A.H. Smith & Morse

Cap: 2–6in (5–15cm)
Spores: white, 7–9 x 6–6μm, smooth
Edibility: edible and excellent

One of the most robust chanterelles, this is also very striking, with its white cap, prominent wrinkled "gills", and stout stem. The cap margin is inrolled, but slowly expands outward. All parts of the mushroom bruise rust-yellow to brown. It is quite common in mixed woods in the Pacific northwest.

Gomphus floccosus (Schweinitz) Singer

Cap: 2–6in (5–15cm)
Spores: ocher, 11.5–14 x 7–8μm, minutely warted
Edibility: doubtful; best avoided

A spectacular fungus, often reaching very large sizes, it starts out as a small, blunt knob or club, but rapidly grows to form a flattened trumpet or funnel. The center of the cap can be hollow all the way down into the stem, and is covered in thick, coarse, recurved scales. The outer surface of the fungus, the hymenium, is a pale pinkish-yellow or buff, and covered in shallow wrinkles and veins running down to the short stem. It is quite common in mixed woods throughout North America.

Polyozellus multiplex (Underwood) Murrill

Cap: 1–4in (2.5–10cm) across (individual caps)
Spores: white, 6–8.5 x 5.5–8μm, angular and warted
Edibility: edible

One of the most remarkable fungi anywhere, this can form huge clusters of caps, all compressed and fused together, of the deepest blue to purple-black. Each cap is irregular, spoon-shaped or funnel-like, smooth on top, with a wrinkled undersurface that is purplish with a white bloom like a grape. There is a strong, aromatic odor present. It grows under spruce and fir in northern North America west to the Rockies, and is, unfortunately, rather rare.

RAMARIACEAE, CLAVARIACEAE, AND RELATED FUNGI
Coral and Club Fungi

A large group with a number of smaller families included, as well as those listed above. As their common name suggests, they resemble undersea corals and clubs. Many are among the brightest colored of fungi and can reach large sizes. Their spores are produced on basidia formed on the outer surface of the clubs.

Ramaria stricta (Fries) Quélet

Cap: 1–4in (2.5–10cm) across
Spores: golden yellow, 7–10 x 3.5–5.5μm, with longitudinal lines
Edibility: edible, but best avoided; easily confused

A distinctive coral fungus in the way in which the slender branches are held in a very upright fashion. The branches fork many times, but always turn directly upward and are colored a dull yellow-brown. All parts bruise darker on handling. The flesh has an unpleasant odor and tastes bitter. It is a fairly common species and grows on conifer logs throughout North America. *R. flava* grows under both deciduous and coniferous trees in the north, and is usually a little taller, has a more unpleasant odor, and is often slightly bitter to taste.

Ramaria botrytis (Fries) Ricken

Cap 2–6in (5–15cm)
Spores: pale ocher, 11–17 x 4–6μm, with longitudinal lines
Edibility: edible, but best avoided; easily confused with poisonous species

This cauliflower-like species has a very broad central stem splitting into numerous smaller branches, each of which is whitish-buff with delicate pinkish-purple tips. The flesh is white, thick, and has a pleasant smell. An uncommon species found under spruce and fir, it is widely distributed.

Clavicorona pyxidata (Fries) Doty

Cap: 2–4in (5–10cm)
Spores: white, 4–5 x 2–3µm, smooth
Edibility: edible

This resembles a rather elegant and much-branched fungal candelabra, with the numerous slender branches gracefully curving upward and tipped with tiny, sharp-pointed crowns. In color it ranges from dull ocher-yellow to pale brown, and the flesh has a peppery taste. It is very common and always grows on dead timber, usually willow, poplar or aspen, and is found throughout North America.

Clavariadelphus pistillaris (Fries) Donk

Cap: 3–8in (7.5–20cm)
Spores: creamy-white, 11–16 x 6–10µm, smooth
Edibility: inedible

Most people are very surprised when told that this is a fungus – it is so unlike anything they consider to be a mushroom or toadstool. The single, large club swells out above and has a wrinkled or furrowed surface when mature. When young it is quite a bright yellow-orange with a paler tip, then slowly turns to ocher-brown or pinkish-brown, often with a lilac tint below. The flesh is white and rather bitter to taste. It grows in small groups, standing up out of the leaf litter of beech woods in eastern North America, while in the west it seems to prefer oaks. There are other, very similar species best distinguished with a microscope.

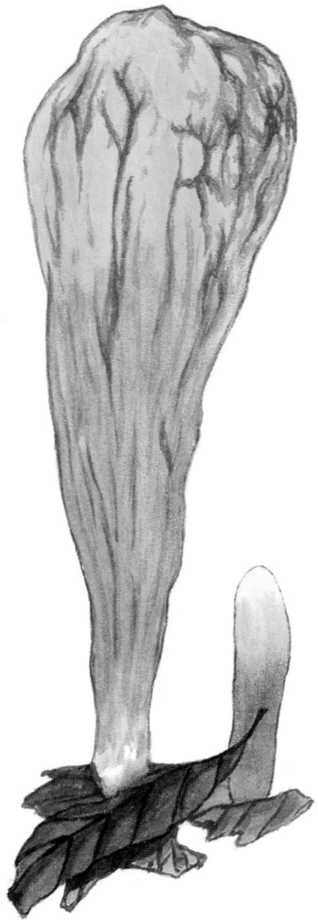

Clavariadelphus truncatus (Quélet) Donk

Cap: 2–6in (5–15cm) high
Spores: ocher, 9–13 x 5–8μm, smooth
Edibility: inedible

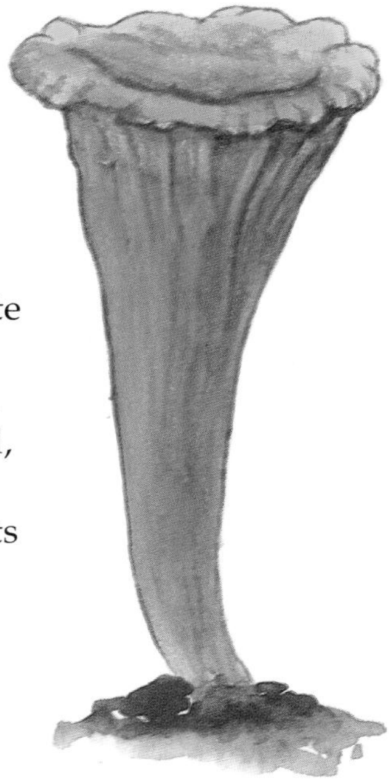

A much rarer species than the previous one, this is nevertheless quite easy to recognize. The broad clubs are flattened at the top, or even slightly depressed, with the sides unevenly wrinkled and ridged. In color they are pinkish-brown to yellow-ocher. The flesh is white and, unlike the previous species, mild to taste. It grows under conifers throughout North America. The similar *C. borealis* has more lilac tints and a white spore print; it is found mainly in the Pacific northwest.

Sparassis crispa (von Wulfen) Fries – "Western Cauliflower Mushroom"

Cap: 6–12in (15–30cm) across
Spores: white, 5–7 x 3–5μm, smooth
Edibility: edible and excellent

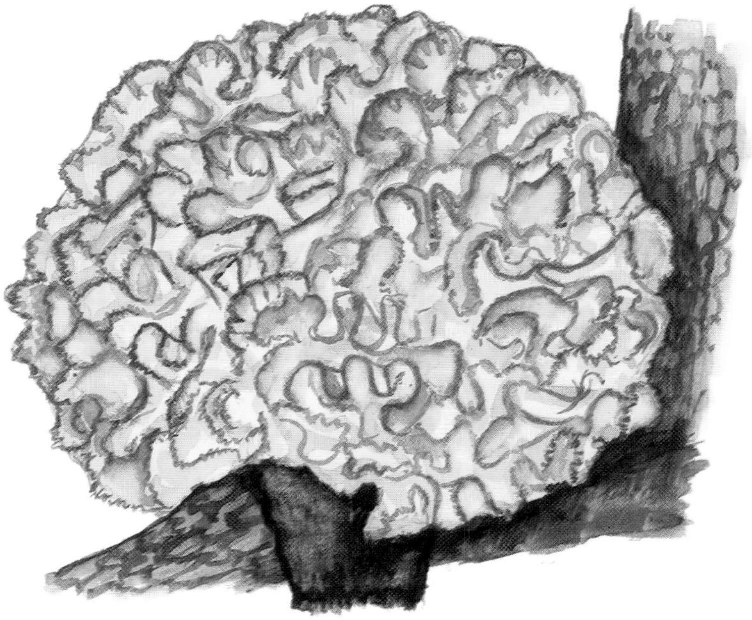

This remarkable species does indeed look rather like a large cauliflower, or perhaps a cabbage, although much paler in color. It is formed of numerous flattened, crispy lobes all twisted together to form a ball, and this springs from a tough rooting base or stem buried deep in the ground. It has a peculiar odor of spice or cheese, and the flavor when cooked is delightfully nutty and crisp. It is a weak parasite of conifers and is usually found at the base of standing trees or near stumps, and is locally common. The related species *S. herbstii* is found in the eastern states and differs in its looser, broader, and more flattened branches; it grows at the base of oaks and is equally edible.

Clavulinopsis fusiformis (Sowerby) Corner

Cap: 2–6in (5–15cm) high
Spores: cream, 5–9 x 4.5–9μm, smooth
Edibility: edible

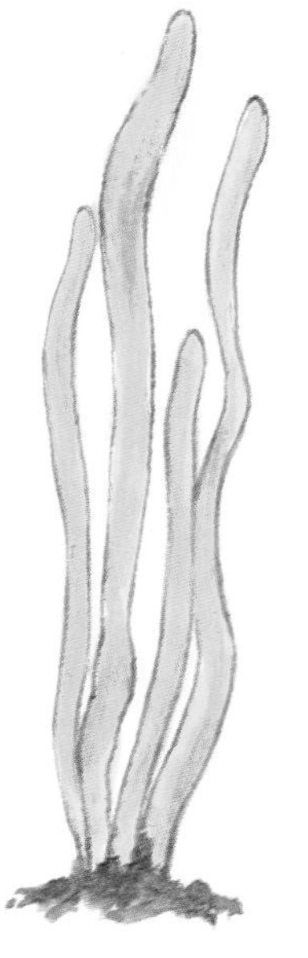

One of the commonest of the club fungi, and also one of the most brightly colored and easy to identify. The simple, narrow clubs are pointed at the tips and loosely clustered. Each club is usually hollow in the center and very brittle. It is common in grasslands and open woods everywhere. Note that the clubs are not truly fused together at a common base, but are separate, unlike some other yellow club fungi. This species has recently been placed in the genus *Ramariopsis,* and the genus *Clavulinopsis* dropped altogether.

Clavaria vermicularis Fries

Cap: 2–6in (5–15cm) high

Spores: white, 5–7 x 3–4μm, smooth

Edibility: edible

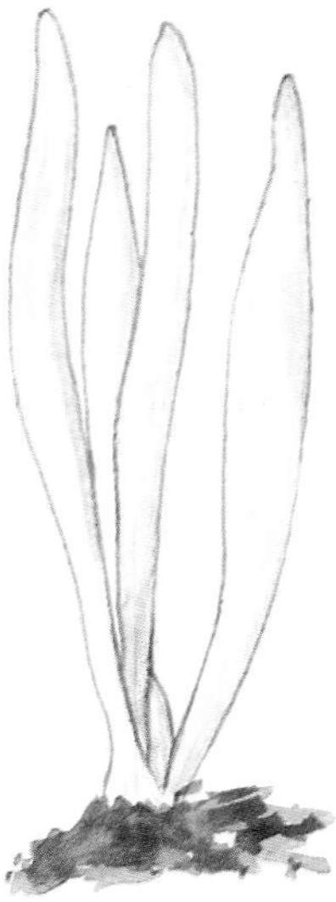

The name *vermicularis* means worm-like, and this species does look a little like a cluster of white, wavy worms. The hollow, pointed clubs are very brittle and are commonly found in grassy areas and open woodlands. The similar *C. fumosa* differs in having grayish-lilac clubs. In both these species the pointed clubs will occasionally become flattened or even divide into two or more points.

Clavulina cristata (Fries) Schroet

Cap: 1–3in (2.5–7.5cm) across

Spores: white, 7–11 x 6.5–10μm, smooth

Edibility: edible

A common species which, although small, is quite attractive. The densely clustered and branched coral is white with finely divided, sharp tips arising from a central stem. The color can vary to cream or yellowish. The similar *C. cinerea* has grayish branches and usually blunt tips, but, once again, this varies. Both can be found in mixed woods throughout North America. This species can become infected by another fungus. It turns *C. cristata* gray, which can make it difficult to distinguish from *C. cinerea*.

Clavulina amethystina (Fries) Donk

Cap: 1–4in (2.5–10cm) high

Spores: white, 7–12 x 6–8μm, smooth and formed on 2-spored basidia

Edibility: edible

Perhaps our loveliest coral fungus, this species is, unfortunately, quite rare, but almost unmistakable. The slender branches are very brittle and a bright, clear amethyst violet or lilac, arising from a central stem. It prefers deciduous woods and seems commoner in the south. The beautiful violet *Clavaria zollingeri* differs in only slightly branching and in having 4-spored basidia with smaller spores.

STEREACEAE
Crust Fungi

These form crust-like sheets on wood, and occasionally spread out into small shelves or brackets.They do not have tubes on the underside like the true Bracket Fungi (Polypores).

Chondrostereum purpureum (Fries) Pouzar – "Silver Leaf Fungus"

Cap: 4–6in (10–15cm) or larger
Spores: white, 5–6.5 x 2–3µm, smooth
Edibility: inedible

This fungus is a common parasite of fruit trees, such as apples, plums, and cherries, as well as woodland trees, and it causes a characteristic silvery blight on the leaves, hence the common name. It can eventually kill the infected tree. The fungus appears as an irregular crust, which then spreads out to form small brackets, and has a lovely lavender-purple edge and undersurface. The top is a dull yellow-ocher to gray-white, and hairy or wooly to touch.

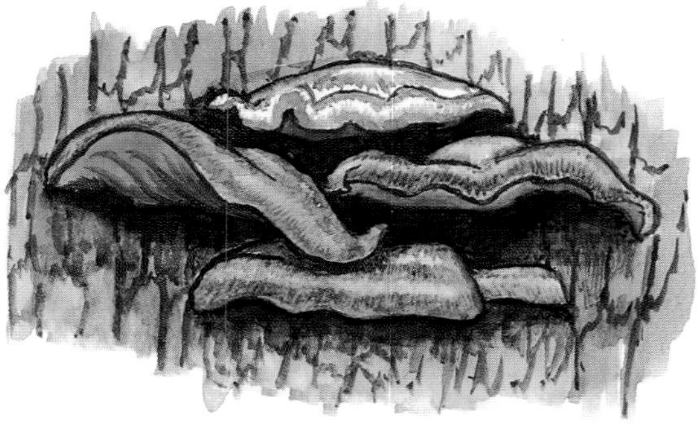

Stereum hirsutum (Willdenow ex Fries) S.F. Gray

Cap: ½–1in (1–2.5cm) across
Spores: white, 5–8 x 2–3.5µm, smooth
Edibility: inedible

A common species in which many individual caps may overlap to form a larger mass, and may even fuse together. The upper surface is concentrically zoned in shades of gray, creamy-yellow, or brown, and is finely hairy or velvety. The undersurface is smooth and yellow-gray. It grows on fallen timber of birch and beech, as well as other deciduous woods, and is widespread everywhere.

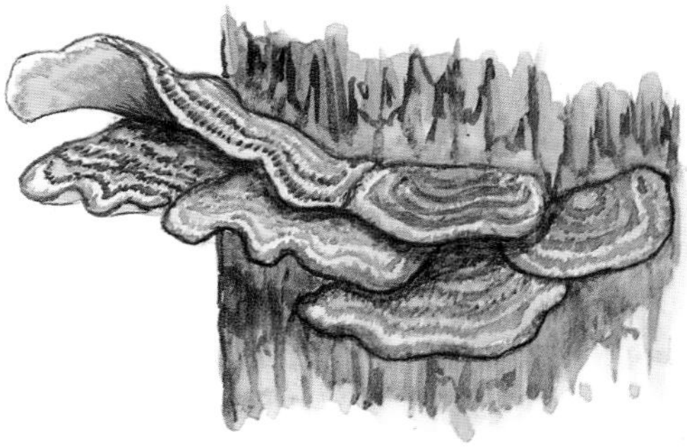

THELEPHORACEAE
Fan Fungi

A group of somber, fleshy fungi with fan-shaped, encrusting or even-stemmed species with dark, spiny spores.

Thelephora terrestris Fries

Cap: 1–3in (2.5–7.5cm)
Spores: purplish-brown, 8–12 x 6–9µm, minutely spiny
Edibility: inedible

Sometimes called the Earth Fan, this species does resemble a cluster of dark, feathery fans hugging the soil. The overlapping fans are often rather ragged in outline, dark blackish-brown to gray-brown, and are tough and fibrous with paler zones. The undersurface is smooth to wrinkled or lumpy. There is usually an earthy or moldy smell present. This species is very common in mixed woods everywhere.

HYDNACEAE AND RELATED FUNGI
Toothed Fungi

These fungi all form their spores on projecting spines or teeth, which usually hang down from the underside of the cap or fruit body. Some species grow on the ground and have stems, while others form brackets on trees. They are now considered to consist of a number of probably unrelated groups which have evolved independently to use similar spiny structures.

Hydnellum spongiosipes (Peck) Pouzar

Cap: 2–4in (5–10cm)
Spores: brown, 5.5–7 x 5–6μm, warted
Edibility: inedible

This thick, heavy species is remarkable for its very robust, bulbous stem. The cap is irregular, reddish-brown, and finely velvety. The short spines on the underside are dark brown and run down the stem, which is dark brown and velvety.The flesh is very tough and two-layered, with a dark, inner zone. This is a common species, growing in the leaf litter of oak woods, and is widely distributed. There are many other species of *Hydnellum*, many with strong tastes and odors, and colored flesh; these include *H. caeruleum*, with blue and orange-banded flesh and a mealy odor.

Sarcodon imbricatum (Linnaeus) Karsten

Cap: 4–6in (10–15cm)
Spores: brown, 6–8 x 5–7μm, with large warts
Edibility: inedible

This coarsely scaly species is gray-brown, and the rounded cap has the underside densely packed with tiny grayish teeth which run down the stem. The latter is white and more or less central. The flesh is pale brown, soft, and tastes rather sharp. A common species, it grows under pines and in mixed woods throughout North America. Other species include *S. scabrosum*, with a blackish-green stem base and very bitter taste, and *S. joeides*, with pale lavender flesh which turns green with caustic soda (KOH) solution.

Hydnum repandum Linnaeus

Cap: 2–4in (5–10cm)
Spores: white, 6.5–9 x 6.5–8µm, smooth
Edibility: edible and good

A well-known edible now appearing quite often for sale in stores that specialize in "exotic" mushrooms. The pale pinkish-orange to orange-buff cap is dry and often irregular in outline. The short spines are pale pinkish-white and descend the short, whitish stem which is usually off-centered. The flesh is white with a pleasant odor and a spicy or bitter taste. It can grow in large quantities in the leaf litter of beech woods and sometimes conifers throughout North America. Two similar but white species found in the south are *H. albomagnum,* which is mild tasting and does not stain when bruised, and *H. albidum,* which is peppery and bruises yellow-orange.

Hydnum umbilicatum Peck

Cap: ½–1in (1–2.5cm)
Spores: white, 7.5–9 x 6–7µm, smooth
Edibility: edible and good

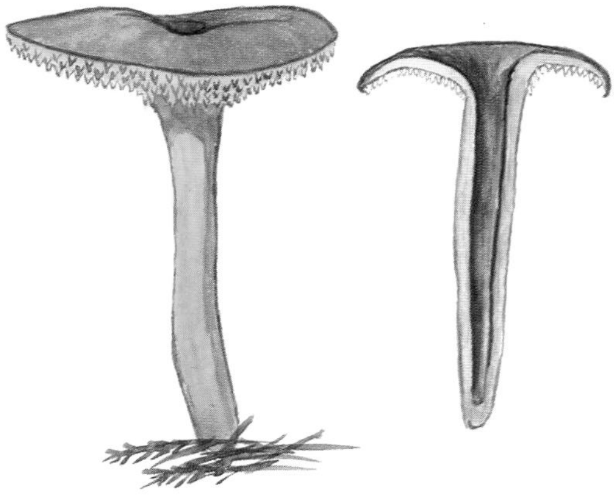

Rather like the previous species, but smaller, with a dark reddish-brown to orange-tawny cap, deeply depressed at the center and with a central hole penetrating down into the stem. The short spines are whitish-orange, while the slender stem is orange and centrally placed. It is common under conifers in the northern and eastern states. This species is so similar to the European *H. rufescens* that one might better be regarded as a variety of the other.

Hericium ramosum (Bulliard ex Mérat) Letellier [=*H. clathroides*]

Cap: 4–8in (10–25cm) across
Spores: white, 3–5 x 3–4µm, finely roughened
Edibility: edible and delicious

This beautiful species looks rather like an undersea coral and is formed of thin, delicate branches from which hang short (½in or less) spines all the way along each branch. The branches can form much denser masses than those illustrated here. The flesh is white and has a crisp, nutty flavor when cooked. It is uncommon to frequent, and grows on old deciduous logs, especially beech, throughout North America. The similar *H. americanum* (=*H. coralloides* of many American authors) has longer spines (½–1½in) clustered at the ends of the branches and grows in similar habitats.

Hericium erinaceus (Fries) Persoon

Cap: 4–8in (10–20cm) across
Spores: white, 5–6.5 x 4–5.5μm, minutely roughened
Edibility: edible and delicious

An uncommon but spectacular species, often found growing high up on beech, oak, or maple trees. It forms a rounded, compact mass without branches, and with very long spines, often several inches in length, hanging down. It is widely distributed in North America and is an excellent edible fungus. This species is most easily distinguished from the other white, toothed fungi by its unbranched, almost globular structure and the much longer spines, almost like a white beard. It can become rather sour and smelly with age, so should be eaten only when young, fresh, and still very white.

Auriscalpium vulgare S.F. Gray – "Earpick Fungus"

Cap: ½–1in (1–2.5cm)
Spores: white, 5–6 x 4–5μm, minutely spiny
Edibility: inedible

The generic name is Latin for "earpick" and refers to a small, fungus-shaped instrument used by the Romans for personal hygiene . The small, spoon-shaped fungus has a dark brown, scaly cap with tiny spines on the underside. The thin stem is dark brown and hairy, and is attached to one side of the cap. It grows only on fallen and partially rotted pine-cones, and, although not uncommon, is easily overlooked in the shady northern pine woods where it likes to grow.

POLYPORACEAE
Bracket Fungi

All fleshy or woody fungi with their spores produced inside tubes (except for the soft boletes already illustrated) are included here. Many are very large and woody, and are common on woodland trees. Some grow on the ground and can look like a bolete, but have much tougher flesh. A number are serious parasites of trees.

Polyporus brumalis Fries – "Winter Polypore"

Cap: 1–4in (2.5–10cm)

Spores: white, 5–7 x 2–2.5µm, sausage-shaped and smooth

Edibility: inedible

One of a group of polypores with a cap and a more or less central, well-formed stem, this species has a smooth, yellow-brown to gray-brown cap, whitish tubes with pores spaced 2–3 per 1/20in, and a slender, gray-brown, minutely hairy stem. It grows on fallen branches, especially of birch, and appears from late fall throughout the winter and into spring, and is very common.

Polyporus varius Fries [=*P. elegans*]

Cap: 2–4in (5–10cm)

Spores: white, 7–10 x 2–3.5µm, sausage-shaped, smooth

Edibility: inedible

A very common species, its pale buff cap is smooth and dry, and the decurrent tubes are yellowish to pale brown, 4–5 per 1/20in. The almost central stem is slender, pale tan with a black lower half. It grows on fallen branches and twigs of deciduous trees. The larger *P. badius* has a shiny, reddish-brown cap and often completely black stem. The closely related *P. arcularius* differs in its large, honeycomb-like pores, and cap margin fringed with fine hairs. It also has a central stem. It is widespread in the USA. *Favolus alveolarius* is similar, with large hexagonal pores, but has almost no stem and a smooth cap margin.

Polyporus squamosus Fries– "Dryad's Saddle"

Cap: 4–12in (10–30cm)

Spores: white, 10–16 x 4–6μm, cylindrical, smooth

Edibility: edible and good when young

Not many polypores are edible, but this one is actually very good if found young and thinly sliced before cooking. The young caps look like strange, blunt knobs growing out of wood, but as they grow, the cap expands to often enormous size. The dull, pale ocher cap is marked with bold, flattened, dark brown scales, while the decurrent pores are pale cream, large, and honeycomb-like. The short, very tough stem is black at the base. It grows, looking very much like a seat or saddle, out of standing or fallen timber in deciduous woods, and is one of the first fungi to appear in early summer.

Grifola frondosa (Fries) S.F. Gray – "Hen of the Woods"

Cap: individual caps 1–3in (2.5–7.5cm); entire fruit body 6–20in (15–50cm)

Spores: white, 5–7 x 3.5–5μm, smooth

Edibility: edible and delicious

Many polypores seem to make use of wounds or injuries in a tree to enter it and thus infect it, and some always seem to fruit at the site of an injury. This species commonly fruits at the base of oak trees which have been struck by lightning, and above the site of fruiting can be traced the long, jagged wound caused by the strike. This large species is formed of numerous caps all fused together in one central mass, and is a smoky gray-brown above with white tubes and pores below. The flesh is tender when young, but soon tough and fibrous. The young, soft tips are excellent edibles and highly esteemed in many countries. It is a common species in many parts of North America, and enormous specimens weighing up to 100lb (45kg) have been found.

Meripilus giganteus (Fries) Karsten
[=*Polyporus giganteus*]
Cap: 10–30in (25–75cm)
Spores: white, 6–7 x 4.5–6μm, smooth
Edibility: edible

This is certainly one of the largest fungi you will see in the USA, and can hardly be mistaken for anything else. The enormous, flattened, and wavy caps spring from a lateral base at the bottom of the tree and gradually grow outward to reach the mature size of nearly 3ft (1 meter) across. The dry upper surface is soft and yellow-ocher or tan, while the pores are white, but all parts bruise rapidly black on handling. It is a fairly common species in North America, growing on beech and oak. It has recently been decided that this is, in fact, genetically different from the European species of the same name, so it has been renamed *M. sumstinei*.

Laetiporus sulphureus (Fries) Murrill – "Chicken Mushroom"
Cap: 4–30in (10–75cm)
Spores: white, 5–7 x 3.5–5μm, smooth
Edibility: edible and delicious when young and tender

The common name originated in the USA, where this is one of the most sought-after edible species. It refers to the fact that, when cooked, the young tips are extremely similar in both taste and texture to chicken. An unmistakable species, it grows on oak, chestnut, and occasionally yew, and forms a series of overlapping brackets of a bright yellow-orange color. In some forms the color verges on pinkish-orange. It can grow both at the base of trees or very high up, and can form masses weighing many pounds. The largest specimen the author has seen required a wheelbarrow to transport it. The fungus causes a serious heart-rot in the trees it infects.

Postia caesia (Schroeter) Karsten – "Blue-cheese Polypore" [=*Tyromyces caesius*]

Cap: 2–6in (5–15cm)

Spores: pale blue, 4–5 x 0.7–1μm, sausage-like and smooth

Edibility: inedible

The common name refers to the bluish hue which soon develops over the entire mushroom, especially when handled. The squat, rather lumpy bracket is soft and fleshy with a slightly scurfy or hairy surface, and begins a pale grayish-white. The odor is quite fragrant and the taste mild, unlike the similar *P. styptica*, which has a bitter or acrid taste and does not bruise blue. It is a fairly common species in some areas, growing on a variety of dead wood.

Hapalopilus nidulans (Fries) Karsten

Cap: 1–5in (2.5–12.5cm)

Spores: white, 3.5–5 x 2–3μm, smooth

Edibility: inedible

This small bracket is a deep orange-brown, rather fleshy and thick, with small, cinnamon-brown pores. The flesh is thick, watery and tawny-brown. A useful chemical test is that all parts turn bright purple-violet with a drop of caustic soda (KOH). It is a common species on fallen logs of deciduous trees throughout the eastern states.

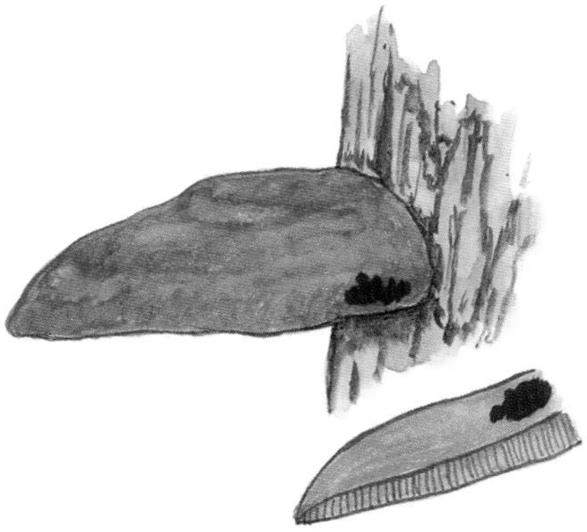

Piptoporus betulinus (Fries) Karsten – "Birch Polypore"

Cap: 2–10in (5–25cm)

Spores: white, 5–6 x 1.5μm, sausage-shaped

Edibility: inedible

This polypore grows only on birch and can be seen in almost any birch wood the world over. It has been used by humans for probably more purposes than almost any other fungus. The soft white flesh when dry makes a good fire lighter, but it has also been used to sharpen razors, as a styptic to halt bleeding, and as display material on which to pin insects in museums all over the world. The rounded, kidney-shaped caps are white to pale tan, with a blunt, inrolled margin. A short stem is often present. The white pores are extremely minute.

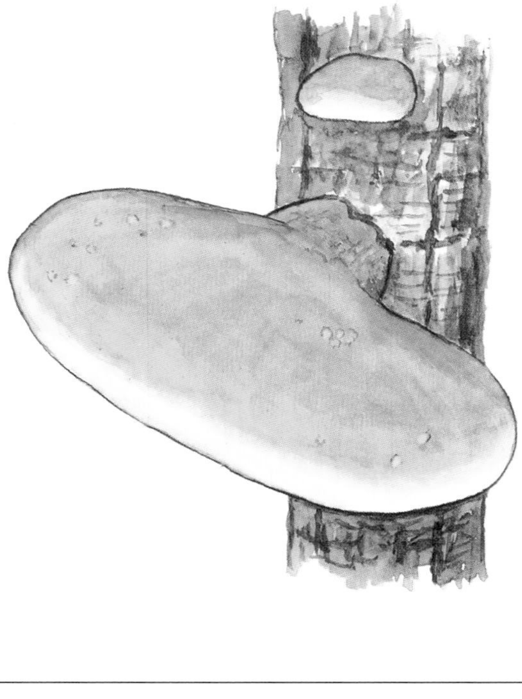

Trametes versicolor (Fries) Pilat

Cap: 1–4in (2.5–10cm)
Spores: white, 5–6 x 1.5–2.2μm, sausage-shaped
Edibility: inedible

One of the commonest and most well-known bracket fungi, its numerous, overlapping caps can be found in almost any woodland. Each bracket is thin, semicircular, and zoned with an amazing variety of colors, from brown to gray, blue-black, yellow or green to purplish. The fine pores are pale yellowish-buff. Old specimens can frequently be seen left over from the previous year.

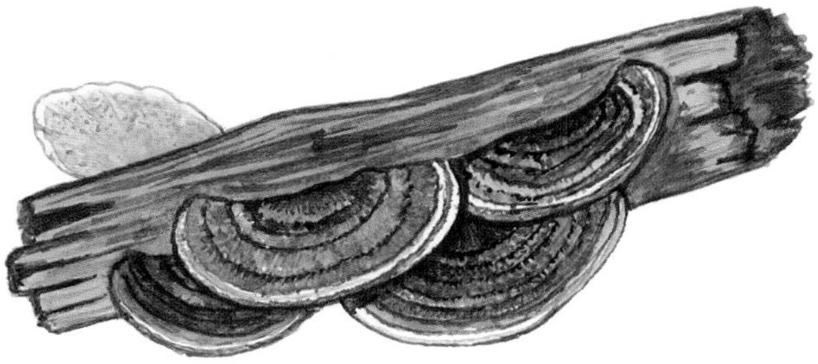

Daedaliopsis confragosa (Fries) Schroeter

Cap: 2–4in (5–10cm)
Spores: white, 7–11 x 2–3μm, sausage-shaped
Edibility: inedible

A very common and very variable species with many described forms. The well-formed, semicircular caps are tough, fibrous, and gray-brown with numerous paler and darker zones. The pores are very variable and may be round to elongated and maze-like, or even gill-like in extreme forms. All will bruise pinkish when handled. It is common on a variety of dead wood and may persist for several years.

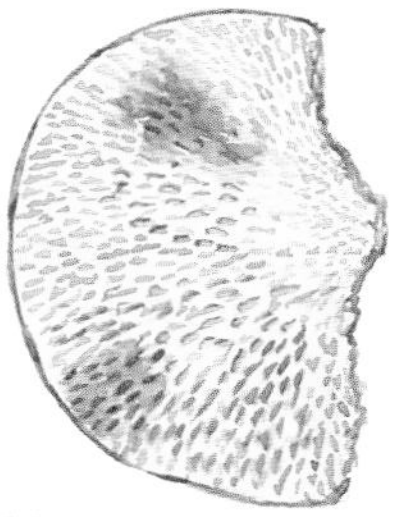

Daedalea quercina Fries

Cap: 2–6in (5–15cm)
Spores: white, 5.5–7 x 2.5–3.5μm, cylindrical
Edibility: inedible

The very thick, tough brackets are smooth to furrowed on the top and a dull white to pale ocher or brown when old. The tubes are extremely thick and elongated to form gill-like plates or strips, and are whitish-buff. It is a common species and grows on dead oak wood from Maine down to North Carolina, and west to Ohio.

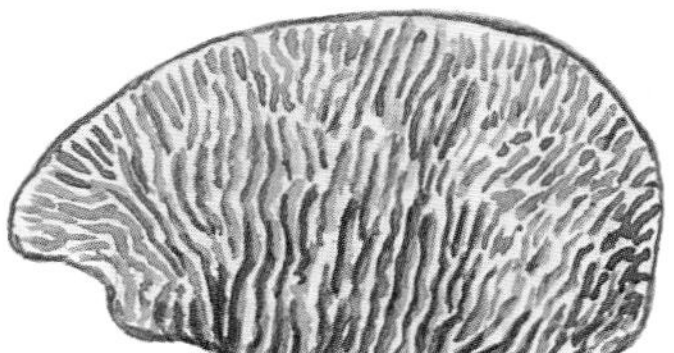

Ganoderma applanatum (Persoon ex Wallroth) Patouillard – "Artist's Fungus"

Cap: 4–20in (10–50cm)
Spores: reddish-brown, 6.5–9.5 x 5–7μm, with a thick, double wall, perforated on the outer layer
Edibility: inedible

This, and the closely related *G. adspersum* form large, very hard, and woody brackets on dead and dying trees everywhere. The hard upper surface is dry and often lumpy, crust-like and gray-brown, but often covered with a layer of bright rust-brown spores. The latter are attracted to and held on the surface by a static charge which forms on the surface. The margin, when actively growing, is white, and the pores on the underside are white and bruise brown instantly when touched. There may be many layers of tubes since a fresh layer is formed each year and some specimens are many years old. The flesh is pale cinnamon-brown with small, whitish flecks. The staining of the pores makes it possible to scratch a drawing on the surface, which is permanent when it has dried. Museums have specimens with such artwork hundreds of years old. *G. adspersum,* which is also widely distributed, has darker flesh without white flecks, and larger spores 8–13μm long.

Ganoderma tsugae Murrill

Cap: 4–10in (10–25cm)
Spores: brown, 7–13 x 6–8μm, ovate with a flattened end
Edibility: inedible, but used to make medicinal teas

Many fungi are being investigated for possible medicinal uses; some are known to be antibiotic in action, others reduce cholesterol, while a few are suspected of having anti-tumor potential for use in cancer treatments. This species is perhaps the most well known for the last-mentioned purpose. It has been widely researched and studies are still continuing today to find its potential. Many people, particularly in China and the Far East, infuse this and related species in hot water to make a medicinal tea which is thought to have many restorative properties. The beautiful brackets have a highly polished, lacquered appearance and vary in color from chestnut to reddish-purple or almost black. A distinct lateral stem is often present. The growing margin and the tubes are whitish-buff. It is a fairly common species on oaks and dead conifers, especially hemlocks, spruce, and pine. The very similar *G. lucidum* grows on oaks and chestnuts.

Fistulina hepatica Schaeffer ex Fries – "Beefsteak Polypore"; "Ox Tongue"

Cap: 3–10in (7.5–25cm)
Spores: pinkish-salmon, 4.5–6 x 3–4μm, smooth
Edibility: edible, but an acquired taste

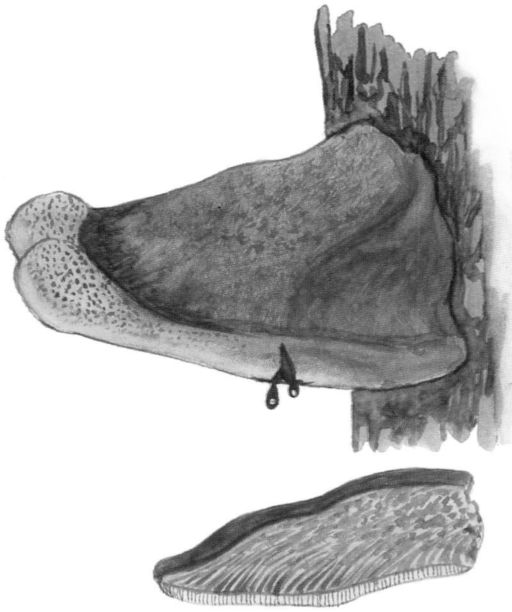

A strange fungus, it really does look like the tongue of an animal, and feels like one too. The soft, reddish bracket is spongy and moist on the upper surface, and usually minutely pimpled and roughened. It may be very viscid when wet. The tubes are pale reddish and very easily separated from each other, while the pores are cream. The flesh is fibrous,very moist, and drips a reddish-brown liquid when cut. The taste is rather acidic, and although some people like to eat it, most consider it rather too unusual. It is an uncommon fungus on old oak trees and occasionally chestnut, and is widespread in eastern North America.

Fomitopsis pinicola (Fries) Karsten

Cap: 2–8in (5–20cm)
Spores: yellowish, 15–20 x 5–7μm
Edibility: inedible

The hard, woody bracket is hoof-shaped, with a dull brownish-red, ruby-red, or even blackish crust, which is usually furrowed and slightly zonate, redder near the margin. The pores are small and whitish, bruising yellow. The thick flesh is light yellow-brown. A new tube layer is added each year, so the age of the fungus can be easily determined. It is a very common species on dead or dying conifers throughout most of North America.

Schizophyllum commune Fries

Cap: ½–2in (1–5cm)
Spores: white, 3–4 x 1–2.5μm
Edibility: inedible

At first sight this might look like a gilled mushroom, but a closer look will show that the "gills" are very strange, split down the middle, and often curled over lengthwise. It is, in fact, closely related to the polypores, and the "gills" are similar to very elongated tubes. The cap surface is white and very hairy, and the margin is usually lobed. It grows in large numbers on a wide variety of woods the world over and can survive droughts by rolling up until wet weather returns.

SUBCLASS GASTEROMYCETES

FUNGI WITH SPORES ON BASIDIA CONTAINED INSIDE THE FRUIT BODY

Although this is now considered by most mycologists to be a rather artificial grouping of fungi which are not really closely related, it is nevertheless a very convenient one for use in guide books, since it brings together all those fungi which produce their spores inside the fruit body, rather than on an external hymenium. The spores in Gasteromycetes are not forcefully ejected by the basidium, so they rely to a great extent on external forces – wind, rain, and insects – to carry off their spores, and they have evolved some of the strangest forms to accomplish this.

ORDER: PHALLALES

Fungi with the spore-mass (gleba) contained in an "egg" and frequently expanding rapidly to produce strange-shaped fruit bodies. The spore mass then liquefies and gives off an unpleasant odor to attract insects, which eat the spores and unknowingly pass them on to germinate elsewhere.

PHALLACEAE
Stinkhorn Family

The stinkhorns can be "hatched" by placing the unopened eggs on a damp paper towel under a glass. The strange, phallic shapes and foul odors are the source of various folktales, usually connected with witches and black magic; other tales relate that they grow where rutting deer have been, while in the Far East they are regarded as aphrodisiacs.

Phallus hadriani Venturi

Cap: 4–6in (10–15cm) high

Spores: 4–5 x 2μm

Edibility: edible only when young

This has the typical stinkhorn structure of a spongy stem emerging from an egg; in this instance the egg is tinted a purplish-pink. At the top of the stem is a ridged and pitted, thimble-like cap over which is spread the olive spore-mass. Shortly after emerging, the spore-mass liquefies and releases the powerful odor – rather like hyacinths mixed with rotting vegetables. It grows in gardens, lawns, and shrubberies in sandy soils, and is common in the western and central states.

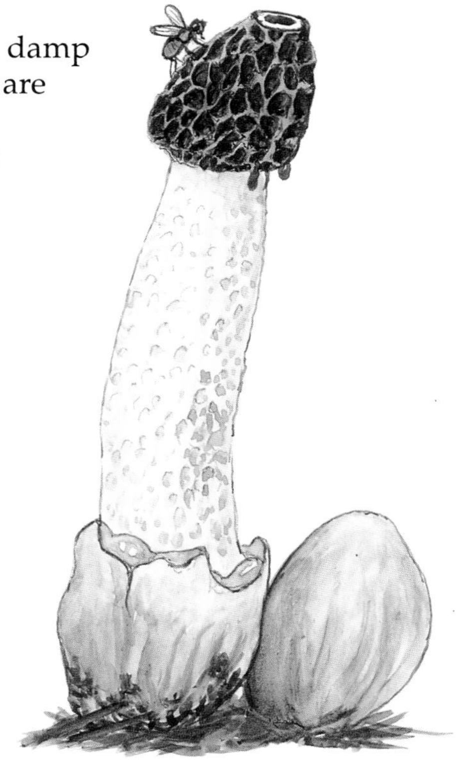

Phallus ravenelli Beck & Curtis – "Ravenell's Stinkhorn"

Cap: 4–5in (10–12.5cm) high
Spores: 3–4.5 x 1–2μm
Edibility: the eggs are a delicacy when unopened

This species can be distinguished from *P. hadriani* by the cap, which is minutely granular under the layer of spores, not ridged and pitted in a network. The spongy, yellowish-white stem emerges from a pinkish egg and it grows on rotted stumps and sawdust, often in large clusters. It is frequent throughout the eastern states down through Florida, especially in disturbed urban areas.

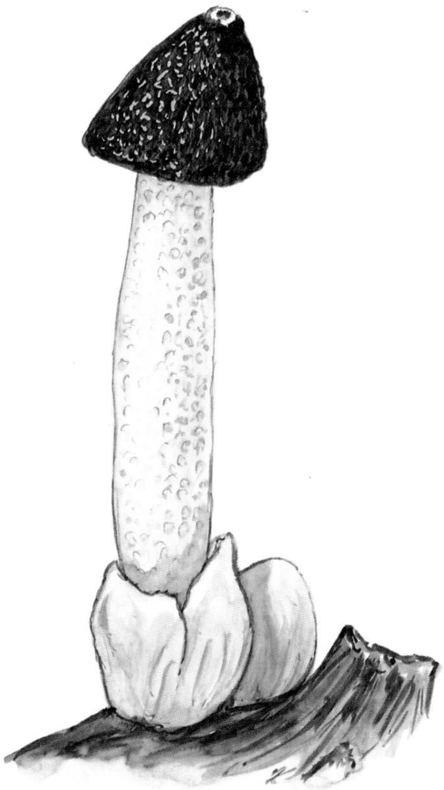

Dictyophora duplicata (Bosc) Fischer

Cap: 4–6in (10–15cm) high
Spores: 3.5–4.5 x 1–2μm
Edibility: edible in the egg stage

In this species the form and structure have been developed to an even more remarkable degree, with the typical stinkhorn shape of spongy stem and cap being adorned with a lacy skirt hanging from beneath the cap. It is not certain what function this skirt serves, but it seems likely that it visually attracts insects that might not be attracted, as many others are, by the repulsive odor. In tropical species this skirt is developed to a fantastic degree, reaching the ground and often colored bright orange or yellow, and may form a ladder for crawling insects to climb up to the spore-mass.

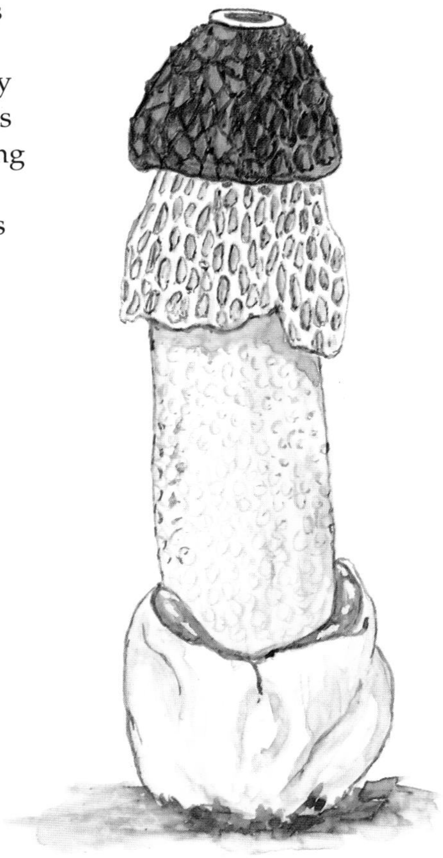

Mutinus caninus (Hudson) Fries
"Dog Stinkhorn"
Cap: 3–5in (7.5–12.5cm) high
Spores: 3–4 x 1.5μm
Edibility: inedible

A slender, delicate species and much less odorous than other stinkhorns – indeed, you may hardly smell it at all. The slender stem emerges from a small white egg and is white to pale orange with a pinched-in, narrow apex which is colored bright red or orange. The cells of the stem are open like a sponge. Over the apex is the dark olive spore-mass, which liquefies shortly after emergence. Note that, as in the previous species, there is no separate cap. This is the most often misidentified species of *Mutinus* in North America. The true *M. caninus* is rather rare and distinctly northern in distribution. The common species are those shown opposite.

Mutinus ravenelii Berkeley & Curtis – Fischer

Cap: 2–4in (5–10cm)
Spores: olive, 4–7 x 2–3μm
Edibility: inedible

Often mistaken for the previous species, this fungus has a strong, fetid odor, a distinctly enlarged, clavate head with much brighter, cerise-red or purplish-red colors, and is shorter and stouter. It emerges from a whitish egg, often grows in conifer woods (a very rare habitat for *M. caninus,* which prefers deciduous woods,) and can be smelled many feet away when a number of caps are present. It is common in the eastern and central states down through Florida. There is some debate over the correct name for this species, and it may be that *M. curtisii* is the appropriate name.

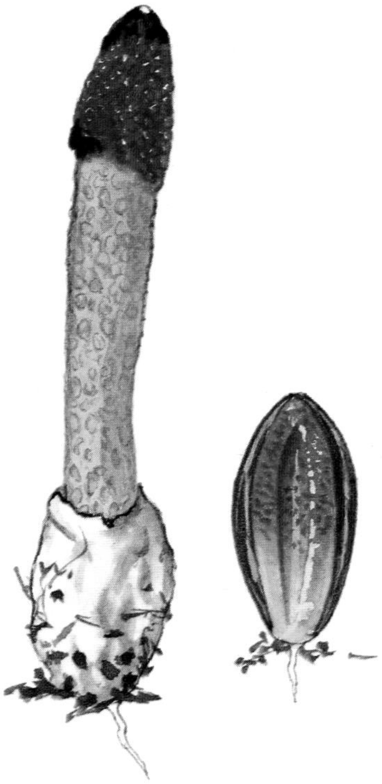

Mutinus elegans (Montagne) Fischer – "Elegant Stinkhorn"

Cap: 4–7in (10–18cm)
Spores: olive, 4–7 x 2–3μm
Edibility: inedible

The commonest species of *Mutinus* in North America, this is also the easiest to identify. The long stem tapers evenly to a point with no clear demarcation of the head. All the spongy cells of this stem are globose and do not form open chambers, unlike the two previous species. The spore-mass may be spread over almost half the stem. In color it ranges from pale orange to rosy-orange, while the eggs have a distinct purplish tint when mature. The odor is rather weak and not particularly fetid, rather sweet or metallic instead. It grows in woodchips and is very common in parks, woods, and gardens wherever these occur.

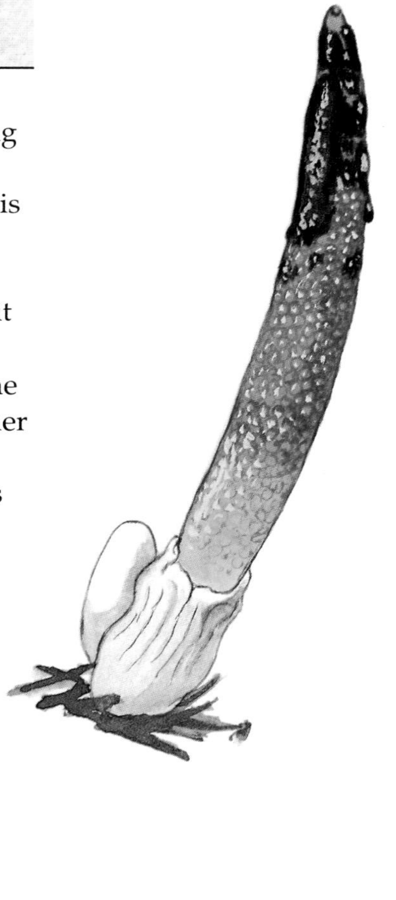

CLATHRACEAE
Cage Stinkhorn Family

Related to the Common Stinkhorns, these fungi resemble cages or baskets, or sometimes squid with tentacles. Like other Stinkhorns, they "hatch" from an egg.

Pseudocolus fusiformis (Fischer) Lloyd – "Stinky Squid"
Cap: 2–4in (5–10cm)
Spores: 4.5–5 x 2–2.5µm
Edibility: inedible

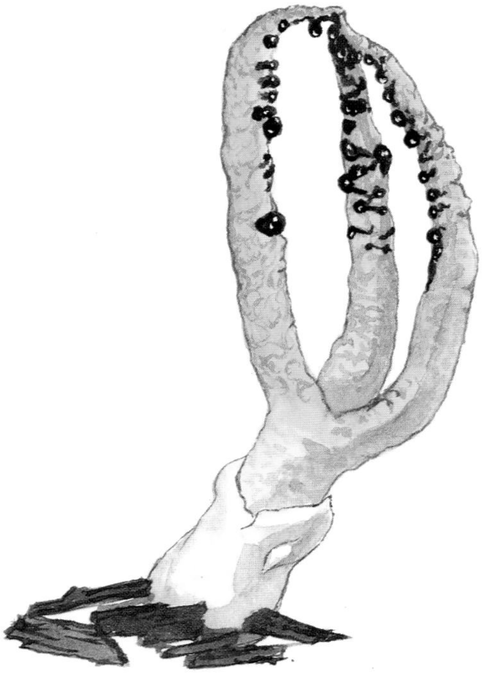

Looking more like an animal than a fungus, it really does have a squid-like appearance, with its strange, spongy "arms" emerging from the small white egg. The number of arms varies from 3 to 4, although 3 is the most common, and they are usually weakly joined at the tips. They are colored bright to pale orange, with the inner surfaces smeared with the deep blackish-green, fetid spore-mass. This soon attracts flies and slugs, which eat the spores and thus disperse them. The species is thought to have been introduced from southeast Asia, but is spreading rapidly throughout the northeast on woodchip garden mulches and even in woodlands along paths.

Clathrus ruber Micheli ex Persoon – "Cage Stinkhorn"; "Lattice Stinkhorn"
Cap: 2–6in (5–15cm)
Spores: 5–6 x 1.5–2.5µm
Edibility: inedible

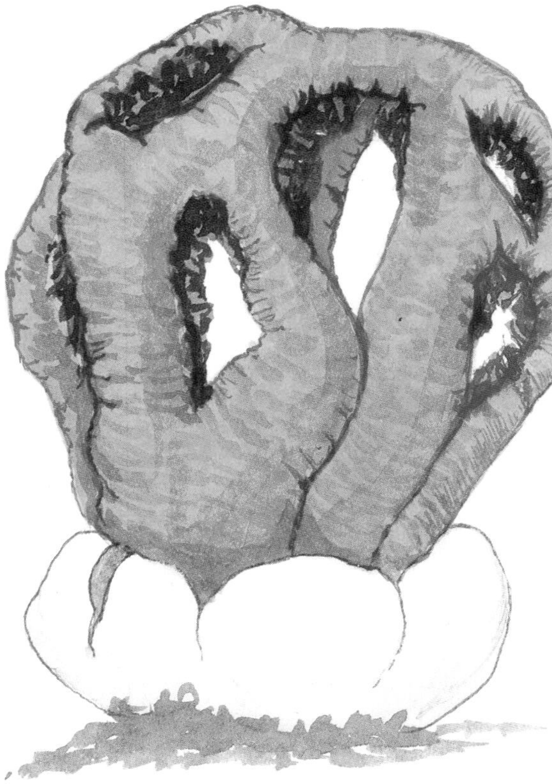

A rare prize in the USA, where it may have been introduced, this mushroom is now naturalized and scattered from Florida to California, but quite rare farther north. Unmistakable, it forms a large spongy, red, cage-like structure which erupts out of a white egg. The inner surface of the cage is smeared with the gleba, which liquefies and gives off the strong fetid odor. Like other phalloid fungi, it attracts insects with its smell in order to disperse its spores.

ORDER: LYCOPERDALES

This large order includes the familiar Puffballs, and the Earthstars, which all produce their spore-mass (gleba) inside a ball-like structure (peridium).

LYCOPERDACEAE
Puffball Family

As their common name suggests, members of this family are ball-like, and the spores inside the ball become dry and powdery and will puff out if the ball is tapped.

Lycoperdon pyriforme Schaeffer ex Persoon
Fruit body: ⅝–1¾in (2–4.5cm)
Spores: olive-brown, 3–4µm, globose smooth
Edibility: edible when young

Growing in large clusters, this is a common sight on old stumps. The pear-shaped puff-balls are white to dull buff when old, and are attached to the wood by thick, white mycelial strands. The skin has a fine, scurfy-granular coating when young, but is soon smooth. The spores begin white, then mature to olive-brown. It is widespread everywhere and quite a good edible when young and firm.

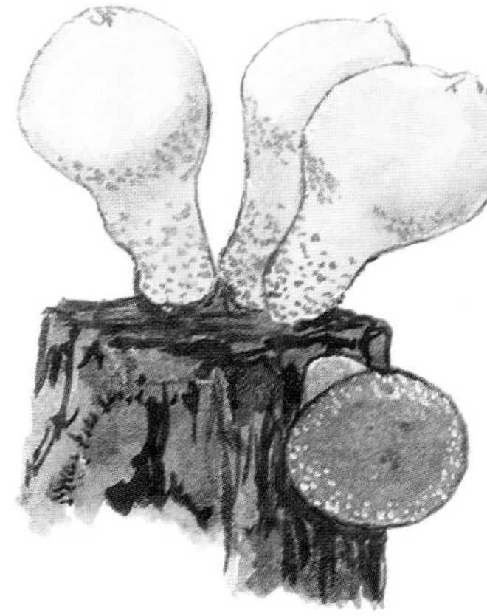

Lycoperdon perlatum Persoon ex Fries
Fruit body: 1–2in (2.5–5cm)
Spores: olive-ocher, 3.5–4.5µm, globose and minutely warty
Edibility: edible when young

An extremely common species, it has a round to slightly club-shaped ball with small white spines or warts, often in tiny rings, which are easily rubbed off, leaving round marks. A short to well-developed sterile base is present. It grows in fields, gardens, and along roadsides, as well as in grassy clearings in woods, and is widely distributed.

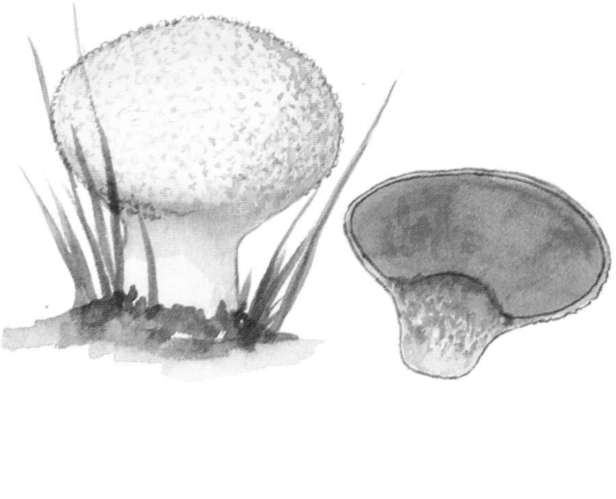

Lycoperdon foetidum Bonord

Fruit body: 1–2in (2.5–5cm)
Spores: dull-brown, 4–5μm, globose and minutely spiny
Edibility: edible when young

This species has tiny, dark brown spines even when young. The puffball is whitish-buff when young, then matures to a dull yellow-brown with darker, blackish-brown spines. The spore-mass is a dull sepia-brown and has a strong, unpleasant odor (several other species also develop strong odors with age). It is a common species, especially under conifers, and is widely distributed.

Calvatia sculpta (Hark) Lloyd

Fruit body: 3–6in(7.5–15cm) high
Spores: olive-brown, 3.5–6.5μm, minutely spiny
Edibility: edible when young

Looking rather like a piece of strange sculpture, this species is covered in large, polygonal warts or spines, which gradually crack apart and fall away with age, exposing the spore-mass beneath. It is fairly common in the mountains of the western states, often under conifers.

Calvatia cyathiformis (Bosc) Morgan

Fruit body: 3–6in (7.5–15cm) across
Spores: purple-brown, 3.5–7.5μm, rounded with distinct spines
Edibility: edible when young

A large and rather common species, it forms a robust ball on a short, stout stem. The ball or club is whitish-buff to grayish and cracks with age. Eventually, it breaks away to reveal the spore-mass, and finally leaves just the sterile base behind. It is commonly found in fields, golf courses, and along grassy roadsides, especially in the eastern and central states.

Calvatia craniformis (Schweinitz) Fries

Fruit body: 3–8in (7.5–20cm) across

Spores: olive-yellow, 2.5–4.5µm, globose and almost smooth

Edibility: edible when young

Often confused with the previous species, but easily distinguished when mature. The spores are a very different color and the outer surface of the large ball is curiously wrinkled, almost brain-like. It is fairly common in open ground, often near oaks, and is widely distributed. The similar *C. bovista,* also with olive-yellow spores, is less wrinkled and brain-like, and has spores 4–6.5µm across.

Langermannia gigantea (Batsch) Rotskovius – "Giant Puffball" [=*Calvatia gigantea*]

Fruit body: 8–20in (20–50cm) across

Spores: yellow-brown, 3.5–5.5µm, minutely warted

Edibility: edible and good when young and still white

One of the monsters of the fungus world, giant specimens are said to have been mistaken for sheep. The rather long, flattened ball is white with a matt, suede-like skin. which slowly erodes away to expose the yellow-brown mature spore-mass. When young and the gleba is still white and firm, the fungus can be sliced and cooked and is an excellent edible. This is one of those species that have distinct flushes in some years and then are very scarce in years that follow. When fruiting well, it may appear by the hundred, and likes banks and hedgerows, woodland edges and gardens, as well as fields. It is quite common in eastern and central North America. *L. booniana,* found in the western states, differs in its thick skin being covered in large, flattened warts and cracks.

GEASTRACEAE
Earthstar Family

These remarkable fungi have a strangely animal-like appearance, with their star-shaped arms lifting them off the leaf litter. The spores are either sucked out by wind blowing over the opening in the inner ball, or by raindrops hitting the inner wall and thus puffing them out. In some species the arms can repeatedly open and close, depending on the weather.

Geastrum triplex Junghuhn – "Earthstar"

Fruit body: 1–4in (2.5–10cm)
Spores: dark brown, 3.5–4.5μm, globose and warted
Edibility: inedible

When young and unopened, they look just like a bunch of dark brown onions lying in the leaf litter. Slowly the thick, leathery outer layer (peridium) splits to form a number of fleshy arms, which curve backward to reveal the inner ball containing the gleba. Surrounding the pale brown ball is a distinct, irregular collar. The spores are released by the action of wind and raindrops via a tiny apical hole in the ball. This is a common species under beech trees and is widely distributed.

Geastrum pectinatum Persoon

Fruit body: 1–2in (2.5–5cm)
Spores: brown, 4–6μm, globose and warted
Edibility: inedible

The small, tough, gray-brown ball splits to form a star, and at the center is a rounded gray-white ball set on a slender stalk. The ball has a narrow, beaked, and deeply grooved opening at the top where the spores are released. This species grows in woods and gardens, especially near cedars, and is widespread but rather uncommon.

ORDER: SCLERODERMATALES

Fungi related by their lack of a true sterile base (common in the puffballs), spore-mass without sterile, thread-like cells (capillitium), and spores coloring before they turn powdery.

ASTRAEACEAE
False Earthstar Family

Resembling Earthstars, these are in fact closely related to the Earthballs (*Scleroderma*), with similar ornamented, dark spores.

Astraeus hygrometricus (Persoon) Morgan
Fruit body: 1–2in (2.5–5cm)
Spores: brown, 7–11µm, warted
Edibility: inedible

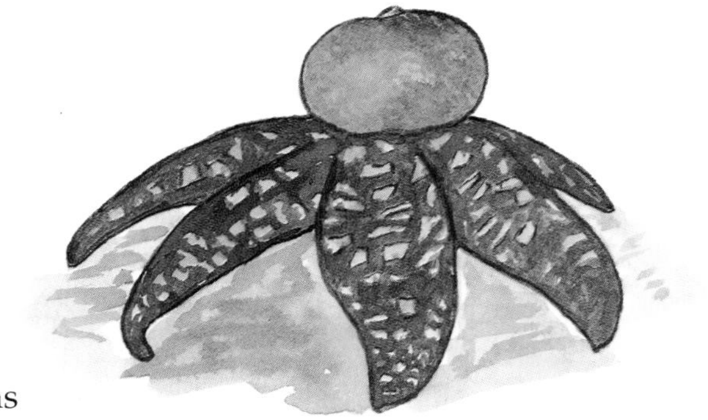

An unusual species which is something of a weather indicator. In moist weather, after the arms have split apart and peeled back, they will remain open, allowing the spores to be released. If the weather turns hot and dry, the arms will close to protect the spore-mass and reduce evaporation. The arms have an irregularly cracked and warty surface, while the ball is pale brown and smooth with a small apical spore. It is common in the northeast, found in sandy soils and sand dunes, often starting buried in the soil and then pushing up as it expands. Although it looks very much like a normal Earthstar, it is much more closely related to the Earthballs described below.

SCLERODERMATACEAE
Earthball Family

The Earthballs resemble Puffballs in some respects but their outer wall (peridium) is much tougher, more leathery, and often warty. The spores are colored and usually spiny or warty to reticulate. Most species are poisonous if eaten in any quantity.

Scleroderma citrinum Persoon – "Common Earthball"
Fruit body: 2–4in (5–10cm)
Spores: purple-black, 8–12µm, globose with tall spines and an indistinct network
Edibility: poisonous

One of the most ubiquitous and abundant fungi in summer and fall, particularly in hot, dry years, this species has a very thick outer wall (peridium) which is pale to bright tawny-yellow, and has fine to very coarse warts. The gleba starts white but rapidly turns purple-black with odd mottlings and whitish streaks. There is a strong, pungent odor, very distinctive but difficult to define – rather rubber-like, perhaps. It grows in mixed deciduous woods everywhere. *S. bovista* is smaller, smoother, and has spores with a very distinct network below the spines.

Scleroderma polyrhizon (Bulliard) Persoon – "Stalked Earthball" [=*S. geaster*]

Fruit body: 3–6in (7.5–15cm)
Spores: olive-brown, 10–14μm, globose with small, sharp spines
Edibility: poisonous

Found in dry, sandy soils, this species begins completely buried before slowly forcing the soil aside as it cracks apart and peels its thick, pale yellowish skin back to form a rough, star-shaped body. At the center is the dark, brownish spore-mass. It is widely distributed wherever the soil and climate are favorable.

Pisolithus tinctorius (Persoon) Coker & Couch – "Dye-maker's Mushroom"

Fruit body: 2–4in (5–10cm) across, 2–8in (5–20cm) high.
Spores: brown, 7-12μm, spiny
Edibility: inedible

This rather ugly mushroom, with a deeply rooting, tough mycelial base, begins life buried in the soil and slowly pushes upward into daylight. The outer skin is ocher to reddish-brown and very irregular in shape, while the spore-mass consists of small, whitish to yellow balls, like small peas embedded in a blackish jelly. This eventually breaks down into a brown spore powder. Despite its ugly appearance, it is highly prized for its use in dyeing. When boiled down it gives a rich golden-brown to blackish dye. It is commonly found in sandy pine woods and is widely distributed.

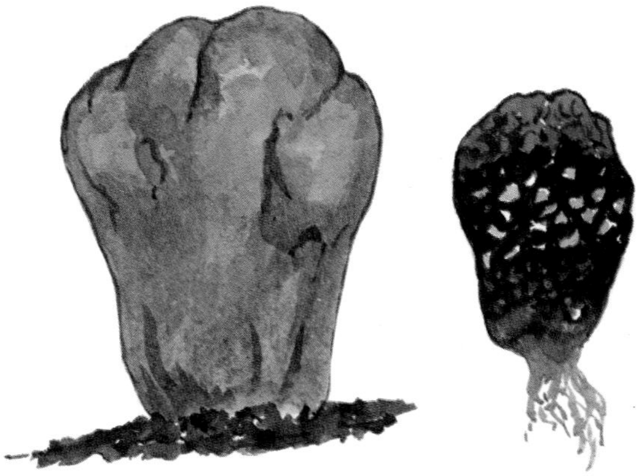

ORDER: TULOSTOMATALES

Sometimes called the Stalked Puffballs, these have the most well-developed stems and often bizarre forms of any of the puffball-type fungi. There are about six genera, of which only two are at all common in Britain.

TULOSTOMATACEAE
Stalked Puffball Family

These resemble a tiny puffball on a long, slender stem.

Tulostoma brumale Persoon
Fruit body: ¾in (about 2cm) across, stem about 1½in (4cm) high
Spores: brown, 3–5μm, globose, minutely warted
Edibility: inedible

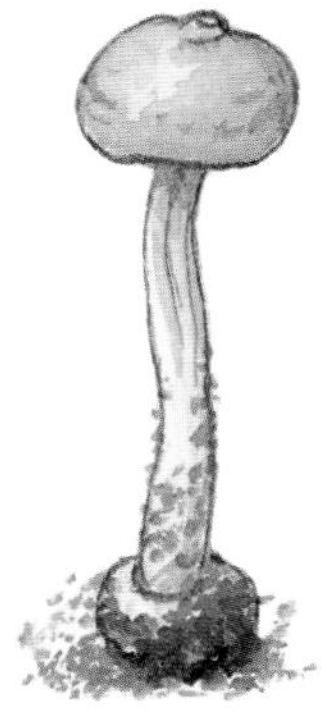

A strange, inconspicuous species, it prefers dry, sandy soils and has even been found in old, drystone walls in towns. The small puffball is a pale whitish-gray and is seated on a slender white stem with a bulbous base, which is often buried in the soil. It is locally common, but it needs a keen eye to spot one. There are a number of similar species which differ in minor details.

Calostoma cinnabarina Desvaux
Fruit body: 1½–2in (4–5cm)
Spores: pale yellow, 14–20 x 6–8.5μm, distinctly pitted
Edibility: inedible

An extraordinary species which is unlike any other fungus, it resembles a tomato raised up on a spongy reddish stem and surrounded by jelly complete with pips. The fungus begins as a gelatinous egg which splits open and reveals the bright red ball containing the spores. This rapidly rises up on the stem, leaving the jelly and fragments of red skin at the base. It is quite common along mossy banks by streams and tracks, and is found throughout the eastern states and south through Florida.

ORDER: NIDULARIALES

As the common name suggests, these remarkable but tiny fungi resemble tiny nests complete with eggs, which are in fact the spore-masses called peridioles. They rely for the most part on raindrops to splash the eggs out of the cups on to surrounding vegetation.

NIDULARIACEAE

Bird's Nest Fungi

The most nest-like fungi of the order, with three genera, of which *Nidularia* is rather rare and not shown here; it forms a globular structure with a thin, simple wall which splits irregularly to reveal its peridioles.

Cyathus striatus (Hudson) Willdenow – "Bird's Nest Fungus"

Fruit body: ¼–⅝in (0.6–2cm)
Spores: 15–20 x 8–12μm, smooth
Edibility: inedible

The urn- or vase-shaped nests are brown and hairy on the outside, but smooth and silvery-gray on the inside, which is distinctly lined and grooved. At the bottom are tiny dark eggs attached by coiled cords waiting to be splashed out by raindrops. This is a locally common species and grows in woodlands on fallen twigs and branches.

Cyathus olla (Batsch) Persoon

Fruit body: ¼–⅜in (0.6–1cm)
Spores: 11–13 x 7–8μm, smooth
Edibility: inedible

The tiny, flared, funnel-like nests of this species are brown and slightly roughened on the outside. The inner surface is smooth and white to pale gray. The eggs are whitish-gray. This species prefers more open, arable land and is common in fields and pastures, as well as sand dunes, on woody debris, and is widely distributed.

Crucibulum laeve (Hudson) Kambly
Fruit body: ¼–⅜in (0.6–1cm)
Spores: 4–10 x 4–6μm, smooth
Edibility: inedible

The almost cylindrical nests are tawny-yellow and begin with a hairy lid covering the opening. This splits open to reveal the smooth inner surface and the creamy yellow, lens-shaped peridioles or eggs inside. It grows on dead wood and woody debris, and is widespread in North America.

SPHAEROBOLACEAE
Catapult or Cannon Fungi

A unique family, with just one genus and species. It is quite unmistakable, but easily overlooked because of its tiny size. It is considered to be related to the other Bird's Nest Fungi, although differing in its method of spore dispersal.

Sphaerobolus stellatus Tode
Fruit body: 1/32–3/32in (1.5–2.5mm) across
Spores: white, 7.5–10 x 4–5.5μm
Edibility: inedible

Although only just qualifying as a larger fungus (it really needs the use of a hand lens), it is included here because of its remarkable method of spore dispersal. It is an almost unique example of a fungal catapult. The tiny whitish balls split open to form a yellowish star with a single brownish ball of spores at the center. The inner layer of the star suddenly flips outward, thus propelling the egg into the air. Eggs have been recorded traveling up to 13ft (4m). This is a common, if rarely seen, species and grows on sawdust, dung, and other organic debris.

ORDER: TREMELLALES

These fungi belong to a large group which shares the common feature of having the spore-producing cells – the basidia – divided (septate) either longitudinally or transversely. They usually have a jelly-like or rubbery consistency.

AURICULARIACEAE
Tree Ear Fungi

A relatively small family, with only a few genera and species worldwide. They all have a more or less rubbery consistency and rather membranous forms. One species, *Auricularia polytricha*, is widely cultivated in the Far East for food, particularly in China.

Auricularia auricula-judae (Bulliard ex St Amans) Berkeley – "Tree Ear"; "Jew's Ear"

Fruit body: 1–6in (2.5–15cm)

Spores: white, 12–15 x 4–6μm, sausage-like

Edibility: edible; considered a delicacy

A strange fungus with an interesting folklore attached. The first common name is obvious, as it does indeed resemble an ear. The second name is a corruption of "Judas' Ear", and refers to the legend that Judas Iscariot hanged himself on an elder tree, one of the favorite hosts of this fungus, and this is supposed to be his spirit appearing in this strange, ear-like form. The dark, purple-brown ears are rubbery in texture and slightly velvety on the outside. It is common everywhere and grows on a wide range of host trees. The basidia are divided transversely. A similar oriental species is widely esteemed as an edible and is commonly served in Chinese restaurants.

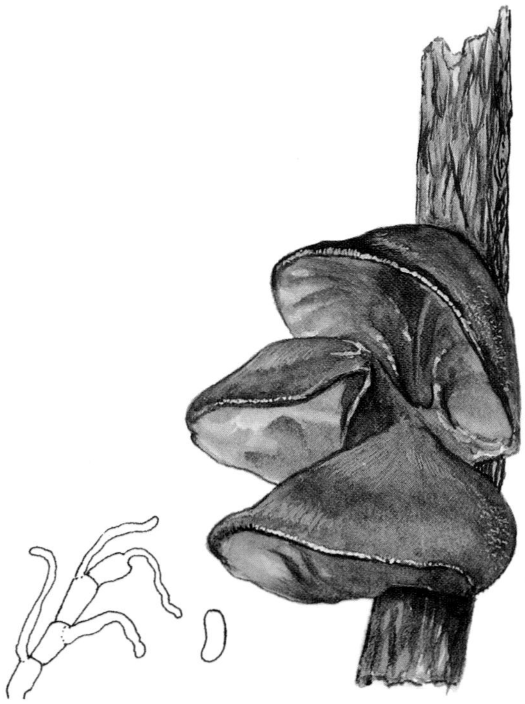

TREMELLACEAE
Jelly Fungus Family (part)

Very variable in shape, from shapeless jelly to rounded or tongue-shaped, or even trumpet-shaped, all species have basidia longitudinally septate.

Tremella mesenterica Retz ex Fries – "Witches' Butter"

Fruit body: 1–4in (2.5–10cm)
Spores: yellowish, 7–15 x 6–10µm, smooth
Edibility: inedible

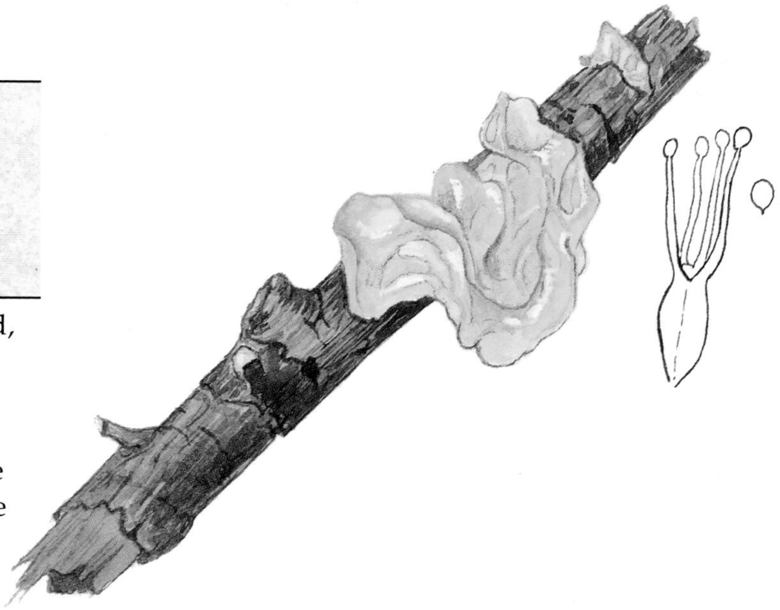

The commonest jelly fungus that most people find, this species varies from a bright yellow to almost white or transparent. It forms irregular lobes and wrinkled masses, and grows from fallen branches and twigs at almost any time of the year when the weather is damp. When the weather turns dry, the fungus shrinks and becomes a shrivelled, hard lump, only to revive again when it rains.

Tremiscus helvelloides (Persoon) Donk [=*Phlogiotis helvelloides*]

Fruit body: 1–4in (2.5–10cm)
Spores: white, 9–12 x 4–6µm
Edibility: edible and considered a delicacy, although rather tasteless; in any case, it is too rare and should not be disturbed

A wonderful species and one which is happily widespread in the USA, although still a rarity; it seems to be most common in the Pacific northwest. The beautiful, funnel-shaped, lobed, and wavy fruit bodies are a clear pink to apricot and quite unmistakable. The flesh is soft and rubbery. The basidia are longitudinally septate. It grows in large groups on the ground below conifers, or even on very well-rotted wood.

DACRYMYCETACEAE
Jelly Fungus Family (part)

Gelatinous, rounded to club-like fungi, with long, narrow, and horn-like two-spored basidia.

Calocera viscosa (Persoon ex Fries) Fries

Fruit body: 1–4in (2.5–10cm)
Spores: ocher-yellow, 9–14 x 3–5µm, sausage-shaped
Edibility: inedible

At first sight this looks very like a coral or club fungus, but if you feel it, the texture is distinctly rubbery and gelatinous, not brittle like a typical club fungus. The bright yellow-orange branches split into smaller points. When dry, it may shrivel into a small, dark orange, and hard lump. The basidia are shaped very much like a tuning fork. It is very common on dead coniferous wood everywhere. The smaller *C. cornea* differs in its single, unforked branches, and grows on deciduous woods.

CLASS ASCOMYCETES

These fungi produce their spores in quite a different way from all the other fungi shown in this book. Their spores are produced in long cells called "asci", usually eight spores per ascus, although this can vary from genus to genus. The spores are ejected from the cell like bullets from a gun, often producing a cloud of spores above the fungus, which you can both see and hear when you pick or disturb it. The asci give the entire group its name – the Ascomycetes. This is an enormous group of fungi with many thousands of species, mostly small and dealt with only in specialist literature. But it does also include such large and well-known edibles as the Morels, as well as some very poisonous species such as the False Morels.

Morchella esculenta Linnaeus ex Fries – "Common Morel"; "Yellow Morel"

Fruit body: 2–5in (5–12.5cm) high
Spores: deep yellow-ocher, 20–24 x 12–24µm, smooth
Edibility: edible and excellent, one of the best

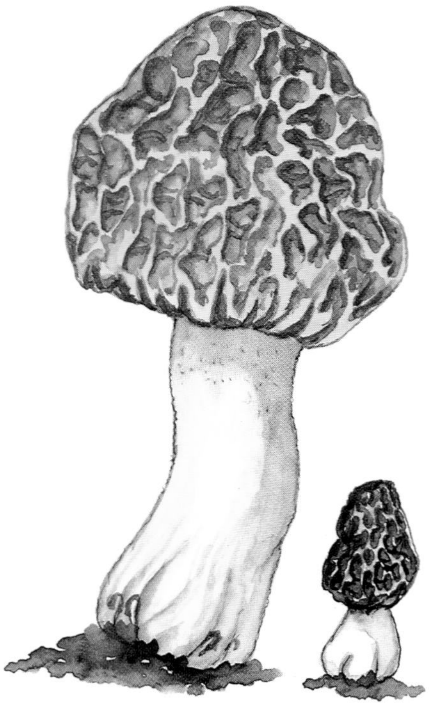

Part of the attraction in hunting for these fungi is the challenge of finding them. They are elusive, fruit only for a short time in the spring, and are very fussy about where they will fruit, preferring the ground around dying apple trees, elms, and ash on chalky soils. The cap begins as a tightly compressed, grayish sponge with lighter ridges, and expands to form a big yellowish sponge with large pits and ridges raised on a large white stem. The entire fungus is hollow (wonderful stuffed and baked!) with a swollen base. The microscopic asci with their spores line the pits and ridges. It begins fruiting around the end of April and finishes around the end of May. Many different forms or species have been described. A small yellow one is common under tulip trees (*Liriodendron*), and a small, tongue-shaped gray one under ash; both are probably undescribed.

Morchella elata Fries – "Black Morel"

Fruit body: 2–5in (5–12.5cm) high
Spores: pale ocher, 24–28 x 12–14µm, smooth
Edibility: edible and excellent

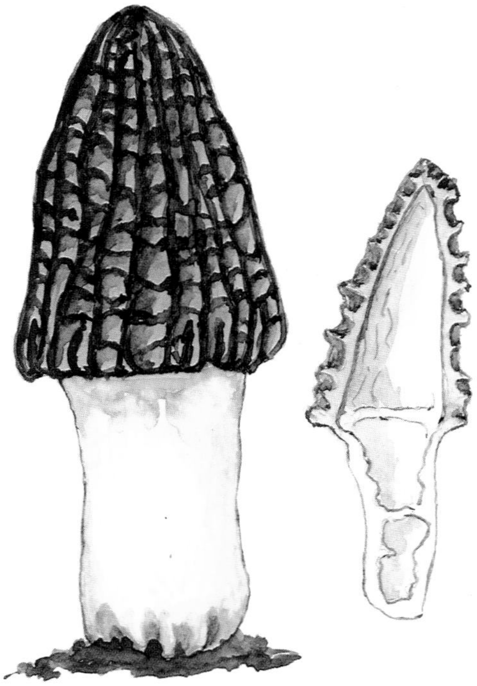

The cap of this species is tall and rather conical, with narrow, more or less vertical ridges connected by cross-ridges. The color is dark brown to smoky gray-black with darker ridges. The stem is white and cylindrical. This species seems to prefer conifers or ash trees, but more research is needed as to habitat preferences. Like the previous species, it grows only in the spring. The Burn-site Morel, *M. atrotomentosa*, differs both in its cap and stem being minutely blackish and velvety, and in growing on the site of recent fires in woods in central and western states.

Morchella angusticeps Peck

Fruit body: 2–6in (5–15cm)
Spores: pale yellow, 24–28 x 12–14μm, smooth
Edibility: edible

An uncommon and little-known mushroom, this is much thinner fleshed than the other species, and is most closely related to *M. semilibera* in this respect. The small conical cap joins the stem directly with almost no division or overhang between them, as is the case with *M. elata,* shown left. The cylindrical stem soon becomes watery and pinkish-brown. It grows in mixed woods in the eastern states, is not as well known as the other species, and is not as good an edible.

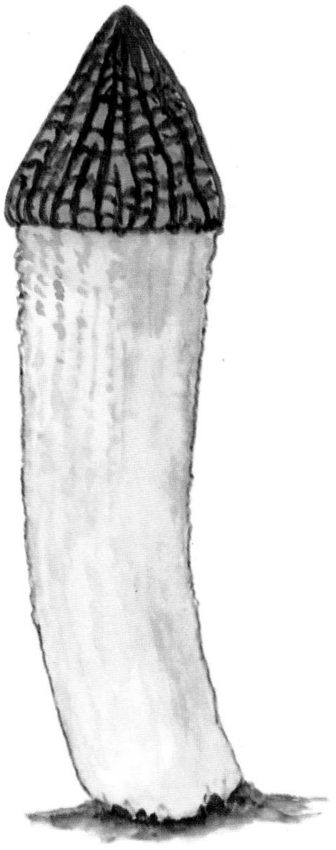

Verpa bohemica (Kromb) Schroeter

Fruit body: 2–5in (5–12.5cm) high
Spores: medium yellow, an enormous 60–80 x 15–18μm, only two found in each ascus
Edibility: edible in small quantities; known to interfere with muscular coordination

The thimble -like cap of this species is dramatically wrinkled and ribbed, almost brain-like. It is completely free from the stem, as can be seen in the cross-section. The brittle stem is whitish and smooth to concentrically ridged. It grows in damp woods and on stream sides in late winter and early spring, often following the snow melt. It is found throughout North America, although it is apparently rare in the eastern states.

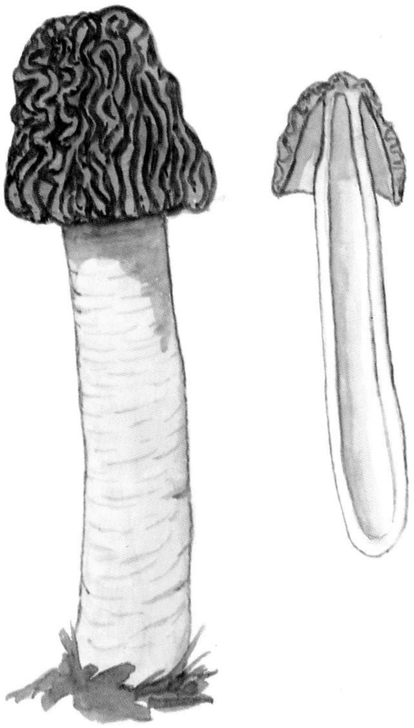

Verpa conica Swartz ex Persoon

Fruit body: 1–4in (2.5–10cm) high
Spores: pale ocher, 22–26 x 12–16μm, smooth
Edibility: edible

This looks exactly like a small thimble raised on a cylindrical, roughened stem. The "thimble" is pale brown and smooth, attached only by its very apex to the white, granular stem. It is an uncommon but easily overlooked species, preferring dense, shady woodlands and old orchards, and is quite widespread.

Morchella semilibera A.P. de Candolle ex Fries

Fruit body: 1–5in (2.5–12.5cm) high
Spores: pale ocher, 24–30 x 12–15µm, smooth
Edibility: edible, but not as good as other Morels

This species varies greatly in the portion of the stem compared to the cap. Some specimens have long, swollen stems like a Stinkhorn, while others have a stem no larger than the cap. The latter is brown and conical with blunt, parallel ridges. The fragile, thin-fleshed stem is white with a granular surface, and is completely hollow. It appears a week or so earlier than the other Morels and grows under mixed trees throughout much of North America.

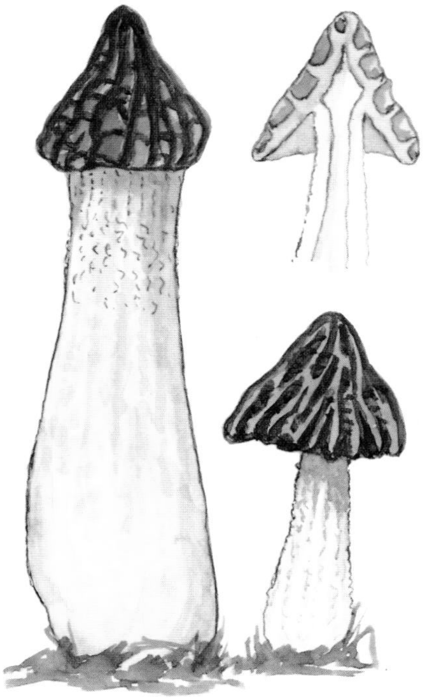

Helvella crispa Scopoli ex Fries

Fruit body: 1–4in (2.5–10cm) high
Spores: cream, 18–21 x 10–13µm, smooth
Edibility: doubtful; best avoided

A lovely species with a white to cream, saddle-shaped cap raised up on a strange fluted white stem. The flesh is thin and very fragile, and the fungus is hollow with several convoluted chambers. It grows in the fall, and is widespread in mixed woodlands everywhere, especially in the west.

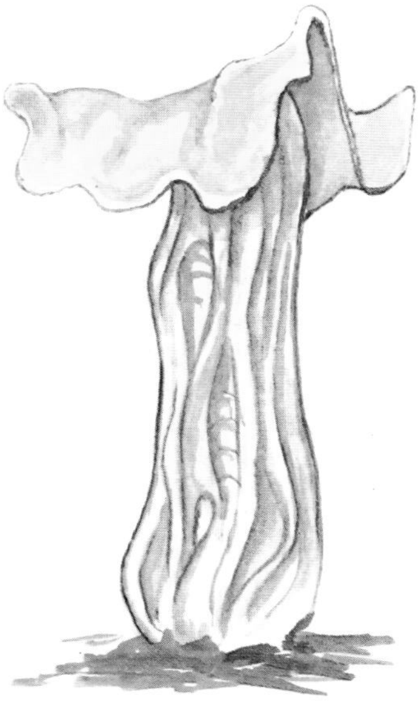

Helvella lacunosa Afzeli ex Fries

Fruit body: 2–4in (5–10cm) high
Spores: pale cream, 15–20 x 9–12µm, smooth
Edibility: doubtful; best avoided

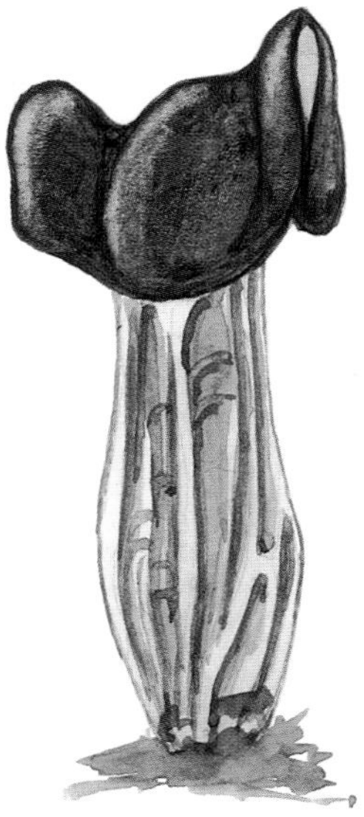

A strange and rather somber fungus, the gray-black saddle-like cap is curled down over the stem. The latter is gray and twisted, fluted with ribs and pits, and is hollow with chambers inside. It grows in mixed woods along tracks and mossy banks, and is quite common in the fall, especially in the Pacific northwest. There is some doubt as to its edibility in any quantity, so it is best avoided.

Gyromitra infula (Schaeffer ex Fries) Quélet

Fruit body: 1–4in (2.5–10cm) high
Spores: cream, 18–23 x 7–8µm, smooth
Edibility: deadly poisonous

An uncommon species, it is most often found farther north, growing on fallen, mossy conifer logs or debris in the fall. The dark reddish-brown cap is lobed and folded down like a saddle, and curiously wrinkled. The stem is white or flushed pale brown, smooth on the outside, but hollow with some chambers inside. This and the following species are notorious for their poisons, which are only removed by thorough cooking. If undercooked, or even if the vapors given off during cooking are inhaled, poisoning can occur. The toxin is now known to be monomethyhydrazine, a constituent of some rocket fuels. It has a cumulative effect, and there have been some serious, even fatal, poisonings from these species in Europe.

Gyromitra esculenta (Persoon ex Fries) Fries – "False Morel"

Fruit body: 2–6in (5–15cm) high
Spores: cream, 18–22 x 9–12µm, smooth
Edibility: deadlypoisonous

An infamous species and the cause of much misunderstanding – even the specific name *esculenta* is confusing. Although this is widely eaten in Europe, and was even purchased in cans in recent years, it nevertheless has caused serious and fatal poisonings. Like the species above, it contains a cumulative toxin which is only destroyed by the heat of cooking. Unfortunately, the cook often got sick from the fumes while the guests were unharmed. It took many years to discover that the culprit was this mushroom. The fungus is called False Morel, but it really looks very little like one. The cap is strangely wrinkled and brain-like, with a glossy surface, not pitted and ridged like a Morel. In section the cap and stem are irregularly chambered throughout, whereas a Morel is completely hollow down the middle. This species is rather uncommon, but widely distributed under conifers, and grows in the spring.

Otidea onotica (Persoon) Fuckel

Fruit body: 1–2in (2.5–5cm)
Spores: 12–14 x 5–6μm, elliptical, smooth
Edibility: edible

A lovely species, one of a group sometimes referred to as "Rabbit's Ears" because of their shape. The irregular, lobed cup is long and ear-like, and a bright peach-yellow to ocher, darker and more orange on the inside (which is lined with the asci). One or more "ears" may be fused together at the base to form a clump. It is rather uncommon and grows on soil and leaf litter in mixed woods. The similar *O. leporina* is a much duller shade of ocher.

Peziza vesiculosa Bulliard

Fruit body: 1–3in (2.5–7.5cm)
Spores: 20–24 x 12–14μm, elliptical, smooth
Edibility: inedible

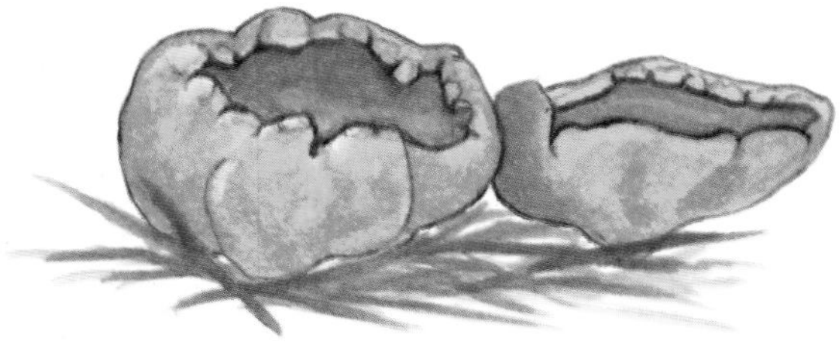

There are many species of *Peziza*, all popularly referred to as cup fungi. They vary in size and color, but are mostly shades of ocher or brown to gray-violet. This is one of the more distinctive species and often grows in large clusters. The yellow-ocher cup is paler, whitish, and very rough and scurfy-granular on the outer surface. The margin of the cup is jagged, tooth-like, or blistered. This species likes areas with old straw, compost, or old manure heaps, and is widespread everywhere.

Peziza phyllogena Cooke [= *P. badioconfusa*]

Fruit body: 1–4in (2.5–10cm)
Spores: 17–21 x 8–10μm, elliptical and finely warted
Edibility: edible

One of a number of dark brown species, this one has an attractive violet or purple hue on the outer surface. The inner surface of the cup is flushed with olive. It often appears a little earlier in the season, perhaps even in the spring, and is found in leaf litter. It is widespread and common.

Aleuria aurantia (Fries) Fuckel – "Orange Peel Fungus"

Fruit body: 1–4in (2.5–10cm)

Spores: 18–22 x 9–10µm, elliptical, with a network of fine ridges

Edibility: edible

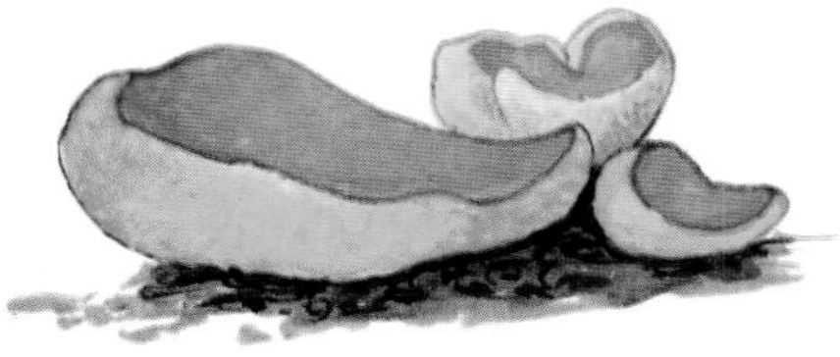

A beautiful species, which really can look like pieces of orange peel, and vice versa. The bright, clear orange cups are round to irregular in outline and much paler on the outside, which is also rather scurfy-granular. It often grows in large groups and may appear scattered along track sides or on disturbed areas, and is quite common in some years.

Scutellinia scutellata (Linnaeus ex Fries) Lamb

Fruit body: ¼–½in (0.6–1cm)

Spores: 18–19 x 10–12µm, elliptical and warted

Edibility: inedible

Although only just making it as a larger fungus, this is included here because under a hand lens it is a truly beautiful species, and is easily spotted in the forest if you look closely at wet, rotted logs. The bright, deep scarlet cups are quite round, and the margin is fringed with a row of black eyelash-like hairs. The underside of the cup is minutely hairy. There are a number of species which are distinguished microscopically and by the length of the lashes. The size of the cup varies, depending on the species concerned, but they are otherwise very similar. Common everywhere.

Trichoglossum hirsutum (Persoon) Boudier – "Earth Tongue"

Fruit body: 1–3in (2.5–7.5cm)

Spores: enormously long and thin, 100–150 x 6–7µm, brown and divided into 16 chambers

Edibility: inedible

Difficult to spot against the forest floor, these black, velvety clubs or tongues are very common. There are a number of species all looking very similar and needing a microscope to identify them. Their spores differ in the number of chambers within. The surface of the club in *Trichoglossum* is minutely velvety, in contrast to the almost identical *Geoglossum*, which is smooth.

Leotia lubrica Persoon ex Fries – "Jelly Babies"

Fruit body: 1–2in (2.5–5cm)
Spores: 17–26 x 4–6μm, spindle-shaped
Edibility: inedible

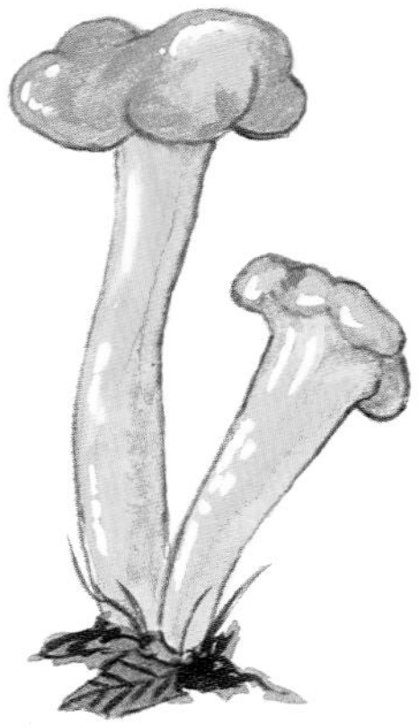

This fungus does rather resemble the candy called jelly babies. There is a rounded, rubbery-jelly cap colored ocher to slightly greenish, with a rubbery yellow stem which may be roughened and granular with darker dots. It can grow in large clusters and is common in leaf litter everywhere. *L. viscosa* has a green head on a yellow stem, while *L. atrovirens* is entirely deep green, but there is some evidence that these may be the result of attack by an imperfect fungus on ordinary *L. lubrica*.

Chlorociboria aeruginascens (Nylander) Karsten

Fruit body: ¼in (0.6cm)
Spores: 6–10 x 1.5–2μm, spindle-shaped
Edibility: inedible

One more often finds the effects of this fungus than the fungus itself. If you walk through any woodland, especially where there are oak trees present, and examine any fallen branches, you will almost certainly find some stained a bright bluish-green. This is the wood, highly valued for its unusual color, that was used to make green inlaid furniture called Tunbridge Ware. The stain is produced by a tiny cup fungus which only rarely fruits. When they are found, the cups are flattened with a tiny stem and are a vivid and intense blue-green. This species is widespread everywhere.

Galiella rufa (Schweinitz) Nannfeldt – "Rubber Cup"

Fruit body: ½–2in (1-5cm)
Spores: 9–17 x 6–7.5μm, the asci contain eight spores, the upper four brown and kidney-shaped, the lower four colorless but similarly shaped
Edibility: inedible

The texture of this fungus is exactly like tough, gelatinous rubber. It has a rough, black outer surface, while the smooth inner surface is a deep reddish-brown. The cup has a short stem. It is quite common and often grows in large groups along fallen twigs and branches throughout eastern North America.

Xylaria hypoxylon (Linnaeus ex Hook) Greville – "Candle-snuff"

Fruit body: 1–3in (2.5–8cm)
Spores: black, 11–14 x 5–6μm, bean-shaped
Edibility: inedible

Growing on fallen timber and old stumps everywhere, this small fungus looks like the snuffed-out wick of a candle. The tough black stem may fork several times and is white and powdery at the tip. The white powder is formed of large, asexual spores; later it will turn black as the sexual spores mature.

Xylaria polymorpha (Persoon ex Mérat) Greville – "Dead Man's Fingers"

Fruit body: 2–4in (5–10cm)
Spores: black, 20–30 x 5–10μm, spindle-shaped
Edibility: inedible

The gruesome common name always intrigues, but once you find this fungus you will see that it is quite descriptive. It does indeed produce clumps (often more than five) of fat, bloated, or misshaped "fingers", which are black and hard. The surface is dry and roughened or granular. If sectioned, the flesh is white inside. The asci are formed in tiny chambers or flasks set in the tough rind with their apertures pointing outward. This species may also sometimes be white and powdery from a layer of asexual spores. It grows on buried wood or old stumps and is very common everywhere.

Cordyceps ophioglossoides (Ehrhart ex Fries) Link

Fruit body: 2–4in (5–10cm)
Spores: enormously long and thin, but breaking apart into 2.5–5 x 2μm, elliptical-cylindrical units, smooth
Edibility: inedible

A strange fungus which is a member of a large group that specializes in parasitizing some other organism, usually insects. In this instance, however, the host is another fungus. If you carefully trace down the golden mycelial threads which emerge from the base of the stem, you will eventually come to a small, brown ball which is the False Truffle, *Elaphomyces*. Although a common species, it is difficult to spot on the forest floor; great care is needed to unearth the False Truffle.

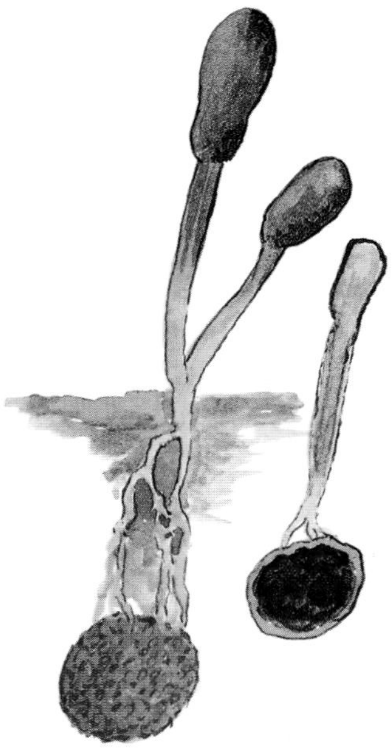

GLOSSARY

Acrid Producing a burning sensation on the tongue.

Adnate Referring to gills, or lamellae, which join the stem for most of their width.

Ammonia (NH_3) A 5% solution (household glass-cleaner with ammonia will often do just as well) is very useful. It causes reactions ranging from bright red to violet or green.

Amyloid A blue-black reaction of fungal tissue or spores to the iodine solution, Melzer's iodine.

Apiculus A point or short stalk at one end of the spore.

Ascus The usually cylindrical cell containing the spores in the Ascomycete fungi.

Basidia Club-like cells on which the spores are produced.

Caespitose Growing in clusters or clumps, with the stems joined at the base.

Capillitium Sterile threads in the spore-mass (gleba) of a Gasteromycete.

Clavate Club-shaped.

Cuticle The outer skin of the cap or stem.

Cystidium Specialized cells on any part of the mushroom, often very distinctive in shape.

Decurrent Referring to gills that run down the stem at the point of attachment.

Deliquescing Gills dissolving into a fluid (liquefying).

Dextrinoid A reddish-brown reaction in cells or spores in response to the iodine solution, Melzer's Iodine.

Ferrous sulfate ($FeSO_4$) A 10% solution is very important in testing many fungi, especially the genus *Russula.* Common reactions are blue, green, or pinkish-salmon.

Fibrillose With fine fibers.

Fibrous With coarse fibers.

Filamentous Composed of fine filaments or thread-like cells.

Floccose Wooly, or with small tufts of fibers.

Gleba The compacted mass of spores and spore-producing basidia formed inside the fruiting body of a Gasteromycete fungus.

Globose Roughly spherical.

Hygrophanous Changing color as the tissues dry out.

Hymenium The fertile layer of cells that produces spores.

Infundibuliform Funnel-shaped.

KOH *See* Potassium hydroxide.

Lamellae Also called gills, these are the radial flaps of tissue on which the basidia are formed in the Agaricales.

Latex The sticky fluid exuded from the tissues of some mushrooms, especially *Lactarius* and *Mycena.*

Mealy Can refer to a granular appearance *or* to an odor of freshly ground meal.

Melzer's Solution A specialized iodine solution made up of 0.5g iodine, 1.5g potassium iodide, 20ml water, and 20ml chloral hydrate. It is an essential reagent for many fungi, for determining the amyloid (blue-black), dextrinoid (reddish-brown), or negative reactions of spores, tissues, etc.

Mycelium The mass of fine threads (hyphae) that make up the fungus, and which runs through the soil or other substrate.

Mycorrhiza A beneficial association in which nutrients are exchanged between fungal hyphae and plant roots or tissues.

Network A fine, often minutely raised, mesh-like pattern of thin ridges running over the stem of a mushroom or the surface of spores.

Peridiole The small seed- or egg-like capsule that contains the spores in a Bird's Nest Fungus.

Peridium The outer wall of the spore case in many Gasteromycetes.

Peristome The opening at the apex of the spore-sac in an Earthstar (*Geastrum*).

Perithecium A flask-shaped chamber of spore-producing asci in some Ascomycetes.

Potassium hydroxide (KOH). Usually found as a 5% solution, this is the standard reagent for testing many mushrooms and for softening dried specimens.

Pruinose Frosted or with a grape-like "bloom".

Reticulum A fine network.

Rhizomorph A root- or string-like bundle of tough mycelial hyphae.

Septate Partitioned with one or more cross-walls.

Sinuate Referring to gills that curve up, or are notched where they join the stem.

Squamulose With minute scales.

Striate With fine parallel lines.

Subglobose Not perfectly rounded.

Substrate The surface on which a fungus lives and feeds.

Tomentose Finely velvety.

μm, micrometer or micron one thousandth of a millimeter.

Umbilicate With a central depression, or navel, in the cap.

Umbo A central hump or dome in the cap.

Vinaceous Wine-red, purplish-red.

Viscid Sticky, glutinous when wet.

Volva Membranous bag, or sac, out of which some mushrooms emerge.

Zonate With cap or flesh concentrically zoned.

Typical Mushroom Classification: Fly Agaric	
Kingdom	Fungi
Division	Eumycota
Subdivision	Basidiomycotina
Class	Basidiomycetes
Subclass	Holobasidiomycetes
Order	Agaricales
Family	Amanitaceae
Genus	*Amanita*
Species	*A. muscaria*

BIBLIOGRAPHY

The following list includes both general field guides and specialist works for the more knowledgeable enthusiast. Most are still in print, although one or two may have to be searched for in libraries. The more guides you can get, the better, since each will have species not included by others.

GENERAL BOOKS

The Audubon Society Field Guide to North American Mushrooms, Gary Lincoff (Alfred A. Knopf, New York, 1981)
A photographic guide by one of the best known mycologists in the USA; over 700 color photographs of species in their natural habitats. A pocket-sized guide and essential reference for all collectors.

Flore des Champignons au Québec, René Pomerleau (Les Editions la Presse, Ottawa, 1980)
A very large and comprehensive set of keys and descriptions to Canadian fungi, with some color plates. Also useful in the northern and eastern parts of the USA.

Mushrooms, Kent H. McKnight & Vera B. McKnight (Houghton Mifflin, Boston, 1987)
Illustrated field guide with useful keypoints of species indicated in the paintings by arrows and other markers. Very comprehensive, with some species not easily found anywhere else.

Mushrooms Demystified, David Aurora (Ten Speed Press, Berkeley, 1986, 2nd edition)
A unique and very comprehensive guide to North American fungi, ideal for beginners, with good keys, color photographs, and a very humorous approach to the subject.

Mushrooms for Color, Miriam Rice & Dorothy Beebee (Mad River Press, Eureka, California, 1980)
A wonderful guide to the art of dyeing wool and other fabrics with dyes extracted from fungi. A fascinating and unique hobby for the budding mycologist.

Mushrooms and Other Fungi, Geoffrey Kibby (Smithmark, New York, 1992)
In the American Nature Guides series with weatherproof cover, this illustrated pocket guide includes over 400 species, many of which are not included in other books.

Mushrooms of North America, Roger Phillips (Little, Brown, Boston, 1991)
A superb photographic guide to over 1000 species – the most comprehensive work yet produced on North American fungi. They are shown at all stages and angles in great detail, with soft studio lighting.

SPECIALIST WORKS

The Agaricales (Gilled Fungi) of California, Harry D. Thiers (Mad River Press, Eureka, California, 1982)
A continuing series of monographs for the region, with detailed keys, descriptions, and color photographs covering such groups as Amanitacea, Cantharellaceae, Gomphidiaceae, Paxillaceae, Hygrophoraceae, etc. Essential works for the more advanced enthusiast.

Amanita of North America, David T. Jenkins (Mad River Press, Eureka, California, 1986)
A major monograph on this large and important group of fungi, which includes some of the most deadly species in North America.

The Boletes of Michigan, A.H. Smith (University of Michigan Press, Ann Arbor, 1971)
Of use throughout the eastern and northern states this is the basic reference work for anyone studying boletes.

California Mushrooms: A Field Guide to the Boletes, Harry D. Thiers (Hafner, New York, 1975)
Essential reference for this popular group of fungi found in the western states; color photographs are issued as microfiche transparencies.

A Field Guide to Southern Mushrooms, A.H. Smith & Nancy Smith Weber (University of Michigan Press, Ann Arbor, 1985)
Beautiful color photographs illustrating the often striking species of the southern states by two of the USA's most famous mycologists.

Keys to the Species of Russula in Northeastern North America, Geoffrey Kibby & Raymond Fatto (Kibby-Fatto Enterprises, 1187 Millstone River Road, Somerville, NJ 08876, 1990)
The most up-to-date and comprehensive set of easy keys to this fascinating group of fungi. Illustrations of spores of all species; no color.

North Amerian Polypores, Vols I & II, R.L. Gilbertson & L. Ryvarden (Fungiflora, Oslo, Norway, 1986–7)
The most important work on these fungi in recent years, and an essential reference by two of the most renowned polypore experts.

North American Species of Clitocybe, Parts I and II, Howard E. Bigelow (J. Cramer, Vaduz, West Germany)
The essential reference to this large and difficult group; black and white photographs.

North American Species of Hygrophorus, L.R. Hesler & A.H. Smith (University of Tennessee Press, Knoxville, 1963)
The first major treatment of these beautiful fungi (see also the more recent monographs on Agaricales of California by H.D. Thiers); black and white photographs.

North American Species of Lactarius, A.H. Smith & L.R. Hesler (University of Michigan Press, Ann Arbor, 1979)
The essential reference work to this large genus of fungi; black and white photographs only.

North American Species of Pholiota, A.H. Smith & L.R. Hesler (Lubecht & Cramer, New York, 1968)
One of a series of important monographs by two great mycologists, covering the major genera of fungi in the USA. This volume covers the important wood-rotting genus *Pholiota*. Black and white photographs.

FUNGAL CLASSIFICATION

CLASS: BASIDIOMYCETES – Fungi with spores formed externally, on basidia

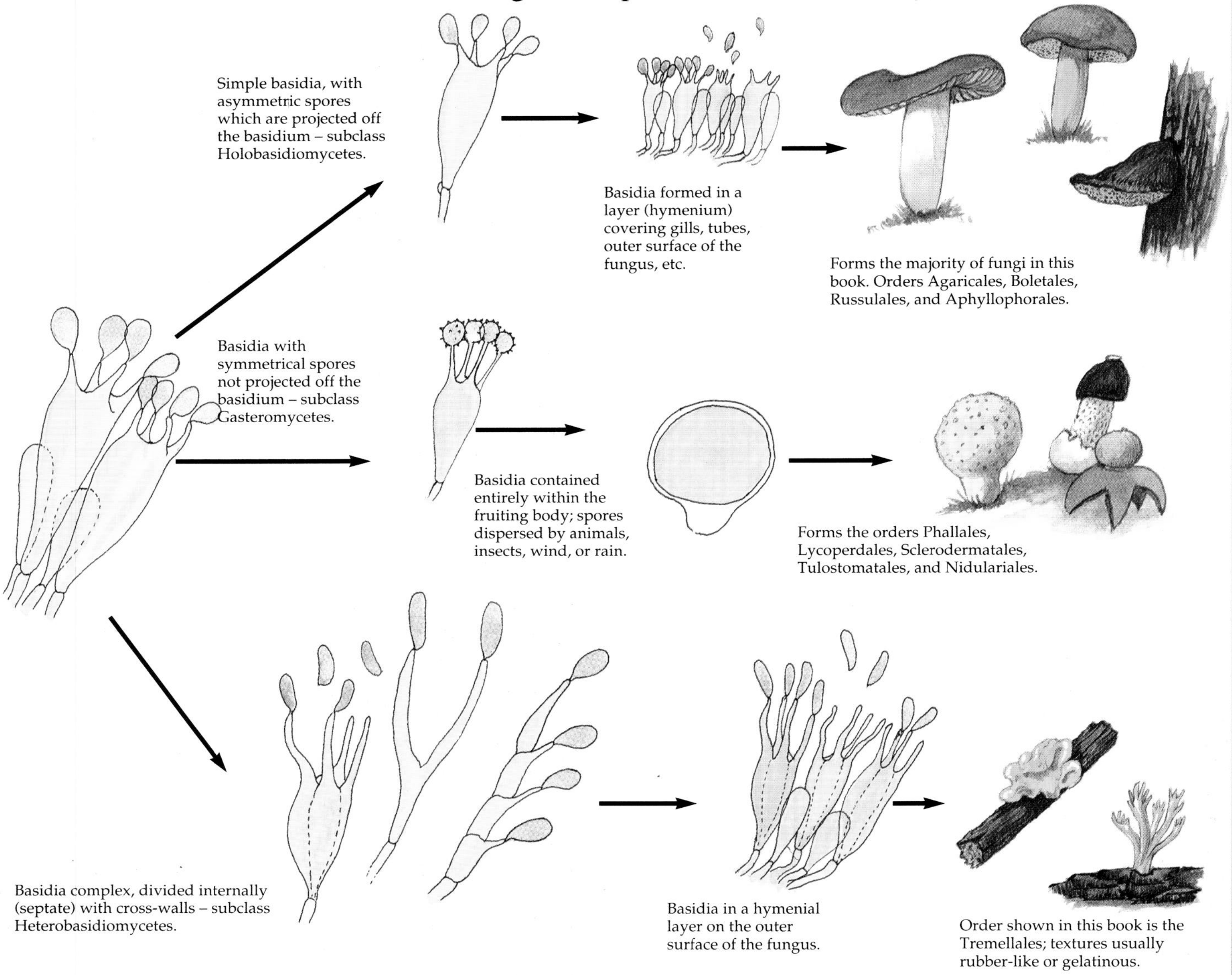

CLASS: ASCOMYCETES – Fungi with spores formed internally in an ascus

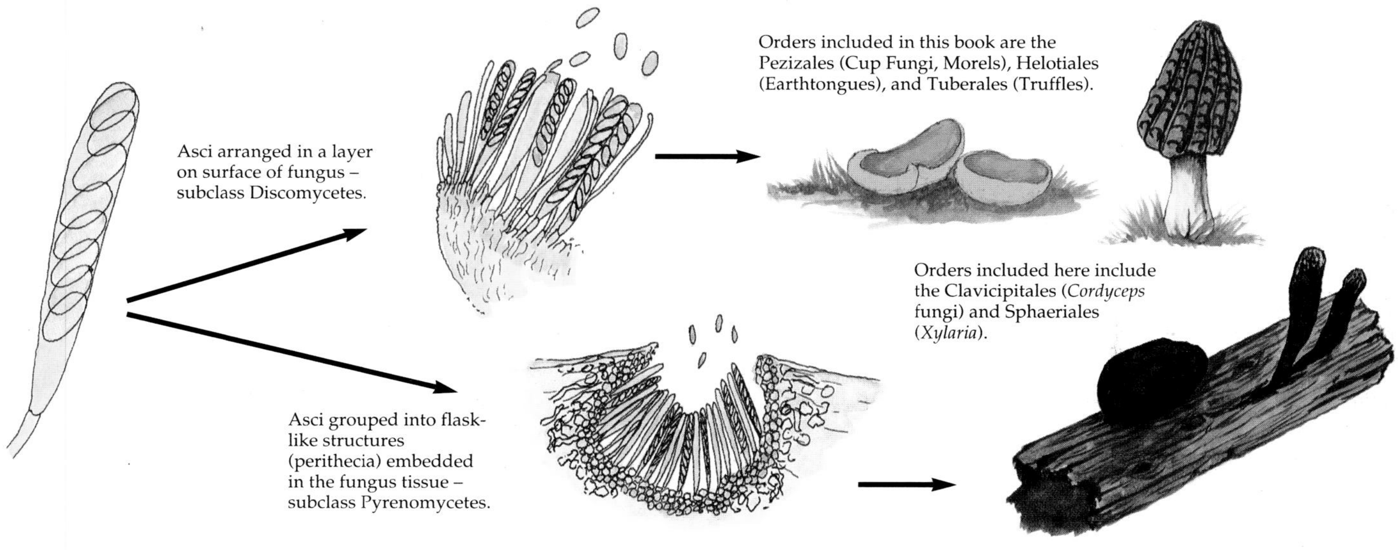

INDEX

C

G

H

I

J

K

L

M

N

O

P

Q

R

S

T

KEY TO SYMBOLS IN TEXT

= Deadly species

= Dangerous and suspect species